THE NICHOLAS & DOROTHY
CUMMINGS FOUNDATION

Re: W.T. O'Donohue, J.L. Cummings & J.L.
Thomas (Eds.) (2002). *The Entrepreneur
in Psychology. The Collected Papers of
Nicholas Cummings, Volume II.* Phoenix:
AZ: Zeig, Tucker & Theisen.

Dear Colleague:

Previously we were pleased to send to the directors of APA approved clinical/counseling
programs and other key leaders in psychology a complimentary copy of Volume I of my
father's collected papers. The reaction was highly positive, and we are now pleased to
send to you a complimentary copy of Volume II.

The first volume selected from over 400 publications three dozen of my father's clinical
research papers that are representative of a span of forty years, and anticipated so much
that occurred in our discipline. We indicated that the second volume would continue this
thrust. However, the recent interest among young colleagues in entrepreneurial
psychology caused the editors to change course. We prevailed upon my father to
chronicle nine of over twenty endeavors that he founded or whose course he significantly
influenced.

Dr. Nicholas Cummings is an entrepreneurial leader, if not the foremost entrepreneur in
psychology. For half a century he consistently not only predicted the future of
professional psychology (Volume I), he helped create it (Volume II). It is in the spirit of
helping those psychologists who would innovate clinical endeavors, thus freeing
themselves and many colleagues from the increasingly problematic experience of
traditional practice, that this book was written and is being distributed.

I hope you enjoy perusing this volume, after which The Cummings Foundation asks that
it be contributed to the library of an institution with which you are affiliated.

Sincerely,

Janet L. Cummings, Psy.D.
President
4400 North Scottsdale Road, PMB 305
Scottsdale, Arizona 85251
Phone: (480) 767-9252 Fax: (480) 451-8758

E-mail: CummFound@aol.com
Website: www.thecummingsfoundation.com

THE ENTREPRENEUR IN PSYCHOLOGY

The Collected Papers of
Nicholas A. Cummings
Volume II

THE COLLECTED PAPERS OF
NICHOLAS A. CUMMINGS

Volume I: *The Value of Psychological Treatment*
  Edited by J. Lawrence Thomas and Janet L. Cummings

Volume II: *The Entrepreneur in Psychology*
  Edited by J. Lawrence Thomas, Janet L. Cummings, and William T. O'Donahue

THE ENTREPRENEUR IN PSYCHOLOGY

The Collected Papers of
Nicholas A. Cummings
Volume II

Edited by
J. Lawrence Thomas, Ph.D.
Janet L. Cummings, Psy.D.
and William T. O'Donahue, Ph.D.

Zeig, Tucker & Theisen, Inc.
Phoenix, Arizona

Published by

ZEIG, TUCKER, & THEISEN, INC.
3614 North 24th Street
Phoenix, AZ 85014

Library of Congress Cataloging-in-Publication Data
Cummings, Nicholas A.
The entrepreneur in psychology : collected papers of
Nicholas A. Cummings, volume II / edited by J. Lawrence Thomas,
Janet L. Cummings, and William T. O'Donahue.
p. cm.
Includes bibliographical references.
ISBN 1-891944-92-4
1. Mental health services — United States. 2. Managed mental
health care — United States. 3. Mental health services — Utilization
— United States. I. Thomas, J. Lawrence. II. Cummings, Janet L.
III. Title.
RA790.6.C85 2002
362.2'0973 — dc21 98-50582
CIP

Manufactured in the United States of America

10 9 8 7 6 5 4 3 2 1

CONTENTS

FOREWORD

J. Lawrence Thomas, Ph.D.

FOR THE BETTER PART of a century, psychology has been evolving from laboratory experiments and philosophical writings (such as those of William James) to an established practicing profession in healthcare. Many battles were fought and won, including qualifying for licensing and insurance reimbursement, establishing professional schools, and proving the legitimacy of psychological interventions in the broad context of healthcare. Those who have been in the field for more than 40 years know something of these hard-won accomplishments, whereas younger practitioners may have only a limited appreciation of the effort it took — thousands of hours of meetings, traveling hundreds of miles by plane (when flying was inconvenient and more costly), giving up practice time, standing up to the status quo, undertaking tricky negotiations, coping with broken promises. Nicholas Cummings was involved in most of these battles, and was usually the central, driving force in waging them.

Those of us who know Nick Cummings' commitment are undoubtedly aware of his role in the development of the profession of psychology, and his more obvious accomplishments are well known. His seminal contributions to establishing that brief psychotherapeutic interventions can reduce overall healthcare costs were described in the 1960s, after he had developed the technique at Kaiser Permanente. These early articles (Follette & Cummings, 1967; Cummings & Follette, 1968) laid a foundation of work that was later to be called *medical cost offset*. In other words, when psychological issues are treated efficiently in a medical-care setting, the savings on the overall medical-care costs will be far greater than the cost of the behavioral health interventions; thus, the work of the psychologist would be "offset," or paid for, by the savings in medical care, and several times over. Cummings proved this on a grand scale with the Hawaii Project, a large prospective study that lasted several years. Using the principles learned from that project, he then founded American Biodyne, the first behavioral healthcare "carve-out," and an extremely successful effort. Along the way, Cummings also founded the four campuses of the California School of Professional Psychology, since he saw that his cherished profession was in danger of becoming extinct: The academic institutions of the day did not appreciate the value of training practicing professionals, and thus did not offer the most adaptable education for the practicing clinician at the doctoral level.

These developments were all results of Nick's seeing a need, and then envisioning, creating, and developing an organization to fill that need. So when I was asked to edit his papers, one of the collections, I reasoned, should include the stories of his founding of these various organizations during a career in psychology that has spanned 50 years. Janet Cummings and Bill O'Donohue, the coeditors of this volume, and I had a conference call with Nick about a year ago, and we talked about the organizations he either had founded solo or was a central figure in their founding. I was amazed to learn that his major undertakings numbered well over a dozen — each serving a crucial purpose in the history of professional psychology. We chose the 10 discussed in this volume, and although Nick does not take complete credit for some of these, which were accomplished in concert with colleagues, it is my distinct impression that the successes would have been much more modest had Nick not been involved. For example, when he sat on committees seeking to convince insurance companies to reimburse psychologists, although a number of players were involved, it was Nick's presence that seemed to have made the crucial difference. An illustration is how, after years of unsuccessfully trying to persuade insurers to recognize psychologists as autonomous providers, he negotiated the impasse by conceptualizing and implementing the legislation that came to be known as "freedom of choice," which mandated that if insurers reimbursed psychiatrists, they must also reimburse psychologists. Although some criticize him for "creating managed care in psychotherapy," it is forgotten that he also helped to make it possible for psychotherapists, and especially psychologists, to get paid by insurance companies in the first place. Second, the reason he founded American Biodyne was to show psychologists how to do it. When no one took up his offer to duplicate it in his or her state or community, he furthered the vision, making it a national and immensely successful behavioral healthcare company.

When I went through the papers Nick had written, however, it became clear that very few of them described how he had put these organizations together. I said, "If we are going to tell these stories, you will have to write them! None of the articles do." Nick is a doer. He loves creating, especially if there is a compelling need. Although he has published more than 400 refereed journal articles and chapters, along with 18 books, he is not one to write about how well he did something. But we twisted his arm, and he agreed to do what we asked. After completing some other works that were in the hopper, he wrote the various chapters in this volume. So this is a unique blend of "Collected Papers." Many of the chapters tell the story of Nick Cummings and his creation of various organizations that furthered the profession of psychology, and these stories are told for the first time in this volume. In a sense, the establishment of these organizations is the psychologist as entrepreneur par excellence. A need was seen, and an organization was formed to fulfill that need. But in another sense his entrepreneurship is unique, and reflects the highest values of our field. Most of these entities were not profit-oriented organizations. They were conceived from the beginning to be of service to the profession (such as COHI), or to our legislators (as the National Academies of Practice), and not for financial gain. That managed care went in that direction is another story, mostly concerned with the fact that the profession of psychology did not heed Nick's warning as to the importance of having clinicians in charge instead of business executives. He saw the industrialization of healthcare as inevitable, and knew that if the outgrowth were not clinician-driven, the fallout for the profession, our patients, and the healthcare industry in general would be nothing less than disastrous. These warnings were ignored; business interests were running managed care and therein lie the problems we have in today's healthcare!

I mused with Nick one time about how it was that he could see the future trends so clearly, and what the factors were that went into this remarkable set of abilities he seemed to possess — aside from an unusual intellect and abundant creativity. I suggested that perhaps it was because his analyst was Erik Erikson, who articulated the stages of life so clearly half a century ago — and was doing so while he was analyzing Nick! "Well, maybe that had something to do with it," Nick said quietly.

Although I am certainly prejudiced, I strongly believe that no one has shaped the profession of psychology in more definitive and helpful ways than Nick Cummings has. He was central to getting psychologists licensed, in getting us reimbursed by third-party payers, in developing training models for educating the practicing doctoral clinician, in establishing the legitimacy of psychological interventions in healthcare and in the resultant cost savings, in offering the services of high-level healthcare practitioners to our country's leaders, and in providing models of how integrated healthcare can be designed to reduce the suffering of those with psychological and medical problems, and, at the same time, saving health-care dollars. So you are invited to read these stories, hopefully with appreciation, of a career that has represented the highest professional and ethical values for over half a century.

INTRODUCTION
William T. O'Donohue, Ph.D.

THE TITLE OF THIS BOOK is meant to be a double entendre. I think Nicholas Cummings well deserves the mantle of "*The* Entrepreneur in Psychology," as his accomplishments are unrivaled in creating organizations that have transformed the profession. But the title is also meant to reflect the general sense of "the," and thus to provide a discussion of an interesting phenomenon: What is the role of the entrepreneur in psychology, and why are there so few?

"Entrepreneur" is an interesting and important construct. To most, it simply means a businessperson who starts a company in an attempt to become rich. If this were all that the term implies (and it does not, as we shall show), it would still be important. This kind of entrepreneur is responsible for creating jobs and for producing products and services that satisfy the needs and wants of others. The U.S. economy, contrary to the stereotypes invoked by some, is not in the main an economy of large corporations. It is a small-business economy, created by this type of entrepreneur.

- Of all nonfarm businesses in the United States, 97% are considered small by Small Business Association standards.
- Small businesses account for 40% of the gross domestic product (GDP).
- The total number of U.S. employees who work in small businesses is greater than the populations of Australia and Canada combined.
- In the 1980s, large companies lost 4.1 million jobs; in 1996, small businesses created a million new jobs.
- Of the nation's new jobs in the private sector, 90% are in small businesses (Nickels, McHugh, & McHugh, 1999).

However, even to the extent that the economy is made up of large businesses, one must remember that even these large businesses were once small entrepreneurial enterprises. The stories of David Packard, Sam Walton, Larry Ellison, and Bill Gates are known to most. Others include:

- DuPont was started in 1802 by Eleuthere Irenee du Pont de Nemours. Eighteen shareholders provided $36,000 in start-up funds.
- Avon was started in 1886 on $500 that David McConnell borrowed from a friend.
- George Eastman launched Kodak in 1880 with a $3,000 investment.
- William Procter and James Gamble formed Procter and Gamble in 1837 with a total of $7,000 in capital.
- The Ford Motor Company began with an investment of $28,000 by Henry Ford and 11 associates.

We will first discuss the narrow conception of entrepreneur because there are some important issues for psychologists. Later, however, we will discuss the fuller, and more important, conception.

THE ENTREPRENEUR AS THE
DEVELOPER OF A BUSINESS

What is fascinating is that in psychology there have been so few examples of these types of entrepreneur. Nick Cummings is the striking exception. In one of the chapters that follows, Nick describes how he conceived, developed, and grew American Biodyne from nothing to a large business, and then sold it. At its peak, American Biodyne employed over 10,000 healthcare professionals serving 14.5 million patients in 39 states. American Biodyne is historically significant as the largest psychological business enterprise ever created by a psychologist. This phenomenon deserves discussion.

In recent years, small entrepreneurial businesses have proliferated in the United States. Many of these have been based on commercializing scientific and technical developments. This commercialization is important as it takes scientific findings and allows the average citizen to benefit from the fruits of these developments. Historically, much of the industrial revolution has been devoted to extrapolating developments in physics and chemistry and transforming these into products and services that people want. Early developments in the understanding of physics created various engines (e.g., steam, internal combustion, jet), which revolutionized transportation. Similarly, knowledge and developments in the understanding of electricity and hydraulics revolutionized machinery used in industrial production. As a final example, developments in chemistry were utilized to produce plastics, unique clothing fibers, and superior construction materials. Entrepreneurs constructed successful businesses that better met the needs and wants of consumers by utilizing these advancements in basic knowledge.

We have recently been witnessing the rise of the information-technology sector. Individuals with knowledge of either computer software or hardware have not simply sold this knowledge or their labor to employers, but have taken the risks, learned business skills, and successfully created companies — some eventually becoming among the largest companies in the world (at least by market valuation). This defied our stereotypes of "the computer nerd" — an interpersonally avoidant geek who knew computers inside out, but beyond being able to sustain the body by soda and pizza, had no knowledge of the real world. These "nerds" learned how to write business plans, make presentations to venture capitalists, form management teams, market, and even manage. They became wealthy and influential individuals.

The next technical revolution, Nick predicts, will be the biotech revolution. Here we will see other kinds of scientists — geneticists, biochemists, bioengineers, physiologists, pharmacologists — spinning off developments in the biological sciences into companies that see opportunities to meet unmet health needs.

For us as psychologists, the question becomes: Why hasn't this become more of a general phenomenon in psychology? Why haven't psychologists seen the manifold psychological needs of human beings as opportunities to extrapolate what they know and to create thriving businesses to satisfy those needs? Why haven't we translated the advances in psychological assessment and treatment over the last decades into organizations that have both the scale and the value proposition that result in a significant business enterprise? Why haven't we produced jobs for others, and so allowed our economic niche to become a relatively unimportant economic backwater? We are generally quite intelligent, and we are supposed to have superior people and problem-solving skills. These attributes make it all the more surprising that there haven't been more entrepreneurs among us.

Is our lack of this type of entrepreneurship attributable to our lack of vision — because we can't think "big"? We partially reject this possibility because many psychologists can have larger visions. In fact, a certain hubris is epidemic among psychologists. One of the editors of this book vividly remembers social psychologists from a large Midwestern university giving a talk at an APA convention recommending that all peace negotiations in the Mideast include a specially trained social psychologist, as we are so skilled at conflict resolution (these might also be useful in faculty meetings). Participants in what Nick calls the "psychotherapy religions" have always proselytized that their therapy secure a monopoly. Other psychologists think big — although locally — and do start and maintain large group practices.

We only partially reject the possibility that vision is partly responsible because psychologists typically have two large blind spots. First, we (as Nick reluctantly likes to point out) are economic illiterates. We generally don't understand basic economic principles. What are opportunity costs? What effect will an increase in the supply of psychologists have on the price of services? Even more surprising is that we don't even understand the economics of healthcare. What percentage of the GDP is represented by healthcare? What percentage of the healthcare dollar goes to mental health? What percentage of the general inflation rate reflects that in healthcare?

These are important macroeconomics questions. And Nick knows the answers. Healthcare accounts for nearly 14% of the nation's GDP, or approximately $1.2 trillion. Mental health is only about 6% of this, or about $70 billion. The inflation rate of healthcare when Nick started American Biodyne was approximately three times the general rate of inflation. Consider the cumulative effect of this: if this multiple continues, instead of one in every seven dollars being spent on healthcare, eventually it will become one in every six, or one in every five — leaving less to spend on food, education, transportation, entertainment, guns, and butter. The national (and even international) healthcare economic problem is huge, and yet we have not allowed ourselves to be an important part of the solution. Nick, in his recent work, sees the unmet behavioral health needs occurring in primary care as an important driver of escalating healthcare costs and is helping to develop the technology and the business to address these needs more efficiently. These efforts are detailed in the last chapter of the book.

These are macroeconomic facts — information about the large economy. But psychologists can also be illiterate concerning microeconomic facts. What are the economic motivations of psychologists as wage earners of practitioners billing for psychological services? Are we motivated to minimize competition (thus decreasing our incomes) by creating barriers to entry into our field? Are we motivated to find more and more "mental disorders" to increase the supply of patients? To what extent are we interested in finding more efficient therapies so that our services can produce more for the buck? Do we become interested in delivering long-term depth psychotherapy, because with a few rich patients, we can be rewarded financially? What are the economic forces that bear on us to be more productive or to produce services of ever-increasing value? Nick understood the micro-economic factors operating on mental healthcare delivery and how developing effective therapy protocols, training his psychologists in these protocols, and having extensive quality-assurance measures could result in a more predictable product, more effective therapy, and more value for the mental health dollar, and thus arrange the economic contingencies more in the patients' and purchasers' interests.

The second major gap in the typical psychologist's vision is an inability to envision a business — a successful ongoing concern creating value for consumers. We believe this is so because of three reasons: (1) Psychologists typically do not have much business knowledge — we don't know how to write business plans, we don't know how to raise capital, we don't know to form exit strategies, we don't know how to form effective governing boards, we don't know how to market, and so on. These matters are rarely, if ever, taught formally, or informally, in our training. (2) Psychologists have mixed emotional reactions to money and business. It is our observation that many psychologists have an approach — avoidance conflict regarding the topic. Many attempt to maximize income by trying to maximize merit raises in academic settings, or growing their private practices, all the while feeling somewhat conflicted about it. There seems to be a very interesting phenomenon in which psychologists want to feel that they are being moral about their incomes, which tends to mean that no matter what they make, they are just below the gluttonous rich. If they make $50,000, then the problematic income is $80,000; they make $80,000, then the problem income is $120,000; and if they make $120,000, then the problematic income is $180,000. The horrors of Republicanism always lie a bit over the horizon.

Another conflict that psychologists have is over the notion of a business. They typically see businesspeople as unethical, as somehow doing shady deals that bilk poorer people out of hard-earned money. Or as defilers of the environment. Or as shallow, crass individuals greedily chasing wealth. However, this interesting prejudice is not consistently applied. Psychologists typically have their favorite businesses; they fall in love with Costco, Nordstroms, Toyota, Apple Computer, or Ben and Jerry's. Moreover, it is not consistent, as they themselves are inevitably businesspeople (although perhaps practicing the "small is beautiful" philosophy).

Universities are businesses (if you doubt this, listen to top administrators talk about selling credits and indirect cost recovery from federal grants). What certainly is clear is that private practices are businesses, as are healthcare delivery organizations. One can attempt to pretend that these are not businesses, but this is simply pretense.

Is business such a bad thing? This antipathy toward business is somewhat surprising. The firm making the medications to keep your children healthy is a business; your favorite restaurant is, of course, a business; your favorite hotel is a business; the publishing house producing this book is a business; your favorite movie was produced by a business, and the farm producing the food you eat is a business. If you wished all the businesses away, you would, by this act, return us all to a primitive hunter — gatherer society. So why this dependence and this use that produces satisfaction, and yet this antipathy? Psychologists ought to think about this and try to resolve some of the perplexing conflict.

The third reason why psychologists haven't been more involved in this type of entrepreneurship is, as Nick points out, that they are generally unwilling to take a risk. We like the comfort of tenure, salaried VA jobs, and low-risk enterprises, such as starting small private practices. However, borrowing a large sum of money (perhaps taking out a second mortgage) or, as Nick did, investing one's entire retirement savings on a startup, and working long hours for a low salary for years is a rare choice in our profession. It is an interesting question as to why so few of us are willing to take these calculated, reasonable, but large risks (particularly because we often, as part of our jobs, advise others to take them).

Because of the importance of these entrepreneurs, they have been studied and attempts made to find their core characteristics. Although there are many descriptions, they share many common features. As an illustration, Farrell (2001) states that the four fundamental practices of the world's great entrepreneurs are:

1. *A sense of mission.* Entrepreneurs believe they are doing something important in the world. They believe they're creating value for customers, employees, and, of course, themselves.
2. *Consumer/product vision.* Steve Jobs, founder of Apple Computer, said: "The computer is the most remarkable tool we've ever built — but the most important thing is to get them in to the hands of as many people as possible." Most entrepreneurs are craftspeople. They have a single, integrated vision of customers and products. They know they need both to survive.

3. *High-speed innovation.* Comfortable bureaucracies are the last place you'll find high-speed innovations and entrepreneurs. Entrepreneurial Davids like nothing better than competing against muscle-bound Goliaths.
4. *Self-inspired behavior.* Entrepreneurs love what they do — they are highly committed to their work. Second, they constantly try to get better at what they do.

THE ENTREPRENEUR AS INNOVATOR

One of the most influential management theorists in the 20th century was Peter Drucker. He maintained that the successful entrepreneur is essentially someone who reallocates resources to produce valued goods and services more efficiently. He was influenced by the economist J. B. Say, who stated in around 1800: "The entrepreneur shifts economic resources out of an area of lower and into an area of higher productivity and greater yield" (Drucker, 1985, p. 21). The entrepreneur, in other words, if successful, finds more efficient ways to satisfy needs and wants. Since goods and services are scarce, the entrepreneur either allows poor people to afford a good or service (because it is cheaper), or allows this good or service to be produced more cheaply so that customers can have more money for other uses, or produces a better good or service for the same price.

In this more penetrating analysis, the entrepreneur becomes the ultimate "green" citizen. Resources are being wasted by being used inefficiently, and the entrepreneur has a vision and an implementation plan to use them more efficiently. We can see Nick's work as embodying this ethic of increased efficiency and value. Students who were planning to become practitioners were inefficiently using the resources of doctoral training in research-oriented departments, and the research-oriented departments were inefficiently utilizing the students' resources. So Nick created a professional school to meet this need more efficiently. The delivery of behavioral health services was a very inefficient institution: patients all too often received therapies that their therapists like, rather than the effective therapies they needed. Nick saw this and was able to create a more efficient delivery system in which healthcare dollars and healthcare labor more efficiently met the needs.

Economists define innovation as changing the value and satisfaction obtained from resources by the consumer. Entrepreneurship is a social enterprise. It requires others to make decisions, presumably to maximize their own interests, to engage in transactions with the entrepreneur. Students saw the value of Nick's professional school. Professionals saw the value of the National Academies of Practice and the American Behavioral Healthcare Association. Health plans saw the value of American Biodyne. And in order for them to survive, they actually had to deliver this value. Successful entrepreneurship is not smoke and mirrors, but actually and consistently delivering increased value to the consumer.

It is this broader, and, we believe, more fundamental, concept of entrepreneur that best fits Nick, and so becomes the title of this second volume of his collected papers. In the chapters that follow, you will read about his innovations. You will see how he saw a problem, a gap, an inefficiency, and in response did not complain, but created a movement, often an organization, to address the need more efficiently. This was no easy task, and below we list some observations regarding how Nick has been able to be such a successful and influential entrepreneur.

NICK CUMMINGS: THE MAN

The number and variety of the accomplishments of Nick Cummings undoubtedly will astonish the reader of this book. Most of these readers will be psychologists and they will wonder what personal characteristics allowed him to accomplish so much. McGrath and MacMillan (2000) have suggested that there are a few rare people who are what they call "habitual entrepreneurs." They often are involved in "startups", profit as well as nonprofit. They suggest that habitual entrepreneurs have the following five characteristics.

- They passionately seek new opportunities. Habitual entrepreneurs stay alert, always looking for the chance to profit from change and disruption in the way business is done. Their greatest impact occurs when they create entirely new business models. New business models revolutionize how revenues are made, costs are incurred, or operations are conducted, sometimes throughout an entire industry.
- They pursue opportunities with enormous discipline. Habitual entrepreneurs not only are alert enough to spot opportunities, but they make sure that they act on them. Most maintain some form of inventory, or register, of unexploited opportunities. They revisit their inventory of ideas often, but take action only when it is required. They

make investments only if the competitive arena is attractive and the opportunity is ripe.

- They pursue only the best opportunities and avoid exhausting themselves and their organizations by chasing after every option. Even though many habitual entrepreneurs are wealthy, the most successful remain ruthlessly disciplined about limiting the number of projects they pursue. They go after a tightly controlled portfolio of opportunities in different stages of development. They link their strategy with their choice of projects, rather than dilute their efforts by applying them too broadly.

- They focus on execution — specifically, adaptive execution. Both words are important. People with an entrepreneurial mind set execute; that is, they get on with it instead of analyzing new ideas to death. Yet they are also adaptive — able to change directions as the real opportunity, and the best way to exploit it, evolves.

- They engage the energies of everyone in their domain. Habitual entrepreneurs involve many people, both inside and outside the organization, in their pursuit of an opportunity. They create and sustain networks of relationships rather than going it alone, making the most of the intellectual and other resources people have to offer and helping those people to achieve their goals as well (pp. 2–3).

Here is a brief outline of our own observations on this important topic.

First, and perhaps foremost, Nick has been a successful entrepreneur because he is visionary. He can see trends and anticipate changes. One of the editors once witnessed Nick speaking to the then president of the American Psychological Association. Nick was explaining how integrating behavioral care with primary medical care was the future of psychology. This would provide excellent business opportunities, jobs, research, and training needs. Nick foresaw this development because it made both clinical and economic sense. The president said that he had no doubt but that this would prove to be correct, as Nick's predictions about the future of healthcare thus far had never been wrong. When asked how he had become so astute, Nick replied that his study of economics and his use of basic economic principles in analyzing the current behavioral healthcare scene allowed him these insights.

Second, like most successful entrepreneurs, Nick's energy level is legendary. It is unclear as to what extent he does not need much sleep versus to what extent he does not allow himself to sleep until certain tasks are completed. He has a "red line" method. Each day, when he looks at his "to do" list, he puts all items that have to be completed above a red line, and he does not allow himself to sleep until all those items have been completed. This energy allows him to accomplish an extraordinary amount each day. The disciplined manner in which his energy is allocated allows him to focus on the ways discussed in the above descriptions of entrepreneurs.

As a side note, an important part of the reason for this energy comes from Nick's excellent health habits. He exercises early every morning. He eats very sensibly and has one cocktail with his wife in the evening. This foundation of good living gives him the physical strength and energy to accomplish so much. This exemplifies what we think is an important distinction between Nick and many others. Many psychologists, perhaps academic psychologists in particular, can cultivate certain foibles or problems as interesting personal quirks. They either dress poorly (Nick says, "Most psychologists dress like they are going to take out the garbage"), or have interpersonal idiosyncrasies, like failing to remember people's names, or have blind sides, like not attending to such "details" as their daily appointments. Nick is very "clean" in this way. The common downsides of many psychologists do not subtract from many upsides.

Another part of the reason for this range of accomplishment is that Nick is an extraordinary problem solver. He is able to think very astutely inside the box, as well as outside. Nick clearly sees problems as challenges to be met creatively. He is realistic and, as discussed above, can adapt his efforts to unsolvable problems.

Part of the reason why Nick can think out of the box is that, like most entrepreneurs, he doesn't mind being out of the pack. He frequently states that part of being an innovator and an entrepreneur is that many people will tell you that you are wrong and crazy. They don't share your vision (if many had the same vision, probably someone else would have already capitalized on the opportunity). Thus, innovators need to be comfortable with operating without the support and approval of many of those around them, particularly their colleagues, who often are highly invested in the status quo. However, there is a certain rule-breaking mentality that is shocking to the conventional mind, but is necessary to progress, particularly progress that is revolutionary and fast, which is in direct contrast with the manager who must be much more closely tied to the conventional and not be in opposition to the opinions of colleagues. This has resulted in Nick's having an interesting relationship with the American

Psychological Association. Although a past president, he often criticizes the organization (he has said, "The APA always can be trusted to do the right thing [pause] after exhausting all the other possibilities"). But this organization represents the conventional, and Nick is always prodding it to face reality and to move rapidly in a better direction.

Nick also has, in the language of the field, "excellent social skills." It is remarkable how comfortable he makes everyone feel. Graduate students often remark on this — that although they were ready to be intimidated, Nick made them feel welcome and important. As a result, he seems to know just about everyone. He remembers people's names, and even the names of their family members. He is a fascinating conversationalist. He can tell a great story. He is extraordinarily persuasive. He can hone in on the points that matter. He is always well informed (he does his homework); he stays on top of current events (particularly events affecting his enterprises) and can speak authoritatively on many subjects. He has a strict personal dress code. He is always well groomed and dresses in a way that shows the appropriate respect for his associates.

And last, but certainly not least, responsible for his success was his extraordinary good fortune convincing Dorothy Cummings to be his wife. The old saying that behind every great man is a great woman is exemplified in this couple. Dorothy is a woman of extraordinary abilities. She has not simply supported Nick's visions and plans, but her astute judgment has played a key role in the formation of the resulting organizations. She shares his ability to take intelligent risks. She, too, is an entrepreneur. It is wonderful to watch this loving couple function as a team. Nick clearly, and fortunately, has not had to blaze his trail to entrepreneurship alone.

A PERSONAL NOTE: A BRIEF BIOGRAPHY
OF NICHOLAS CUMMINGS

Janet L. Cummings, Psy.D.

MY FATHER, Nicholas Cummings, was born in Salinas, California, in 1924. At that time, the town of Salinas was the thriving hub of Monterey County, and was also known as "Steinbeck Country." (In fact, *East of Eden* in John Steinbeck's novel by that name was Salinas, with *Eden* being Monterey to the west.) This celebrated author lived three blocks from my father's childhood home and was a good friend of my grandfather's. As a child, my father liked Mr. Steinbeck, and knew he was somehow an important man, but also someone most of the townspeople did not like. Steinbeck was quite controversial, and Salinas did not resolve its love-hate relationship with him until the city founded the Steinbeck Museum in 1996. My father grew up reading Steinbeck's novels and short stories, and has always respected and appreciated him. When the Steinbeck Museum was founded, my father purchased 24 bricks, which were inscribed with my parents' names, my brother's name, my name, my daughter's name, and the names of other family members who had a nexus in Monterey County. I remember the look of shear delight on my father's face as he told the family about these bricks in the Steinbeck Museum. At first, I was disinterested, but then recalled my father's upbringing in Salinas and his affiliation with Steinbeck and realized how important "Steinbeck Country" had been to him.

My dad's father (my grandfather) owned the leading hotel in Salinas, along with his three brothers. Immigrants from Greece, they came to the United States by way of Australia, where they stayed until they had earned enough money to book passage to this country. Thus, they landed in California instead of coming through Ellis Island in New York. Great-Uncle George was the first to arrive. He had bought a ticket to San Francisco, but the captain of the schooner misnavigated, thought Monterey Bay was San Francisco Bay, and made harbor there. George got a job as a waiter, not realizing that he was not in San Francisco. When they were reunited, all four brothers (my grandfather was third in age) each took two jobs, one at the famous Del Monte Lodge and the other at various small restaurants. They saved their money and bought the Abbott House, which they transformed over the next several years into a four-story, 150-room modern (for the time) hotel, where John Steinbeck was a frequent guest.

My grandmother came to the United States from Greece as a teenager. She had only received the equivalent of a third-grade education in Greece and was raised to be a very traditional woman. As a result, she read very little, was quite superstitious, and remained very dependent upon her family, never learning to pay bills or to drive an automobile. She lived with her family in the San Francisco Bay Area, but my grandfather spotted her from more than a hundred miles away in Salinas, and when she was 19, and in accordance with the custom of the day, he asked for her hand in marriage. My father was the first of many children born to the extended family, and my great-grandmother Mary, who lived in the household, doted on him. When he was barely older than a toddler, she taught him public speaking and instilled a confidence, extroversion, and a sense of self-reliance that have stayed with him all of his life. My great-grandmother was a very intelligent woman, although she had never attended school and did not know how to read. She had memorized all of the Greek oral tradition (mythology), which she taught to my father through repetition. At a very young age, my father could recite Homer's *Iliad* and *Odyssey* in classical Greek. He loved the stories he learned from his grandmother and became a marvelous storyteller who could mesmerize his family as they listened to him recite Greek myths with the dramatic skill of a Shakespearean actor. Since my great-grandmother did not speak English, the family spoke Greek to accommodate her.

Although my father always downplayed this, our original family name was Comnenus, also the name of the ruling family of the Eastern Roman Empire. When, in the 16th century, the Ottoman (Turkish) Empire under Solyman the Magnificent overran most of southern Europe, the family fled Constantinople (now Istanbul) and settled on a Mediterranean island that was under the control of the Venetians until the 18th century. On one occasion, my father took my brother and me into St. Sofia Cathedral in Istanbul and showed us the family names carved into the royal pews. Other than that, he has said little. Comnenus, because of the double consonant, is difficult to pronounce, and over the centuries, it became Cominos, and eventually Cummings. My father inherited the scourge of many Comnenus males, partial hemophilia, which could have been fatal had it not been for my great-grandmother's knowledge of folk medicine. She would prepare a powder from eggshells that she would roast until they were golden brown. Then, with a centuries-old brass hammer and pestle, she would grind them into a fine, almost weightless, powder. Applied to the many cuts my father suffered because he refused to curtail his normal, exuberant boyish play, clotting occurred almost instantly. The same would be true for his three or four daily nosebleeds. The real danger, of course, was internal bleeding, but he survived and, when in his early teens, modern medicine came up with a permanent remedy.

From all evidence, my father had a very happy early childhood, until age 4, when his father died. The family was vacationing, and when my grandfather developed severe abdominal pain, my grandmother called the resort doctor, who prescribed castoroil over the telephone instead of making a house call. My grandfather's appendix ruptured and within hours he died of peritonitis in that age long before antibiotics. My grandmother went into a deep depression that lasted three years and my great-grandmother, Mary, raised my father and his sister (who was 3 when their father died) during those years.

When my father entered school, he had the disadvantage of not speaking English, as only Greek had been spoken in his home. He also was disadvantaged by his depression at losing his father (literally) and his mother (psychologically). The teacher maintained that my father was mentally retarded and referred him to the school psychologist, who gave him a psychological test. One of the test items was to arrange a series of various sized blocks according to weight. Not understanding the English instructions, my father guessed at what the task was and arranged them according to size, from the smallest to the largest. He probably similarly misunderstood instructions for the other test items. He was diagnosed as mentally retarded, and two weeks later, a social worker arrived at the house with papers for my grandmother to sign, committing my father, who subsequently was rediagnosed in the genius range, to the Sonoma State Hospital for the Mentally Retarded. My great-uncle, Mitchell, happened to be visiting my grandmother, who was too depressed to understand the significance of the social worker's demand, and he unceremoniously threw the woman out of the house. My father had forgotten this incident until his personal psychoanalysis many years later. His training analyst, Erik H. Erikson, rightly interpreted that this had a great deal to do with my father's choosing the profession of psychology. He himself later realized that this had laid the groundwork for his lifetime of impatience with incompetent, poorly trained psychologists, and even greater impatience with flimsy, nonevidence-based psychodiagnosis and psychotherapy.

In addition to being deemed mentally retarded by his teacher, my father's early school experience was further complicated by the constant ridicule inflicted by his peers because of his inability to speak English. However, he learned English amazingly quickly. Bolstered by extroversion and storytelling abilities, he soon became very popular among his classmates. Whenever they sought a leader, whether as a team captain or a student body president, they looked to my father.

When my father was 7, his mother re-married and his stepfather moved his new bride and her two children to the San Francisco Bay Area, where my father lived for the rest of his childhood and adolescence. This was a glorious time for him. His mother was free of depression and he adored his stepfather, whose every move and gesture he emulated. His stepfather was a successful businessman who instilled in my father many of the values that later in life, and after a series of innovative clinical careers, made him psychology's most successful entrepreneur.

I have very fond memories of my stepgrandfather who lived into his 90s. He had received only the equivalent of an eighth-grade education in Greece, but by studying on his own, he made himself into a well-educated man. In addition to the daily newspaper, he received a newspaper from Athens by mail every day, which he devoured. He also read many books, and could carry on an intelligent conversation on any subject. When I was in college, he loved to have me visit just to sit and talk with him about what I was learning, whether in core courses or in electives. He was his happiest when he was able to learn right along with me, or when he could teach me about the things he enjoyed, such as gardening. One of the greatest honors I have received in life was when, on his deathbed, my stepgrandfather asked that I be the one to deliver the eulogy at his funeral.

The happiness that his stepfather brought my father unfortunately was short lived; at the age of 9, he had poliomyelitis and was told he would never walk again. While in the hospital, he delighted the staff and the other children on the ward with his storytelling. However, when he was discharged from the hospital and remanded to a wheelchair, he became despondent, lost his self-confidence, and his grades in school suffered. Once again, great-grandmother Mary came to the rescue. She espoused the belief of Sister Kenny, a nurse nun who maintained that even passive exercise could help regenerate destroyed spinal nerves. The prevailing wisdom in medicine until recently was that the central nervous system (CNS) never regenerates. (I can't help but laugh when I read the "latest" medical research indicating that the CNS can regenerate itself, at least under some conditions.) My great-grandmother supported, cajoled, shamed, and bullied my father into riding his bicycle by pushing down from his hips, as his legs were useless. My father recalls her saying over and over, "You are too young to give into being a cripple for the rest of your life." She actually used the word "cripple," emphasizing its negative connotation, to shame him for even thinking of accepting his state. He remembers waking up at night and hearing his mother sobbing that her son would never walk again. With his mother's wailing and his grandmother's cajoling, plus the merciless teasing of his peers at school, he decided that it was preferable to believe that he could walk again. Day after day, he would creep downstairs like a snake and with the aid of a series of water pipes, pull himself up onto his bicycle. Out he would go, defying his mother's prohibition. When he fell, he was helpless until someone came along to help him. His mother was frantic, often calling the police to find him and bring him home. In time, my father began to see improvement, and within three years, he was walking so well that the telltale signs of polio were not discernible.

So instilled was his grandmother's admonition that he not be "crippled," he never told his draft board that he had had polio or was a partial hemophiliac, which might well have spared him from serving in World War II. Instead, he entered the army, and in basic training, he would sneak out of the barracks at night to secretly practice close-order drill so that no one would discover his limitations. He has succeeded in hiding his polio-stricken limbs from everyone but my mother, who knows very well that he was never able to master the rhythm and coordination necessary for ballroom dancing. In his mid-60s, my father noticed symptoms that recalled his childhood polio days, and he diagnosed himself several years before the medical profession recognized the postpolio syndrome that besets polio victims decades later. For many years, my father had run daily, until a piece of shrapnel in one knee, a souvenir of World War II, made running impossible. He then started walking daily, generally between five and seven miles, but eventually found that long walks aggravated his postpolio symptoms. So, once again, my father turned to his bicycle, which he now (in his late 70s) rides 15 miles each morning, defeating for the second time the so-called inevitable polio aftereffects. I know better than to accompany my father on his bike rides. Even though I exercise regularly and am in good physical condition, I know that I have no chance of keeping up with him. My husband has made the mistake of going bicycle riding with my father on several occasions, and each time, he has returned out of breath, complaining of difficulty walking owing to sore leg muscles, and grumbled constantly over the next three days, "Your father tried to kill me!"

A wounded veteran of World War II, my father never talked of his combat experiences. Instead, he regaled us as children with stories of every snafu that occurred during his three years of service. He described these with such humor that we had no idea of what he had really done in the war. I learned some of the facts at the Biodyne boot camp, where he descried how his military experiences had influenced his psychological career. My husband, a Vietnam veteran, assembled my father's medals and citations in a frame, and presented the display to my father on his 76th birthday. When I naively asked my father why he had never bothered to collect all of his medals where he earned them, he simply stated, "We were all kind of busy back then." I know that World War II had a profound effect on my father, and he is proud to have been one of the generation that history credits with saving the world. Only recently has he expressed some concern that the U.S. Capitol boasts a memorial to every war we have fought, except for the biggest and most important one. We even have a memorial to the holocaust survivors (and rightly so), but not to the men and women who rescued them. With World War II veterans dying at the rate of over 1,000 per day, he hopes that the recent actions of the Congress and President Bush, 60 years after Pearl Harbor, may result in a World War II memorial on the Washington Mall while he and his friends are still alive to see it.

My father repeatedly states that the best thing that ever happened to him was meeting Dorothy Mills in an advanced statistics class at the University of California, Berkeley. She was 20 and he was a returning war veteran of 23. They shared a lab bench, but for the first two weeks, she was cold and distant, having taken an initial dislike to him. Three months later, they were married in Reno, Nevada, between semesters, and as of this writing, they have been together for 55 years. It was 11 years before I was born, allowing them both to finish school in New York's Adelphi University. My mother obtained a master's degree in social work, and my father underwent psychoanalytic training and received a Ph.D. in clinical psychology. After a couple of false starts in doctoral programs that my father considered a waste of time, they chose Adelphi because it was truly a professional program, unabashedly training graduates to enter independent practice. In almost every other APA-approved program, the mere suggestion that one might be interested in private practice was enough to warrant expulsion from the program.

My father graduated with the faculty's declaring him their best and most promising student. Gordon Derner, founder of the radical program at Adelphi, advised my father to spend a few years on the faculty of an Ivy League university, and was instrumental in obtaining for him an appointment to the graduate faculty at Cornell. My father reluctantly accepted the position, moved with my mother to Ithaca, and then quit within the first three weeks of the fall semester. He later made another attempt at a faculty position, but quit that one after only two weeks. He remains disenchanted with the bureaucracy called academia, stating that it is the last vestige of the Middle Ages, compounded in its inefficiency by the modern invention of tenure. When my father decided to found the California School of Professional Psychology, he told me of his false starts in graduate school and his two briefly held faculty positions. I am certain that these negative experiences with graduate education in psychology greatly influenced his decision to recreate graduate education in the field. Had it not been for those early experiences, the professional school movement and the Vail Conference might never have taken place.

When my father and mother left Ithaca, they returned to San Francisco, where my father began a psychoanalytic practice, only to become dissatisfied and convinced that this was the most inefficient therapy devised by humans since leeching. He saw it work, but lamented that it took so long that he would be fortunate indeed if he were to live long enough to treat (with completed psychoanalyses) a mere 80 to 100 patients. He accepted the position of chief psychologist at Kaiser Permanente, where he experimented for 25 years with efficient/effective psychotherapy, and extended these techniques to his coexisting private practice. My parents built a spectacular three-story home on Twin Peaks overlooking downtown San Francisco, the Bay Bridge, the San Francisco Bay, and Oakland/Berkeley. My brother and I were born in San Francisco, in the Kaiser Hospital where my father worked, and lived in that house on Twin Peaks throughout our childhood.

When I was born, my father confesses, he was beside himself with happiness. I remember that he had always held at least two, and sometimes three, full-time jobs while I was a child. He required very little sleep, and I have often been amazed at how much he could accomplish while the rest of the world slept. But no matter how busy he was, he always managed to come home for dinner and see me before returning to the office to work late into the evening. When my brother and I were preschoolers, my father's work schedule changed so that he was unable to come home for dinner on one particular evening of the week. On those evenings, my mother, my brother, and I would buy take-out food and bring it to my father's office, where we would all sit in child-sized chairs at the child-sized table he used when doing play therapy, and eat our dinners. My father kept a collection of toys to use when seeing child patients, and he would take a few minutes to play a game with my brother and me before sending us home so that he could resume work.

One of his traits that I recall from my childhood was my father's playfulness. When I was an infant, he would stand behind my crib, peering down at me and calling himself my "upside-down daddy." We played this game so often that my eyes began to distort upward, and he had to quit it. Before I could speak, he would read to me, and as he came through the door, I would greet him with my favorite book, *Mimi the Merry-Go-Round Cat*. My father was a master at inventing games, and managed to keep my brother and me occupied during long automobile trips. When my now 5-year-old daughter, Amy, was 10 months old, she, my husband, my parents, and I went on a three-hour car trip. At that time, Amy hated her car seat, and fussed constantly when restrained there, thus making even very short trips miserable for anyone else in the car. On that particular trip, Amy had with her a Beanie Baby duck. My father sat next to her and held that duck while making quacking noises for three hours. Amy was so entertained that she forgot to fuss about being in the car seat for so long.

My father began private practice as a master's-level psychologist in the late 1940s. Realizing how scary this was with no licensure for psychologists, he became instrumental, with a handful of others, in California's becoming one of the first states to provide statutory recognition of psychologists. Even though he had been "grandfathered" on the master's level, he recognized the importance of the doctorate and, following several false starts in other programs, traveled to Adelphi University to obtain his Ph.D. and analytic training.

In the 1950s, no insurance company reimbursed for psychotherapy, claiming that it was not economically viable to do so. Believing that psychotherapy should not be reserved for the wealthy and should be made available to working-class people, my father was able to persuade Kaiser Permanente, the first health maintenance organization (HMO) in northern California, to make psychotherapy a covered benefit. He and his colleagues conducted extensive research demonstrating that psychotherapeutic interventions could save medical and surgical dollars far beyond the cost of the psychological services. He found this to be especially true for somatizing patients, who were among the highest medical utilizers. What became known as the "medical cost offset phenomenon" is now in its third generation of research, and my father remains its seminal investigator.

Growing up in the 1960s and 1970s, I watched my father intently as he conducted his medical cost offset research and developed early protocols for the efficient and effective treatment of various psychological conditions. Of particular interest to me were his innovative and radical approaches to treating both substance-abusing and suicidal patients without hospitalizing them. Eavesdropping on my father's telephone calls to patients from home, I was fascinated by his ability to manage the patients, skillfully utilizing a wide variety of techniques and tailoring his interventions to each individual patient. As a result, I became very interested in the suicidal process and the management of suicidal patients. For my dissertation research on the subject of suicide, I performed a psychological autopsy on a suicide victim and produced a teaching videotape on suicide that is used throughout the United States and the United Kingdom for training purposes. Many of my ideas in this regard came from those early years of listening to my father handle emergencies over the telephone.

I was also intrigued by my father's model of treating substance abuse without hospitalization. Unknown to him, I would often set my alarm clock to go off every two hours, as I knew he called his detoxing heroin addicts every two hours, day and night, during the "cold turkey" horror of withdrawal. I particularly enjoyed listening to him tell the addicts what to expect during the next two hours and giving their "babysitter" friends a pep talk to prevent them from being conned into allowing the addicts to obtain heroin.

No matter how many times his patients relapsed, my father was always there for them. Even though we seldom were able to get through a family dinner or weekend outing without his being called to respond to an emergency, he treated each patient as important, giving him or her his full attention during these phone calls.

When my father eventually caught me eavesdropping, he reminded me that the conversations were private and very personal. He said that he would gladly discuss his model of psychotherapy with me, explaining in general what he does and why. Even though he refused to talk about specific patients, he allowed me to ask general questions, which he answered on a level I could understand.

I recall one very important early experience. At the time, psychedelics were believed to expand one's consciousness, yet my own impression in observing people who dropped acid (LSD) or other hallucinogens was that their consciousness had actually narrowed. They seemed to focus on minutia with the illusion that these were expansive, while missing or misinterpreting important stimuli and events. I discussed my observations with my father, who indicated that my observations were in agreement with his clinical findings. Both my observations and his findings were later confirmed by clinical research, which he shared with me to validate my perceptions further. That my observations were confirmed gave me confidence. Not only was drug abuse understandable, but even I could understand it. This confidence contributed to my decision to learn more by becoming a psychologist. By the time I had completed my doctoral training, I was very comfortable with treating substance abuse.

My father realized that I inevitably would be exposed to drugs and peer pressure as a teenager to use them. Instead of simply lecturing me, he managed to provide some unforgettable object lessons. He arranged for me to sit in on some of his addiction groups, where I was able to talk with his patients and listen to their stories. I have never met a heroin addict who had not first used marijuana, so the belief that pot use did not lead to hardcore addictions, which was popular at the time, seemed naive to me. I was amazed that 30-year-olds could have done themselves in so quickly that they looked much older.

This was not the only unique object lesson my father provided. My parents loved to travel, and took my brother and me along on most of their trips. We owned a motorhome in which we toured North America. We also made several trips to Europe, trips to Australia and the South Pacific, and a trip around the world. As a result, I have been to all 50 states and about 30 other countries. My father used our travels to instill patriotism in my brother and me. In each country we visited, he pointed out the uniqueness of the culture, making sure we were able to appreciate each country's art, religion, and values. He made sure we saw the positives that each culture had to offer, but he also made certain that we saw the negatives. When I was in high school and college, it was popular to idealize India and to consider a trip there the ultimate spiritual experience. Having visited India at the age of 12, I had seen the terrible poverty produced by that country's caste system and so easily avoided being influenced by my peers concerning India. Even though my brother and I are both realistic about the problems the United States faces, we have a patriotism that is quite exceptional for people our age because we were given the opportunity to compare our country with many others throughout the world.

My father had some very creative ways of curtailing his children's rebellion. For example, when I was a teenager, I was entrenched in a power struggle with my mother over how I could or could not wear my hair. He intervened in a most reasonable way. He told me that I could wear my hair however I wished, as long as it was clean, combed, and out of my face. Neither my mother nor I could find fault with his reasoning. When my daughter, Amy, was in the midst of the "terrible twos," my father invented a character he named "Sad Sack Sally." He told Amy about the dire consequences that awaited Sally if she misbehaved in a restaurant, ran away from her mother in a public place, or committed other offenses of which Amy was guilty. Amy listened intently to these stories, and asked to have them repeated over and over. Whenever Amy misbehaved, we could simply ask her if she wanted to be like Sad Sack Sally. Invariably, she would answer, "No!" (a favorite word for 2-year-olds) and set out to prove that she was different. Hearing my father tell my daughter these marvelously creative stories reminded me of how he had similar stories when I was a small child.

In 1977, the APA membership elected my father president, to take office in 1979. Between the election and the time he assumed office, my father visited every state and large county psychological association in the country and confirmed that, except for a few isolated practitioners, neither psychologists nor social workers treated substance abuse. The few who did were looked down upon as inferior and incapable of treating a more interesting and worthy clientele. My father decided to use his presidential address, which he delivered during the 1979 APA convention in New York City, to make substance-abuse treatment a respectable therapeutic endeavor. I listened proudly to his landmark address, "Turning Bread Into Stones: Our Modern Anti-Miracle," in which he played upon a biblical text and the drug vernacular of the time. In this address, he outlined his model for substance-abuse treatment, succeeding in elevating it to the level of a respectable and worthy endeavor for psychologists. The address subsequently was published in the *American Psychologist*. The APA received more than 7,000 requests for reprints, far outnumbering the usual few dozen requests for reprints of presidential addresses.

Although my father's research on medical cost offset persuaded insurers to pay for psychotherapy, only psychiatrists were eligible for reimbursement. As the first chair of the APA's Committee on Health Insurance (COHI), my father developed the freedom-of-choice legislation that amended the insurance codes of every state so that if an insurer reimbursed psychiatrists, it must also reimburse psychologists. When this legislation passed in a significant number of states, the private practice of psychology really began to flourish.

I watched my father become increasingly frustrated during the many years he spent attempting to influence the APA's Education and Training Board to change its rules so that practitioners could serve on faculties with the same prestige as academicians. Failing to do so, he founded the four campuses of the California School of Professional Psychology (CSPP), the nation's first such professional school. This resulted in the Vail Conference and the changes in graduate education whereby psychotherapy and other subjects are taught by practitioners.

As a child, I had heard my father talking about his vision of forming the first professional school in psychology. I was astounded at how quickly that abstract vision became a reality. However, the amazement and pride I felt soon turned to sadness as I watched my father go through one of the most difficult periods in his life, which, in turn, became one of the most difficult for me, and the rest of our family as well. My father spent several years being disdained by the APA and undergoing merciless attacks by a mutinous faculty. He undoubtedly was depressed as he struggled to remain president of CSPP, which the accreditation bodies said he needed to do until the school became accredited. At the same time, many faculty members whom my father had considered close personal friends, as well as colleagues, tried everything possible to force his resignation. My father lost his zest for life, becoming increasingly irritable. He was constantly on edge, had trouble sleeping, and seemed to forget how to relax and enjoy being with his family. Eventually, after the Board of Trustees refused his resignation four times, which he submitted every six months over two years, my father was dismissed from CSPP. Although this was quite difficult for him at the time, it did allow our family to return to normal. After recovering from the shock of being fired, my father felt liberated and was able to engage in fun activities again. A year later, he was overwhelmingly elected APA president.

When I decided to become a psychologist and was investigating doctoral programs, I did not consider the California School of Professional Psychology. Instead, I attended the School of Professional Psychology at Wright State University in Dayton, Ohio, one of many professional schools my father helped to establish in an advisory capacity. I have often been asked why I did not attend CSPP. But seeing my father treated so poorly there and then unceremoniously ousted, I had no desire to subject myself to the same type of treatment at the hands of some of the same individuals who had tormented him. At Wright State, I received an out-standing education with clinicians teaching the same practical, clinically oriented courses my father had envisioned to prepare students for clinical practice. I did not want to be known as the founder's daughter, as I un-doubtedly would have been at CSPP, which would have severely hampered my educational experience.

When I received my Psy.D. degree from Wright State, my father was the commencement speaker. The Wright State faculty figured he would be there and so would have the opportunity to invite him to speak at a time he was turning down such requests weekly. When it was my turn to be hooded, the dean of the School of Professional Psychology, Dr. Ron Fox, stepped aside and allowed my father to do the honor. My father had always called me his "favorite daughter," and even though I was his only daughter, I knew this meant I was special. After I received my doctorate in psychology, he began referring to me as his "favorite daughter and favorite colleague."

After leaving Kaiser Permanente, my father served as executive director of the Mental Research Institute (MRI) in Palo Alto, California, where he continued his work in brief therapy. At MRI, he further refined his protocols and made his model of Focused, Intermittent Psychotherapy Throughout the Life Cycle, which he had begun at Kaiser, even more time efficient and cost-effective.

In 1981, my father established the Foundation for Behavioral Health, which conducted the seven-year longitudinal study on behavioral-care services known as the Hawaii Project. This landmark research once again demonstrated the medical cost offset phenomenon and the validity of my father's model of focused, intermittent, psychotherapy. It remains *the* definitive research the government uses in planning. During those seven years, my father maintained a condominium in Honolulu near Waikiki Beach, which he and his colleagues used during their frequent trips to Hawaii to oversee the project. Both my brother and I accompanied our father to Hawaii on separate occasions, and enjoyed touring the islands and engaging in water sports while Father worked. We both went snorkeling in Hanauma Bay, where our father had taught us to snorkel when we were 7 and 8 years old by having us hold onto a rubber raft he towed while snorkeling.

My father was able to foresee all the trends in healthcare delivery that have taken place during his career. Most notably, he foresaw the impending industrialization of healthcare, about which he warned the profession of psychology in his article in the *American Psychologist* in 1986, "The

Dismantling of Our Healthcare System: Strategies for the Survival of Psychological Practice." This article provided a blueprint for how psychologists could own what came to be known as managed care and keep business interests out. To demonstrate that his ideas could actually be implemented , he formed American Biodyne, a practitioner-driven national company, as a model that he intended to limit to 500,000 enrollees. When his colleagues ignored the plan, calling it grandiose, he took his foot off the brake and American Biodyne grew to 14.5 million enrollees in 39 states. Prior to its sale to MedCo/Merck in 1992, Biodyne had never been the subject of a malpractice suit or complaint to a licensing board or ethics committee.

When American Biodyne was still a small demonstration project with fewer than 500,000 enrollees, my father told us of his plan to retire. However, when colleagues made it clear that they had no intention of following his blueprint, he decided to allow the company to grow. This was one of several times that my father has flunked retirement. Every time he retires from one position, he manages to find one or two new endeavors to take its place.

Shortly after I moved to Ohio to attend Wright State University, Biodyne began operations in that state. As was usually the case when Biodyne moved into new territory, local practitioners would express fear that the company would affect their jobs. I called my father and asked, "Did you have to piss off the state of Ohio as soon as I moved here?"

When I was completing my course work for my doctorate, I decided I wanted to do both my internship and postdoctoral fellowship at Biodyne. Although I knew quite a bit about my father's model of focused, intermittent psychotherapy (also called the Biodyne model), I wanted supervised experience in using it. When I began my internship at the Biodyne center in Tempe, Arizona, I was assigned a very difficult patient who had been seen unsuccessfully by every therapist in the center. I remember asking myself, "What would my father do?" I recalled my eavesdropping on his telephone conversations with patients and the many speeches I had heard him deliver, and simply did what I thought he would probably do. I treated the patient successfully in two sessions. Because all the professional staff members had failed with this patient, my supervisor had me present the case at the weekly clinical case conference, after which he said, "You did an adequate job by resolving that case in two sessions. But your father would have done it in one."

During the four years I worked for Biodyne as an intern, postdoctoral fellow and staff psychologist, I grieved to see my father's model become increasingly eroded as his clinically driven company was taken over by the business interests of MedCo/Merck, then Merit, and now Magellan. Nonetheless, his blueprint of a practitioner-driven national behavioral healthcare delivery system still stands as the model to be emulated. It earned him the appellation "Father of Behavioral Healthcare Delivery," which was conferred on him at the opening session of the 1997 Behavioral Healthcare Tomorrow conference in Washington, D.C.

When my father started American Biodyne, he saw training as integral to the model's success, and created a program that all Biodyne clinicians were required to attend. This intensive 130-hour two-week program later became known as the "Biodyne boot camp." Even after his model no longer was utilized at American Biodyne, he continued to teach the Biodyne boot camp on occasion. As a veteran of the boot camp who has utilized the model both while working for Biodyne and later in private practice, I have helped my father by teaching segments of it in Scottsdale, Arizona; in London, England; and most recently, in Reno, at the University of Nevada.

In advancing psychology, my father has served on two Presidential Mental Health Commissions, those of Presidents John Kennedy and Jimmy Carter. He was advisor to the U.S. Senate Subcommittee on Health, chaired by Senator Edward Kennedy, for three years. He was on the U.S. Senate Finance Committee for four years and with the Health Economics Branch of what is now the U.S. Department of Health and Human Services for six years. He has testified before the Congress 18 times on behalf of psychology and mental health, and his research has been entered into the *Congressional Record* eight times. My mother, brother, and I sometimes accompanied my father on his trips to Washington, and my brother and I each accompanied him on separate occasions, during which he arranged for us to observe sessions of the Senate and the House of Representatives. He introduced us to some of the senators who had become his friends, and who gave us an insider's perspective on the workings of the U.S. government.

Along with his various other undertakings, my father managed to find time to found the National Academics of Practice in Washington, D.C., the nation's interdisciplinary national health forum composed of 100 of the most prestigious practitioners in each of nine Academies: dentistry, medicine, nursing, optometry, osteopathic medicine, podiatric medicine, psychology, social work, and veterinary medicine. He also founded the National Council of Schools of Professional Psychology, the American Managed Behavioral Healthcare Association, and several other national organizations. At the present time, he is the president of the Foundation for Behavioral Health and chair of the Nicholas & Dorothy Cummings Foundation.

Shortly after I became a psychologist, my father told me of his desire to leave some money to endow a nonprofit behavioral health foundation after his death, and asked if I would be willing to establish and oversee such a foundation. I suggested that he not wait that long, as he might enjoy seeing another of his dreams become a reality during his lifetime. Thus, the Nicholas and Dorothy Cummings Foundation was born. As the foundation's president, I have thoroughly enjoyed giving our annual Cummings PSYCHE Award to distinguished practitioners who have made significant and enduring contributions to time-effective psychotherapy and/or proven innovations in behavioral health delivery systems, especially as these pertain to behavioral health in primary care, and whose contributions reflect a career and lifetime of achievement. Each recipient of the award has been a giant in the field and worthy of the prize of $50,000 tax-free, a statue of the Greek goddess Psyche after whom psychology and psychiatry were named, and a calligraphied citation. However, I thought my father was excited enough to do cartwheels when I told him that his mentor during his days at Kaiser Permanente, Dr. Morris F. Collen, had been chosen by the Selection Committee to receive the 2001 award.

In 1997, the Nicholas and Dorothy Cummings Foundation endowed the first chair in organized behavioral healthcare delivery, the Nicholas Cummings Professor of Organized Behavioral Healthcare Delivery, at the University of Nevada, Reno. The chair is currently held by William T. O'Donohue, Ph.D., who is one of the editors of this volume. The endowed chair has three missions: (1) to rewrite the curriculum for professional psychology in the 21st century, (2) to establish a research arm dedicated to the healthcare delivery research of the future, and (3) to form an entrepreneurial endeavor with the University of Nevada to bring behavioral health into primary care. All three missions are in operation, with the last called the University Alliance for Behavioral Care (U/ABC). My father serves as chair of its board, and I serve as a board member (secretary/treasurer).

Along with these many accomplishments, my father has found time to publish 24 books and over 400 refereed journal articles and book chapters. He and I have collaborated in writing two books (*The Essence of Psychotherapy: Reinventing the Art in the Era of Data*, and, more recently, *The First Session with Substance Abusers*), and together have produced two edited volumes (*Surviving the Demise of Solo Practice: Mental Health Practitioners Prospering in the Era of Managed Care*, as well as *Behavioral Health in Primary Care: A Guide for Clinical Integration*). My father now refers to me as his "favorite daughter, favorite colleague, and favorite coauthor."

I have seen my father receive every honor and award the profession of psychology can bestow, as well as four honorary doctorates for his work in education, practice, and the Greek classics. However, his greatest joy is that he has been married to my mother for 55 years. His most rewarding accomplishments were raising his psychologist daughter and his son, whom he boasts is one of the five honest lawyers in the nation. And he is most proud of his granddaughter, Amy, who has his extroversion, his flair for dramatic storytelling, his seemingly unlimited energy, and his endless creativity. After practicing for 45 years in his birthstate of California, my father is now a proud resident of the nation's fastest growing state, Nevada, There he holds the position of Distinguished Professor at the University of Nevada, Reno, and is chairman of the Board of Directors for U/ABC. He still travels, both for pleasure and to share his vast clinical experience in workshops and keynote addresses, and writes for publication on a regular basis. Thus, he continues to flunk retirement.

{ 1 }

THE FOUNDING OF THE
KAISER PERMANENTE MENTAL HEALTH SYSTEM:
HOW THE FIRST COMPREHENSIVE
PSYCHOTHERAPY BENEFIT WAS WRITTEN

FEW PSYCHOLOGISTS PRACTICING TODAY are aware that until the early 1970s, psychotherapy was not a covered benefit in health insurance. In most plans, it was specifically excluded in the contract language, as the conventional wisdom was that psychotherapy was too ethereal to be understood by actuaries, and too intangible to be financed by insurance. Psychotherapy was paid for "out-of-pocket," which meant that those in treatment had to be able to afford it. There were sufficient numbers of patients affluent enough to support the limited number of psychologist pioneers who ventured into private practice, but without a psychotherapy insurance benefit, the saturation point of psychologists in independent practice would have been reached by the mid-1970s. Once psychotherapy became a prepaid insurance benefit, psychologists, disenchanted by having to be under the heel of psychiatry in their jobs, stampeded into private practice in droves.

This is the story of how that first comprehensive prepaid psychotherapy benefit was successfully implemented, and how the demonstrated cost savings in medicine and surgery that resulted from the psychological interventions that were provided moved the entire insurance industry to make psychotherapy a covered benefit. It is also a second, and more important, story. In order to move policy into the future, it is often first necessary to form an organization that, through its success in doing the impossible, disproves the conventional wisdom. In essence, this has been my career, or actually a succession of careers: forming organizations designed to move psychology forward.

ORIGINS OF THE
KAISER PERMANENTE HEALTH PLAN

When I first joined the staff of Kaiser Permanente in San Francisco in the late 1950s, as chief psychologist, psychotherapy was excluded from its list of insured benefits. How this changed, and why, can only be appreciated if preceded by a brief history of what is generally accepted to have been the prototype of the modern health maintenance organization (HMO), a term that was not to be coined until decades after the founding of Kaiser Permanente.

The building of Boulder Dam, subsequently renamed Hoover Dam, was well underway when the government sought bids to construct the aqueduct leading from the newly formed Lake Mead to Los Angeles. A small gravel-hauling contractor from Oakland, California, won the contract, having bid fully a third less than the next lowest bidder. The head of this small company was an unknown by the name of Henry J. Kaiser, destined to become one of America's great industrialists. Once the contract was signed, he systematically set about creating the infrastructure (literally, the company) to do the job, acquiring a fleet of trucks and earth-moving equipment, and buying a bankrupt cement plant in Fontana, California, on the edge of the Mohave Desert. It was from Kaiser that I learned the sequence of getting the business first, and then creating the structure to deliver that business. Henry would say, "By doing it backward, you can bid lower than anyone else because you are not carrying a lot of useless overhead while you're waiting to get the business." Of course, there are few people who can do it "backward" as he could. He did it again with the shipyards that did not exist until he got the contract to build the Victory ships that saved Great Britain and supplied the Allied forces in World War II. Not only did he create the shipyards in record time, but once they were operational, he delivered the ships in five days from laying the keel to launching. I attribute a lot of my success in forming organizations to Kaiser's example of doing it backward while everyone else does it forward. It served me particularly well in forming American Biodyne. The centers to service the contracted populations were never formed until I got the contracts. That way, the company could leapfrog across the country, going to the states with the best opportunities, rather than being tied to the locale where the infrastructure was waiting to be utilized.

A little-known fact is that Kaiser almost failed on his first big project, the aqueduct, not because he lacked business acumen, but because he could not get healthcare for his employees. Even though it was the Great Depression, marked by the greatest rate of unemployment in U.S. history, construction workers were reluctant to relocate their families to the desert where, on the dirt roads of the era, the nearest doctor was 15 to 20 hours away. When things looked bleak, a young physician from Los Angeles made Kaiser an offer he could not refuse. For 5 cents an employee-hour, he would build the facilities and staff them with full medical/surgical care not only for the employees, but also for their families. This young physician/visionary was Sidney Garfield, whom Kaiser welcomed with open arms and a healthcare contract. Capitated healthcare was born on the Mojave Desert in 1934.

Shortly after the aqueduct was completed, World War II began and Kaiser took Garfield with him to provide healthcare to the tens of thousands of new shipyard employees he was recruiting from the farms of the Midwest. Complete healthcare was one of the biggest inducements for them to leave the farms and move west to Richmond, California, where Kaiser would train them in various shipbuilding trades.

FIND A NEED AND FILL IT

When the war was over, Kaiser prevailed on Garfield to continue the concept of a capitated staff-model health plan and offer it to the public. This was consistent with another of his cardinal principles: *"Find a need and fill it."* He always maintained that if one finds a real need, marketing will be minimal, as the market will come to you. This principle served me well many years later when I discerned the need for carving out behavioral care into a separate managed health system.

Garfield joined Henry Kaiser in this project, named it the Kaiser Foundation Health Plan, and staffed it with the Permanente Medical Group, a name borrowed nostalgically from the bankrupt Permanente Cement Company in Fontana that helped launch Kaiser's construction company. As Henry had anticipated, it was an instant success. Among the first to join were the former shipyard workers, but more important was its large-scale acceptance by the labor unions in Northern California. In the postwar era, organized labor began to agitate for employer-paid healthcare for all workers and their families, a radical concept at the time. The new plan was attractive because it was lower in cost and provided greater benefits than the indemnity plans of the time. Garfield would not accept a group into healthplan membership unless it offered an employee a choice between the Kaiser Foundation Health Plan and an indemnity health-insurance plan. This assured patient choice and increased the probability of patient satisfaction. Overwhelmingly, employees chose the Kaiser plan because it had none of the deductibles, co-payments, and other limitations common in the indemnity plans. Soon the health plan caught the attention of nonunion employees in white-collar jobs, and by the time I had joined the Permanente Medical Group in the late 1950s, Kaiser had over two million subscribers and 39 hospitals/medical centers scattered throughout Northern California. Furthermore, the Southern California health plan was well underway, as was that in Portland, Oregon, which was soon to be followed by Hawaii.

THE PHYSICIAN EQUITY MODEL

Garfield was meticulous in making certain that Kaiser-sponsored healthcare would always be clinically driven. Additionally, he maintained that "doctors work harder when they work for themselves." Combining these two concepts, he created the physician equity model in which the practitioners owned the delivery system. New physicians had three years to prove their ability and productivity, after which they could be elected "participants." This meant that they could be part of the decision-making process, but could not receive dividends. At the end of five years, the physicians would be eligible for ownership. If elected, they became partners and shared in the divisible surplus (money saved by doing the job for less than the capitation rate). This surplus was further predicated on the productivity of each practitioner as rated by his or her peers. When the outmoded laws governing the corporate practice of medicine were eliminated, the partnership became a corporation and each physician was a shareholder.

Typically, the divisible surplus could equal or exceed the annual "salary" (actually, a participant/owner's regularized drawing account) received by each shareholder. At retirement, the practitioner turned in the shares in exchange for a pension. In working at Kaiser Permanente, it was obvious to me that the productivity, vitality, clinical integrity, and general success of the system were the result of the clinician control and physician equity. I adopted both of these concepts in founding American Biodyne, the only clinically driven system of managed behavioral care.

THE ROLE OF THE SOMATIZER IN THE DEVELOPMENT OF THE HEALTH PLAN

Early in the 1950s, the Permanente physicians discovered that 60% of all visits to physicians were by patients who either had no physical illness, or had a physical illness that was being exacerbated by psychological factors. Today, this is a nationally recognized phenomenon, and the American Medical Association (AMA) accepts 60% to 70% as the national figure. The reason it was first discovered at Kaiser Permanente was the nature of the health plan itself. Kaiser physicians were capitated and did not have to fill out reimbursement forms that demanded diagnoses before payment, as is typical of an indemnity plan. At Kaiser, all care was prepaid, and the physician was not compelled to render a working diagnosis whenever a definitive diagnosis was not possible.

Sidney Garfield had anticipated such a phenomenon and had conceptualized a mental health system into which the somatizing patient would be triaged from the medical system. He insisted that the new system be staffed by psychologists rather than psychiatrists. The latter are physicians, and Garfield argued that they would ultimately contribute to the patient's belief that the condition was physical rather than psychological. Timothy Leary was hired as chief psychologist to create such a system, and soon an impressive staff of psychologists hired by him was seeing patients triaged from the medical system. The only way a patient could see a psychologist was to be referred by his or her physician. There was a co-payment of $5, about one-third to one-fourth of the private-practice rate in the early 1950s.

Friction soon developed between Garfield and Leary, who was more research oriented than delivery committed. He refused to have his psychologists do psychological consultations for hospitalized patients when requested, and he was totally opposed to his staff's serving on-call in the late evenings and on weekends. Consequently, psychiatrists had to be brought in at high private fees to do these consultations and perform the on-call services. After three years, Garfield had had enough, and he fired Leary and his entire staff.

This was before Timothy Leary went to Harvard and soon thereafter became the so-called high priest of LSD. It is interesting to speculate what might have happened had Leary remained at Kaiser, and had entered his LSD phase while there. I would never have gone to Kaiser, and the entire history of psychotherapy as a prepaid benefit might have been different. On the other hand, it is doubtful that Kaiser Permanente would have tolerated Leary's LSD priesthood in the same way that it was tolerated at Harvard by Professor McClelland, to whose psychology department Leary went when Garfield fired him.

I knew Tim as an excellent researcher, and his interpersonal theories were intriguing. He was an intelligent man who drank too much and later asserted to me that LSD had cured what potentially might have been serious alcoholism. After he left Harvard and became a 1960–70s guru, he was the first person to go to a federal prison (at Lompoc) for attempting to smuggle marijuana *into* Mexico. I saw him again after he was released from prison, and by that time, he seemed to have "fried" his brains. He described how he was a visitor from the 25th century who was trapped in the 20th century, a time that he found very boring and intellectually trite. Then, about five years before he died, he confessed to me that he had to take that long sojourn through LSD, only to discover ultimately that the best high was Ripple wine. Knowing Sid, I doubt if he would have tolerated even the first phase of Tim's sojourn.

KAISER PERMANENTE AND ORGANIZED MEDICINE

Organized medicine aggressively opposed the Kaiser Health Plan, which it labeled "socialized medicine." Consequently, Permanente physicians were not eligible to join the county medical societies, severely limiting their ability to hold hospital privileges or to conduct other forms of practice outside the Kaiser health plan. No wonder that Garfield chose to build his own hospitals and medical centers, thus freeing the health plan from AMA interference and control.

Henry Kaiser was not aware of the circumstances that barred Permanente physicians from membership in the county medical societies until he and Garfield were traveling from the West Coast to Chicago by train. When Sid told him about it, he asked who would be the person to talk with at the AMA headquarters in Chicago, and was told that it would be

Morris Fishbein, physician and long-time executive director. At Henry's insistence, at the next stop, Sid alighted from the train and phoned (it must be remembered this was long before cellular telephones) Fishbein, who was delighted to grant an appointment to the celebrated industrialist. At the meeting two days later, Henry informed Fishbein that in his view, he was conducting a health boycott, illegal according to federal law, and that he could expect a lawsuit if the practice was not rectified immediately. Fishbein buckled, Kaiser accepted a compromise, and Permanente physicians were admitted to the county medical societies after receiving Kaiser's promise that the health plan coverage would never exceed one-sixth of California's population. The Permanente physicians joined the county medical societies and, because of their large numbers, became a significant, if not dominant, force.

Enter Nick Cummings

After Leary left, Kaiser Permanente went for about a year without a psychologist, and then embarked on a search to find a replacement. This time, it was decided to center the project in San Francisco instead of Oakland, where Leary had his offices. The task of finding a psychologist fell to Morris F. Collen, a physician cofounder with Garfield of the Kaiser Permanente system. He headed the West Bay series of hospitals and medical centers that stretched from Santa Rosa on the north through San Francisco to Santa Clara on the south. Morrie, one of my early mentors, is now in his late 80s and remains one of my closest friends. An electrical engineer he became so interested in capitated medicine that he attended medical school at Johns Hopkins so he could join Garfield in the postwar Kaiser Permanente effort. I decided to apply for this job.

I had completed my training in New York and returned to my hometown of San Francisco, where I began a psychoanalytically oriented private practice. Although I always enjoyed working with patients, after a few years, I became concerned that with an analytic practice, I might in my lifetime be able to treat perhaps 80 to 100 persons. Furthermore, they would be affluent patients who might not be the most in need of therapy, as the majority of Americans could not afford to see me four to five times a week over several years. I learned of the job at Kaiser Permanente, and I applied, more out of curiosity than serious intent. There were several dozen other applicants, and I was willing to defer to them until I had my interview with Morrie Collen, and subsequently, Sid Garfield. I was told by both that at Kaiser Permanente, psychologists were not highly respected, and that if I were to be offered the job, I would have to agree that I could be fired within six months for no stated reason. They confided that they were still smarting from the Timothy Leary fiasco, and I was essentially guilty until I proved myself innocent. They recited a mythical story about nuclear bombs exploding in the Bay Area. The physicians dropped everything else and treated the injured around the clock while psychologists continued their research and published a dozen books describing the calamity. This was tantamount to waving a red flag in front of a bull. I was determined to get this job and show them what a psychologist could really do.

It should be noted that in spite of the previous experience, Garfield held to his concept that the mental-health triage system should be created by a psychologist rather than a psychiatrist. I got the job, and I was fired and rehired four times within the first two years, usually because I went forward with various projects or publications without bureaucratic approval. The last time I was fired, it was by Morrie. Actually, this was the last firing and rehiring I counted. I was fired several more times, but I took the position that since Dr. Collen had fired and rehired me, the only one left who could fire me was Dr. Garfield himself. This worked, and I was rendered essentially untouchable, allowing me to achieve my ultimate goal of making psychotherapy a covered benefit on a large scale, and to develop the focused psychotherapy that years later was named Brief Intermittent Psychotherapy Throughout the Life Cycle (for more information, see Cummings and Sayama, 1995).

In the beginning, I was working with a chief psychiatrist, Bernard I. Kahn, who had preceded me by several years. Barney was a likable man, easy to work with, but limited in psychiatric skills. Nonetheless, he had the ability to persuade his nonpsychiatric physician colleagues of the importance of psychological treatment. Before becoming a psychiatrist, he had practiced as an internist, which gave him credibility with primary-care physicians. From the beginning, Barney and I agreed that we had to move from the "courtesy" psychotherapy system with its mandatory physician referral and co-payment to making psychotherapy a covered benefit. We spent a great deal of time pricing the benefit, and our figures clustered around a pm/pm (per member/per month) of 25 cents. Everyone else at Kaiser Permanente thought this was much too low. It was finally decided to embark on a pilot project involving certain specified subscriber groups, but at a pm/pm of 75 cents. Unfortunately, Barney died in his office of a heart attack shortly after the demonstration project began, and so did not see the final results. Time demonstrated that the capitated rate as we originally estimated it was amazingly accurate.

THE PSYCHOTHERAPY DELIVERY SYSTEM

As described in Volume I, my psychoanalytic background logically dictated that all the psychologists and social workers who came to work with us would use couches in the treatment process. The ludicrous series of events that led to our divesting ourselves of the couches will not be repeated, but it does bear repeating that our new, essentially blue-collar population necessitated a major paradigm shift in our developing treatment model. It required more of a focus and more activity on the part of the therapist. For lack of a better term, it was initially called HMO therapy, but eventually it came to be known as Brief Intermittent Psychotherapy Throughout the Life Cycle (Cummings & Sayama, 1995; Cummings & Cummings, 1997) and resembled the way in which most therapies practice today.

Of importance is the fact that the Kaiser Permanente system provided an atmosphere free of theoretical pariahs, and one where innovation was encouraged and rewarded. To say that I took advantage of the opportunities this accorded would be a gross understatement. I experimented constantly and flourished in the nondoctrinaire environment that was in such contrast to my original psychoanalytic orientation. Throughout all of this, I had the support of Sid Garfield and the invaluable prodding, chiding, and encouragement of Morrie Collen. When I complained that certain innovations did not work, or that the Kaiser patients seemed not to be "psychologically minded" (a prevalent copout at the time), they both stated with all seriousness, "If you can't solve a problem, try looking at it upside down. Nick, why not stand on your head? You will be amazed to see what you've been missing." It was reminiscent of Henry Kaiser's dictum that when everyone else does it one way, it is best to do it backward.

Once the mental-health service was well established in San Francisco, we began expanding the concept to the other medical centers. Chiefs hired to head clinics in other centers either spent several months working and training in San Francisco, or persons from San Francisco transferred to the new facilities. In this way, the new HMO therapy was diffused throughout the system.

It might be noted, however, that in spite of his otherwise iconoclastic behavior, to the day Barney died, he used a psychoanalytic couch. This was a source of constant amusement to us all.

THE MEDICAL COST OFFSET PHENOMENON

The discovery of the medical cost offset phenomenon with its subsequent impact was thoroughly addressed in Volume I (Thomas & J. Cummings, 2000). It refers to the body of research demonstrating that (1) patients with emotional distress manifest this in physical symptoms that baffle the doctor, and (2) brief psychological interventions reduce this "somatization" with a savings in medicine and surgery that is more than sufficient to pay the cost of the behavioral interventions. In the present context, it is important to note that this research not only led to Kaiser Permanente's making psychotherapy a covered benefit, but also was the economic basis for the national policy change that now saw psychotherapy as doable in the insurance sector.

After the demonstration project had been in operation for three to four years, it was time to perform outcome research to determine whether we had been effective or ineffective. Most of the staff favored the traditional outcomes variables: return to work, divorces avoided, patient reports of satisfaction and improvement, success in school, and other hard-to-measure factors. I insisted that since our avowed mission to address somatizing, the best outcome variable would be a reduction in medical/surgical costs for the somatizers. In support was my psychiatric colleague William T. Follette, who from the very beginning saw this as the important variable. Although most of the staff was less than enthusiastic, Bill and I went ahead, following an initial pilot study that had been conducted while Barney was still living. The results were surprising to us, since even brief or single-session therapy (when the latter is by patient, not therapist choice) was effective far beyond the cost of providing the psychological interventions.

The initial pilot project was first reported at a White House conference and caught the attention of the Health Economics Branch of the Department of Health, Education, and Welfare. It was after this White House conference that Morrie Collen fired me for releasing the study without permission. Morrie worried that the study would end up on the negotiating table, with employers using the results to demand psychotherapy benefits without an increase in premiums. I held my ground and

Morrie relented. His previous engineering background had made him too much of a scientist to suppress any evidence-based results.

In the next few years (circa 1965–1970), I, and, to a lesser extent, Bill Follette, spent a great deal of time working with Agnes Brewster, who headed the Health Economics Branch, and her colleague, Royal Crystal. Roy became particularly enamored of the mental-health system at Kaiser Permanente and awarded us a series of research and demonstration grants. This enabled us to continue our cutting-edge research, and also guaranteed the continuing support of our clinical innovations within our own system. It also focused national attention on medical cost offset, with the National Institute of Mental Health (NIMH) sponsoring a series of replications, all yielding positive results, and culminating in the Bethesda Consensus Conference in 1980 under the auspices of the Carter Administration. This verified the phenomenon of medical cost offset, noted that the magnitude of the offset was higher in organized settings, and set the research priorities for the next decade.

HELP FROM ACROSS THE SEA: MICHAEL BALINT

When I first joined the staff of Kaiser Permanente, the term entered on a patient's chart when exhaustive tests over a long period elicited no demonstrable physical illness was "hypochondriac." I found this term distasteful, as it implied that it was the fault of the patient, and I immediately set about to change it. Every term I came up with was rejected until late one night, during a brainstorming session, I used the term somatization, with the person somatizing being a somatizer. Both Sid and Morrie accepted this term, saying it sounded medical and would be acceptable to physicians. But even though we were able to rid ourselves of the offending terminology, the relationship between stress and physical symptoms was not well understood at that time. We searched the literature for help and found Michael Balint's illuminating 1957 book, *The Doctor, the Patient and His Illness.*

Great Britain had instituted universal healthcare under a government-sponsored system shortly after World War II. Almost immediately, they, as we were years later, were inundated by so-called hypochondriacs, and they instituted a psychological system to deal with it. Balint's approach was that primary-care physicians had to be retrained to think more like psychologists, and psychologists had to be retrained to practice more like primary-care physicians. His book was like manna from heaven, and we invited Dr. Balint and his wife, a psychotherapist, to join us for a one-week training seminar. They accepted, and spent six days with us, teaching from early morning until late at night. They met not only with our mental health staff, but also with all of our primary-care physicians, offering their rich clinical experience and suggesting solutions that we had not yet considered. The concept of psychologists as primary-care providers took a giant leap forward in our system that week in 1961. The Balints' fee was $1,000 for the week for both of them, plus their expenses, a modest sum even for that era, and a pittance in retrospect. Since most practitioners today know Balint only secondhand, I would be remiss if I did not say something about him. He was an effective physician, an incisive psychologist, a patient but meticulous teacher, and a compassionate and charming human being who imparted his vast knowledge freely, with the assistance of his wife. Although what he had to say was radical at the time, he made it sound simple and plausible because he had discovered his insights in the trenches familiar to all overworked and harassed primary-care physicians.

DIFFERENCES WITH SIDNEY GARFIELD

In conceptualizing the treatment of the somatizer, Garfield believed that such a patient should be triaged from the medical system to a separate psychological system. This conceptualization is described in one of the papers I published before my own thinking about collaboration and integration between psychology and primary care had gelled. It is reprinted in Chapter 10 of Volume I, and represents Garfield's model as we had implemented it. As I began to develop my own ideas, my views came into direct conflict with those of my superior. The presence of Michael Balint was, therefore, critical in orienting the primary-care physicians in an integrated model rather than in a model of triage into a separate system.

It was not easy for me to disagree with such a brilliant innovator as Sidney, and it was doubly difficult because of his and Morrie's support of the radical innovations we had already implemented. Among these was the dropping of the intake procedure, a familiar practice now, but unheard of in any other clinic in 1959. Quite simply, the therapist who saw the patient for the first time saw that patient throughout the course of treatment. Additionally, the psychotherapist was trained in psychopharmacology and was the one who recommended that a specific psychotropic be prescribed. Only in complex cases did the psychiatrist actually see the patient. By conducting the prescribing in this manner, the intrusion of a physician did not dilute or otherwise interfere with the transference to the psychotherapist. This, too, has become a familiar procedure in many practice settings. Our colleagues in the community predicted that the many malpractice suites that would swiftly follow would put an end to both such "irresponsible" practices. In spite of these threats, the leadership (Sid and Morrie) approved the practices, but made certain that the training of the nonphysicians was sound and comprehensive, and in the best interest of patient care.

Not a single untoward event occurred, so when we implemented the next radical innovation, it went unnoticed in the psychiatric community. Psychologists and social workers were trained to be on call, handling psychiatric emergencies by telephone and in the emergency room after hours, and to provide consultations to physicians throughout the day. Since we were doing this in our own hospitals, we did not need to apply for hospital privileges for our psychotherapists — which elsewhere most certainly would have been denied. Of particular importance was the confidence of the administration in our innovations in spite of the efforts of two of our own psychiatrists to stop them. The rest of the psychiatrists were supportive, and became increasingly so as the arrangement proved itself over time.

All of these innovations were still a separate system, housed in a building across the street from the hospital and most of the medical clinics. What would happen if psychologists were to invade the primary-care setting itself?

THE NOBLE EXPERIMENT

In 1962, we decided to do just that as a demonstration project in the San Francisco Kaiser Permanente Hospital and Medical Center. A social worker or psychologist would be physically present in every clinic during its hours of operation, whether an appointment clinic, a drop in clinic, or the emergency service. Because none of the salaried mental health practitioners wanted a full-time assignment to one of the medical clinics, a schedule of rotating coverage was implemented that proved satisfactory in providing total coverage on the premises of each clinic.

During a six-month trial period, psychologists and social workers were rotated by schedule through all of the primary-care clinics so that each was actually on the premises at one point. A primary-care physician (PCP) who wanted to involve a behavioral health practitioner had only to explain the reasons to the patient, and both would walk a few feet down the hall to the psychologist's or social worker's office. Then, instead of leaving the patient there, the physician would remain and would be involved in the subsequent examination and disposition. The behavioral-care practitioners wore white coats, as did the physicians, and a number of other deliberate steps were taken to blur the line of demarcation between medicine and behavioral health, in order to provide unified, seamless primary care.

The PCPs made full use of the arrangement, with a surprisingly large number of patients, and learned by participating in the behavioral-care process. Weekly clinical case conferences attended by all involved reviewed the interventions and the course of the most difficult cases. At the end of the six-month trial period, the PCPs had nothing but praise for the arrangement and were enthusiastic about its being continued. The psychologists and social workers, however, were lukewarm, and preferring that the project be discontinued. The PCPs were insistent, and the arrangement was extended for six months, at the end of which the psychologists and social workers threatened to mutiny rather than participate. The project collapsed.

The resistance on the part of the mental health practitioners was surprising and unexpected. Attempts during the second six months of the project to address and ameliorate some of their concerns were unsuccessful, and by the end of the year, they were adamant in their opposition. In retrospect, this outcome might have been anticipated when these same practitioners initially expressed reluctance to spend more than two hours a day in the primary-care clinics. The major lesson learned was that most mental health practitioners are unsuited to participating in primary care, and the psychologists and social workers who do must be carefully selected.

The objections voiced by the mental health workers evidently were deeply felt, but sometimes seemed ludicrous. They resented wearing white coats, for example, complaining that this contributed to a loss of identity. All were insistent that a separate mental health clinic was like a temple, wherein patients were partially cured by merely walking through its portals. This esoteric, and perhaps amusing, version of the placebo effect was proffered with all sincerity, underscoring how far the participating psychologists and social workers would go to avoid conceptualizing anything even remotely like primary care. But the most outspoken opposition had to do with the issue of confidentiality. The argument that confidentiality belongs to the patient; that it can, and often must, involve a team of healers; and that in one year, not a single patient complained, or even expressed concern about it did nothing to mitigate the stridency of the mental health practitioners' stance. With considerable emotion, and not a great deal of logic, they had unanimously concluded that the psychotherapeutic process had been violated.

There was a lesson learned from this early noble experiment: there are no differences in outlook, flexibility, and the ability to work with physicians between traditionally trained mental health practitioners and those we learned to call behavioral-care providers and who were willing to learn how to work in primary care. As new programs developed within Kaiser Permanente, so did departments of behavioral medicine involving psychologists, physicians, and other health personnel that hired their own behavioral-care specialists, leaving the traditionalists to toil in the temple.

THE NATION'S FIRST AUTOMATED MULTIPHASIC HEALTH SCREENING

Computers in the early 1960s were cumbersome, relatively slow devices that made input difficult and data retrieval a challenge. The personal computer (or anything resembling a desktop version) was still 20 years away. The instruments were so sensitive that they were housed in hermetically sealed rooms, lined up like a row of refrigerator-sized boxes with whirling tape wheels. To enter the computer room, one had to shed all dust, don special smocks, and refrain from eating, drinking, or smoking there. As early as 1963, however, Kaiser Permanente had an automated multiphasic health screening with 29 on-line tests that were capable of processing 10,000 patients every six months. The patient entered the system and walked quickly from station to station, and all the results were in the hands of the physician at the end of the procedure. A series of tests that ordinarily required several days were accomplished in one hour. This remarkable early system was the brainchild of Morrie Collen, and it earned for him, along with Lester Breslow, the title of "fathers of computer medicine." Shortly thereafter, Morrie became one of the founders of the field now known as medical informatics.

From the beginning, Morrie and I agreed that the multiphasic program should include automated psychological screening, but that it must be a part of the one-hour total multiphasic screening. Therefore, the psychological screening could not exceed 10 minutes. This was during an era in which the conventional psychological screening was the MMPI, which took 45 minutes to two hours for a patient to complete. I viewed the assignment as daunting; Morrie was unhappy with even the 10 minutes, as this would leave only a total of 50 minutes for the other 28 tests.

There were other technical problems as well, as this was long before mark-sense and other scoring devices had been invented. Each patient's responses to a questionnaire had to be punched into cards by a clerk known as a keypuncher. Actually, it required two keypunchers, and any differences between them had to be resolved with a third keypunching. This was a costly, labor-intensive procedure that threatened the inclusion of the psychological screening device. The patient could not respond to an 80-item questionnaire, and have it keypunched, and in the physician's hands by the end of the one-hour procedure. When I told Morrie that it could not be done, he replied, "I guess you'll have to look at it again, this time while standing on your head." *It can't be done* simply was not in his vocabulary.

I was desperate. We had spent almost two years validating an 80-item questionnaire that used terminology familiar to physicians instead of the characteristic psychological jargon. It was called the NMQ (Neuro-Mental Questionnaire), and the primary-care physicians were eagerly expecting its help in identifying patients who were in emotional distress of sufficient magnitude to justify behavioral interventions. I stayed awake several nights seeking a solution. When it came to me, it was sudden and simple, as any breakthrough appears to be in retrospect.

Instead of punching the questionnaire answers into a card, a computer card was used that had the question in bold print that could be easily read by the patient, and also was prepunched with the question so that it could be readily read and recorded by the computer. Each patient received a deck of 80 cards, each with a printed question corresponding to the prepunched question. The patient was given a box with two slots, one marked "yes," and the other "no." In a forced-choice manner, the patient read each card and inserted it into the appropriate slot. All the "yes" responses were put through the computer, and this constituted the patient's NMQ profile. Then all 80 cards were put through a sorter that automatically placed them in a required sequence. The deck was now ready for the next patient. Several patients could be doing their NMQs at the same time, and the average time was seven minutes. The recording of the patient's profile took only seconds.

I wondered why no one had thought of the prepunched card before, but it was probably because there was no Morrie Collen entreating the upside position. IBM, which was doing our complex computer assemblies, was so enamored of the idea that in exchange it gave us two computer programmers free of charge for one year. Until it was replaced by newer technology, the prepunched card became standard in computer work, and eliminated up to 75% of all keypunching.

More difficult was the disagreement between Morrie and me as to whether the NMQ should be used to triage patients to a separate mental health system, as conceptualized by Garfield, or to an integrated primary-care system, as I was advocating. This was crucial because it determined the nature of the information printed out and conveyed to the practitioner. Morrie's loyalty to Sid had him favoring the triage system, but in time he saw the wisdom of an integrated primary-care approach and approved my taking the NMQ in that direction.

THE VALUE OF KAISER PERMANENTE
MENTAL HEALTH: A SUMMARY

I was not a founder of the Kaiser Permanente Health Plan, having arrived a decade after the system was in existence. However, I was a late arrival in the first generation of management (Kaiser Permanente is now in its third generation) and was privileged to work with the founders, who shaped my future professional life in several profound ways, and for long after I left that HMO. I was given the opportunity not only to be integral to the creation of an extensive psychotherapy delivery system, but to help design the first comprehensive prepaid psychotherapy benefit in the nation. In my writings during that time and afterward, I noted that we had demonstrated that there could be no comprehensive health system without a mental health component.

The discovery of medical cost offset and its role in the recognition of psychotherapy as a prepaid benefit in health insurance was perhaps the greatest contribution of the mental health system we established. Kaiser Permanente recognized that much of its success was the resolution of the somatizers, whose utilization of healthcare was inundating the system. Consequently, in the 1974 federal HMO Enabling Act, a minimum of 20 sessions of psychotherapy annually was mandated for federally chartered HMOs.

It was at Kaiser Permanente that I learned that often the best way to move public policy (or such slow-moving bodies as the APA) is to form an organization that accomplishes that which was previously regarded as impossible or undesirable. This resulted in my founding of a series of organizations, all of them surprisingly effective and successful. It is probable that not only the importance of establishing new organizations to move policy was learned at Kaiser Permanente, but also the organizational techniques that made them successful in spite of conventional wisdom to the contrary. These included (1) doing it backward, (2) finding a need and filling it, and (3) standing on one's head to see the matter differently. Undoubtedly my early mentors indoctrinated me with the belief that failure is not an option. Furthermore, having been fired and rehired several times, I developed for all time a persistence that could not be deterred by the threat of losing my job.

During the three decades from 1955 to 1985, I founded a number of organizations, but the innovative, entrepreneurial spirit that I first saw at Kaiser Permanente was not seen again until the birth of the Silicon Valley and my subsequent involvement with it beginning in the early to mid-1980s. This will be described in a later chapter.

{ 2 }

The Success of COHI
and How Psychology Became
an Autonomous, Reimbursed Profession

As DISCUSSED in the previous chapter on the founding of the Kaiser Permanente mental health system, it was the findings of the research into medical cost offset that persuaded the insurance industry to include psychotherapy as a covered benefit. Once this became standard, however, psychotherapy services were reimbursed only if provided by a psychiatrist. This was an ironic turn of events inasmuch as psychologists had conducted the research that established the precedent. In addition, the first comprehensive prepaid psychotherapy benefit, which was at Kaiser Permanente, was delivered overwhelmingly by nonpsychiatric providers; that is, psychologists and social workers. How psychology became an autonomous, reimbursed provider of psychotherapy is the second part of the saga. The organization that was instrumental in bringing it about was the APA's Committee on Health Insurance (COHI, pronounced "co-high").

AHCIRSD

In the mid- to late 1950s, a growing group of professional psychologists began agitating that the APA take an active role in establishing psychology as an autonomous profession. These psychologists were responding to the alert by Leonard Small, who maintained that soon most Americans would have some form of mental health insurance, and if psychologists were not recognized providers, we would wither as a profession. Len was a New York private practitioner who circulated a biweekly mimeographed letter under the auspices of what he called the National Clinical Liaison Committee (NCLC). Two of Len's early recruits to the mission were Milton Theaman of New York and Rogers Wright of Long Beach, California. For some time, the NCLC was a handful of activists who were persistent and noisy enough to have the APA throw them a bone to pacify them.

An ad hoc committee was established to address the concerns of this small group, which appeared to be much larger and better organized than it was. Whether the APA knew this was essentially a pesky gnat, or whether it misinterpreted the group as more of a fox terrier nipping at its heels, the real purpose of this new committee was to slow down the drive for professional autonomy. The APA argued that insurance was not respectable enough to warrant a standing committee; hence it was given ad hoc status. The further agreement was that insurance was not sufficiently important to absorb the work of an entire committee, so "related social developments" was added to the committee's name. Thus was established the Ad Hoc Committee on Insurance and Related Social Developments (AHCIRSD, pronounced affectionately by professional psychologists as "ah-curse-ed"). The charge of "related social developments" was never adequately defined, and AHCIRSD did not waste any time trying to understand it or any of its precious resources on pursuing it.

Milt Theaman was appointed chair, and the membership included Melvin Gravitz, Rogers Wright, William Schofield (who wrote a book describing psychotherapy as "paid friendship"), and George Coppel. Milt was an able chair, but the firebrand was always Rog. About a year later, William Smith of Clearwater College in Florida and I were added to the roster. Bill brought the important perspective of diversity and I brought my recent work in medical cost offset. AHCIRSD met regularly and there was always more to do than was possible in the time allotted. Meeting early in the morning and continuing until after midnight throughout the weekend was common practice. In contrast to most APA committees, which met on weekdays and whose members were salaried academicians, the members of AHCIRSD were practitioners who did not get paid if they met during the week.

Even by meeting on weekends, all of us sacrificed a substantial amount of income because AHCIRSD was an activist committee and we met with the insurance industry in attempts to persuade its decision makers to recognize psychology as an autonomous profession. This was an APA taboo that we consistently violated, as APA committees were constituted to be deliberative, not action-oriented, bodies. As would be expected, all of these meetings took place during regular business hours, and for Rog and I, who were coming from the West Coast, a one-hour meeting in New York or Hartford involved a minimum of two days' travel and a significant kick in the pocketbook.

Meeting with leaders of the insurance industry was one of our main activities, and in the course of five years, AHCIRSD succeeded in persuading only two small insurance companies with a subscriber population that represented 0.03% of the insured population to recognize psychology. At this rate of success, it would take 150 years to persuade 10% of the industry to do so. Clearly, a different strategy was needed, but AHCIRSD never found it. We met with Abe Fortas, the well-known trust buster from the 1930s who failed to win U.S. Senate approval for his nomination to the Supreme Court. He had been appointed APA's outside counsel, and we asked if there were a possible legal challenge to the insurance industry's refusal to recognize psychology. There obviously was none, but Fortas did not say so, consistent with a lawyer's keeping alive the possibility of a fee for continuing to look into the matter. Even if the outcome potentially might be an optimistic one, there was no money to mount a thorough investigation. We were becoming increasingly discouraged.

Our internal activities were more successful, however. We had definitely graduated from being a pesky gnat to the APA to being a barking, biting fox terrier. We began to attend meetings of the Council of Representatives, where we lobbied its more sympathetic members. We were winning friends and allies in unexpected places, making the APA decision makers uneasy. In the last year of AHCIRSD, we had made arrangements to fly to Washington to attend the Council meeting when we were informed that our trip would not be reimbursed. When Rog and I decided to pay for our own plan tickets, we were flatly forbidden to attend. Our reply was that the Council was an open meeting and we had a right to attend as APA members. As chair, Milt Theaman did everything he could to prevent our attending the meeting, and he succeeded in scaring away most of the committee members. Rog and I remained adamant that we would be there, and we were bravely joined by Bill Smith. The three of us did attend, and we were very active in presenting the cause of AHCIRSD to anyone who would listen.

Shortly thereafter, the APA decided to get rid of AHCIRSD, as it had become the rallying point for practitioner activism. This could not easily be done without arousing the ire of the troops, so a presumably conciliatory plan was adopted. The lowly AHCIRSD would cease to exist, and would be replaced by a prestigious standing committee, something we all wanted. Hidden in the proposal was the fact that a standing committee would be more under APA control than the former ad hoc committee was. In the process, Rog Wright would not be reappointed, and I would be named chair, thus quietly getting rid of the troublesome Wright. The new Committee on Health Insurance (COHI), however, had as members such soon to be recognized activists as Jack Wiggins, who would be a future APA president, and later Eugene Shapiro and Herbert Dorken, all of whom were psychologists and eventually succeeded me as chairs.

THE REINVENTING OF COHI

If the APA had hoped that COHI under my leadership would cease to be an action-oriented body, it was seriously mistaken. From the very beginning, I was determined that it would be an action committee, violating the APA's prohibitions in this regard, but I was further determined that COHI would be externally effective, which AHCIRSD was not. I was aware that progress has to be incremental, but the snail's pace of AHCIRSD was unacceptable. I was looking for a new direction, and it came from an unexpected source.

In one of our many futile visits with executives of the insurance industry during which AHCIRSD pleaded the cause of professional psychology, Rog introduced me to Red Halverson, the executive vice president of the Occidental Life Insurance Company. Red and I became instant friends, and since he was based in Los Angeles, I visited him frequently over the next several weeks to seek his advice. He was liberal with his time, and during a succession of lunches and dinners together, Red grew very sympathetic to our cause. He arranged for us to get together with H. Paul Brandes, a key attorney in the office of the California Insurance Commissioner. This resulted in the conceptual breakthrough I had been seeking.

At that meeting, 45 years ago, Paul Brandes and I bonded, and we have remained close friends ever since. He is retired now, but at one point, when he expressed unhappiness with the state bureaucracy, I was able to help him join the large legal staff of the Kaiser Health Plan.

Red and Paul pointed out how three words inserted by amendment into the insurance codes of the states would make it mandatory for insurers to reimburse psychologists if they reimbursed psychiatrists. After the word "physician" would be inserted "which includes psychologists." They also pointed out this would be relatively easy to do if a stealth campaign were mounted with lightning rapidity. What we had failed to do by persuasion, and what was not possible judicially, we could do legislatively. We immediately seized upon the idea, for we had reinvented COHI.

BIRTH OF THE FREEDOM-OF-CHOICE LEGISLATION

It was not surprising that the APA would have none of this. When I refused to promise that I would not go forward with the idea, COHI's staff support was withdrawn. So I went ahead using other resources available to me. We contacted every state psychological association to ask their participation. But first we had to resurrect most of them.

State psychological associations were created to fight for the enactment of licensing or certification laws. As each state succeeded in obtaining this statutory recognition, the respective state association became dormant. In 1968, most states had succeeded in this legislative fight, and other than California, New York, and New Jersey, the state associations that won the fight had all but evaporated. COHI asked each state association to reactivate itself and appoint an insurance committee with an energetic psychologist as its chair. Then we invited these insurance chairs to an all-day meeting preceding the annual APA convention in San Francisco.

Since we had not informed the APA of what we were doing, we could not ask it to provide a room large enough to accommodate an all-day meeting. To be entirely truthful, I had not kept my committee members completely informed because, as psychologists are wont to do, they would have deliberated about the plan for another year or two. This would be especially true as they realized the APA's fierce opposition to the concept. The meeting room problem was quickly resolved. As the 1968 president of the California Psychological Association, I persuaded the Mark Hopkins Hotel atop Nob Hill that, as president of the hosting state organization, I should be given the presidential suite. This was luxurious and had ample space.

When the insurance chairs assembled the day before the convention, we were delighted to see that 42 states were represented. I chaired the panel of Red Halverson and Paul Brandes, who walked the group through a do-it-yourself legislative kit. The response was enthusiastic, as the insurance committee chairs present had been chosen from among the most committed professional psychologists in each state. Several attendees, and particularly Gene Shapiro of New Jersey and Jack Wiggins of Ohio, took hold and were determined to go forward in their respective states with the newly conceived legislative thrust.

Bills were introduced in several states, with New Jersey succeeding within months and California within the next year. Remarkably, in a brief period, six states had enacted what had initially been termed the psychology reimbursement legislation. By that time, Jack Wiggins had renamed it the freedom-of-choice legislation, which identified the consumer as the main beneficiary, rather than the profession of psychology. State legislators liked the new name as they felt justified in running with it, and it was surprisingly compatible to the APA governance. Soon the APA Board and Council declared the drive for freedom-of-choice legislation to be APA policy.

THE AFTERMATH

As each state enacted the legislation, the economic base for the private practice of psychology was established, and professional psychologists entered it in droves. There were difficulties along the way, with court challenges, and with the legislative language becoming more sophisticated. The first problem was that the law was interpreted to be applicable only in the state where the policy was written, not where it was delivered. Amendments soon rectified this difficulty. Then Blue Cross and Blue Shield asserted that this did not apply to them as they were medical-services organizations rather than insurance companies, and this had to be resolved through a series of lawsuits. Only about half of the states ever passed the legislation, but since insurance companies are national, it was more trouble to have differential policies from one state to another. At such a time, the reimbursement of psychologists had become standard in fee-for-service indemnity plans. Then came the ERISA laws that exempted employer-sponsored plans and threw everything up in the air again. In all of these subsequent struggles, however, it was not a handful of outsiders who were waging the fight, but the dedicated resources of the APA.

The important point is that, once again, a successful organization, in this case, the reinvented COHI, having succeeded in accomplishing the unacceptable and the seemingly impossible, was able to change the direction of the APA, as well as that of professional psychology. Where medical cost offset had rendered psychotherapy reimbursable, COHI made psychology a reimbursable profession.

{ 3 }

THE PROFESSIONAL SCHOOL MOVEMENT: THE DIRTY DOZEN'S EMPOWERMENT OF THE CLINICIAN IN EDUCATION AND TRAINING

EACH PROFESSION HAS A MAJOR, if not decisive, influence on its training. This is accomplished by an approvals process conducted by its professional society. Such professional approval is above and beyond the determination of academic excellence that is the sole prerogative of the regional accrediting body in higher education. The latter restricts its accreditation to academic matters, and leaves to the professional society the responsibility of determining its standards of training, as well as the subsequent standards of practice for those so trained. In the mid-1960s, this was true of every profession except clinical psychology. Whereas every other profession had a truly professional society, the education and training of professional psychologists were vested in the APA, an essentially academic organization with a decidedly antiprofessional bias.[1]

---

[1] This history reflects the personal experiences of the founder of the professional school movement. The intent is to convey the nature of the activism, which often required getting one's hands soiled, and earning the appellation of the "Dirty Dozen" for its leadership. For a more formal, expurgated delineation of the events, see: Stricker, G., & N. A. Cummings, (1992), The professional school movement. In D. K. Freedheim (Ed.), *History of psychotherapy: A century of change* (pp. 801–828). Washington, D.C.: American Psychological Association.

Approval of a doctoral program in clinical psychology was based on evaluations conducted by site teams under the aegis of the APA's Education and Training Board (E&T). The standard of evaluation was the Boulder Model, so-called because the Boulder (Colorado) Conference on the Education and Training in Clinical Psychology enunciated the following dictum: "The science of psychology has not progressed sufficiently to warrant the existence of an independent professional practice. Therefore, clinical psychologists are trained first as scientists, and only secondarily as clinicians."

The evaluation of a doctoral clinical program stressed the importance of academic/scientific aspects, and glossed over the quality of clinical training. If the laboratories and other scientific necessities were firmly in place, it did not matter whether field placements were mediocre, or even nonexistent. Clinical courses typically were taught by faculty who had never been in practice, and many of whom had never worked with a patient. This was so because clinicians did not possess the number of publications and other prerequisites necessary for faculty appointments. Those who taught and trained us were openly disdainful of anyone in practice, and any doctoral student who planned to enter practice knew that success in the program was depended on hiding these facts from the faculty, or else be flunked. The APA approvals process had its beginnings in the late 1940s, but it was not until the mid-1970s that a program would be denied APA approval solely on the basis of slipshod clinical training. Herbert Dorken, Ph.D., was a member of a site committee and insisted that a particular program be failed on the basis of inadequate field placements, even though its laboratories and other aspects of scientific training were superb. This was a landmark declaration that was quickly forgotten, as Dr. Dorken and other psychologists like him who might stringently examine clinical, rather than scientific, training were not again appointed by the E&T Board to its site committees.

Academia promulgated and tolerated the emerging Boulder Model doctoral programs in clinical psychology because of government funding. First the Veterans Administration, which was later joined by the National Institute of Mental Health (NIMH), sought to address the shortage of mental health professionals by providing training stipends for psychologists, along with those for psychiatrists. These government agencies required professional standards and an approvals procedure, and the universities acceded to these demands in spite of academia's distaste because the psychology departments used this influx of money to expand and upgrade their experimental programs and faculties.

ENTER THE DIRTY DOZEN

The Dirty Dozen were practitioner activists, predominantly from California and New Jersey, who foresaw that there would come a time when most Americans would have prepaid health coverage, and if psychologists were not reimbursed as autonomous providers by insurance companies, psychology as a profession would be severely crippled, and might cease to exist altogether. They confronted the opposition of psychiatry, but realized that their own APA also was essentially opposed to the independent practice of psychology. Therefore, they targeted both APAs, as well as a reluctant insurance industry that did not want an increase in the number of providers it would have to reimburse. The appellation "Dirty Dozen" was conferred by their opponents, who abhorred the group's guerrilla tactics, but the group itself came to cherish the name. There were actually 14, giving rise to the accusation that they also did not know how to count.

The members of the Dirty Dozen were painfully aware that training in clinical psychology was woefully inadequate to meet the challenges confronting the increasing numbers of psychologists who were entering independent practice, and they had every intention of addressing the issue. However, the escalating psychiatric opposition to insurance reimbursement for psychological services, coupled with a stiffening resistance from the APA on various issues, consumed all of the Dirty Dozen's time, energy, and very limited resources. The few attempts to meet with members of the E&T Board were effectively rebuffed. The education and training process seemed more insulated and aloof than other functions of the APA that were beginning to feel the brunt of constant attacks by the Dirty Dozen and a growing army of followers. So training was regarded as a paramount issue that nonetheless, received little attention from the activists until fortuitous events would present an avenue through which the E&T Board might be successfully approached.

ENTER THE NCGEP

A group of graduate students from Washington University in St. Louis contacted me in 1965. Led by Norman Matulef, who subsequently received his doctorate in clinical psychology and entered independent practice in Missouri, they expressed gross dissatisfaction with graduate training in our profession. They were naive as to how they might approach the

APA to express this dissatisfaction, and they sought the help and advice of the Dirty Dozen. They had created a loosely formed organization they named the National Council on Graduate Education in Psychology (NCGEP), certainly a grandiose title in view of their small number. I flew to St. Louis and met with the three graduate students who led the NCGEP.

At that meeting, we developed a brash strategy that unfolded over the next several months. By invitation, Matulef and I were joined by the late Herbert Freudenberger, Ph.D.; Stanley Moldawsky, Ph.D.; Eugene Shapiro, Ph.D.; and Don Schultz, Ph.D. Shapiro, Schultz, and I were members of the Dirty Dozen, and Freudenberger and Moldawsky were to emerge as the first wave of successors to that group. Freudenberger and I served as the working marshals, and Matulef was proffered as the grand marshal of the NCGEP. Impressive stationery, bearing a prestigious address, was printed listing Matulef as chair and Freudenberger and me as co-chairs. A newsletter was widely circulated among graduate students and practitioners. We contacted the Council on Professional Approvals (COPA), which accredits the accreditors out of Washington, D.C., and declared our intent for the NCGEP to become the approvals body for professional psychology. A copy of our COPA application was sent to the E&T Board, along with the information that the NCGEP represented psychology graduate students nationally. The NCGEP was preparing a petition in which 2,000 graduate students would attest to their dissatisfaction with the work of the E&T Board in particular, and with the lack of real clinical training in general. This petition would be sent not only to COPA, but also to what was then the U.S. Department of Health, Education and Welfare (DHEW). Fearing that we were a powerful new organization with clout, the E&T Board quickly granted us an audience at its next meeting.

Once before the E&T Board, Matulef, Freudenberger, and I continued our brashness. We demanded that the approvals process be amended to permit practicing clinicians to have faculty status, that all APA-approved programs have affiliations for field placement with settings that were truly clinical in nature, and that clinical courses be taught only by clinicians. Unless our demands were met, we were prepared to expose the APA's dereliction in approving slipshod clinical training, thus jeopardizing those whom these graduates one day would be treating. None of these demands were met, but the E&T Board began taking them seriously and actively engaged the NCGEP in seeking a compromise. We continued to play the game, buying valuable time in the education and training arena while the Dirty Dozen was meeting issues that could not wait head-on.

What Is a Professional School?

A professional school is an autonomous or semiautonomous (if part of a university) program that trains its future practitioners, and is administered by a person with the rank of dean or higher. We are all acquainted with dental, medical, and nursing schools, but few psychologists realize that these are of more recent origin, and the first professional schools were in theology for the training of the clergy. Until a few years ago, all health professional were trained in professional schools, except for clinical psychologists, who continued to be trained in departments of psychology in colleges of arts and science. Even social work, which seems to have followed psychology by 10 or 15 years in licensing, insurance reimbursement, and other practice issues has had professional schools since the 1890s.

Why has psychology lagged behind every other profession? The reason is that psychology as a practice as we know it today emerged as a post-World War II phenomenon. Up until then, psychology was essentially academia and science, with a few practitioners in independent practice scattered around the country, most of whom were women who saw children and whose training was the master's degree. Defining professional psychologists as doctoral-level practitioners has been APA policy only in the last 30 to 35 years. In fact, the Dirty Dozen and its practitioner activist successors demanded, and got, this doctoral-level policy through the APA Council of Representatives, and it stands to this day.

By virtue of its professional schools, for which it sets the standards and curricula, a profession controls its training. It became increasingly apparent to those of us in the NCGEP who were wrestling with the APA's E&T Board that we would not be a fully autonomous profession until we had our own professional schools. It is no longer clear in my memory whether I was chosen by the Dirty Dozen to lead the charge, or whether I grabbed the bit in my teeth and ran with it. Nevertheless, my founding of the professional school movement had to await two other priorities. First, by becoming the first chair of the APA's Committee on Health Insurance, I designed, and saw passed, the first freedom-of-choice legislation that finally opened the door to insurance reimbursement (1965–1968), and, second, my presidency of the California Psychological Association (CPA), had become the main power base nationally through which the Dirty Dozen operated (1968–1969). It was during my CPA presidency that events occurred that catapulted me headlong into what came to be known as the professional school movement.

THE HARVARD–STANFORD PHENOMENON

It would seem unlikely that the launching of the Russian earth-orbiting satellite "Sputnik" would have given impetus to the creation of the professional school movement, but that is exactly what happened. The American people were stunned when the U.S.S.R. beat the United States in orbiting the earth by fully two years, even though Sputnik was "unmanned." There followed a national obsession with the reaffirmation of science in our schools and colleges, with deemphasis on the liberal arts.

In response to this concern, psychology departments began cutting back their clinical programs, and with new government funding for science, they could afford to give up the VA and NIMH clinical stipends. Some universities, led by Harvard on the East Coast and Stanford on the West Coast, eliminated clinical/counseling psychology programs entirely. I dubbed this the "Harvard–Stanford Phenomenon," as I talked about its threat to the future of professional psychology. Two other events took place in rapid succession that fueled the fire and drew large audiences to hear me. The first was the fact that the largest higher-education complex in the world, the University of California system with nine UC campuses and 19 California state universities, graduated only eight doctoral clinical psychologists in 1968. Even worse, the estimate was that in the following year only four would graduate. Then, in 1970, the president of the APA, George Albee, Ph.D., was quoted in the magazine *Psychology Today* as predicting the death of clinical psychology. This appeared in a featured version of his presidential address, "The Short Unhappy Life of Clinical Psychology: Rest in Peace." I made much of these two events as I literally crisscrossed the nation championing the need for psychology to have its own professional schools.

The idea that the profession of psychology should have its own professional schools captured the imagination of rank-and-file clinicians everywhere I went. More than anything I said, I had inadvertently tapped the almost universal dissatisfaction of the professional psychologists of the era with their graduate education and training, and for the first time, they saw a way to vent that dissatisfaction by supporting the professional school movement. My speeches were rewarded with standing ovations and an increasing army of adherents.

During this time, there were three friendly debates between Albee and myself, known in the literature as the Albee-Cummings debates. The first was at an APA Division 29 meeting in the Bahamas before about 150 attendees, and the last was in San Diego, before a psychology audience of

2,000. In that debate, I lauded Albee for alerting us to the need to have our own house in which to practice, and extended this truism by pointing out that we first needed our own house in which to train. George, in turn, conceded that in his predicting the demise of clinical psychology, he had not foreseen the coming of the professional school movement that was giving rebirth to the profession. Subsequently Albee and I came to be known, respectively, as the mortician and the obstetrician of clinical psychology.

THE NUMBERS OF PROFESSIONAL PSYCHOLOGISTS

With the current overproduction of professional psychologists, it is difficult to imagine that in the mid- to late 1960s there was a shortage of practitioners. The demand for psychologist clinicians in all sectors of our society was tremendous, and generated a great deal of interest on the part of prospective students. In fact, during this period, psychology became the most popular undergraduate major. The attraction of the subject itself, coupled with the career opportunities it offered, were irresistible. However, of every 340 persons graduating with a bachelor's degree in psychology, only one eventually received a doctorate in professional psychology. Much of this had to do with the limited number of openings in clinical programs. Getting into an APA-approved doctoral program was reputed to be even more difficult than getting into medical school.

So severe was the lack of available training that I used to chide us by saying, "For a profession obsessed with sex, we have not yet mastered the art of reproduction." To this I would add for California audiences, where the shortage of professional psychologists and the lack of training facilities seemed to be the most acute, "California's leading import is clinical psychologists trained in New York." Even if these words were said in jest, the message they intended to convey resonated with the growing number of practitioners who supported the professional school movement.

The present generation of practitioners who face the glut of both doctoral- and master's-level psychologists are prone to blame the professional school movement for the oversupply. That this blame is unwarranted will be addressed later in the discussion of what went right and what went wrong with professional schools.

THE LAUNCHING OF CSPP

The California School of Professional Psychology (CSPP) was founded in 1969 and classes begin simultaneously on its first two campuses, San Francisco and Los Angeles, in September 1970. To say that it was launched on a shoestring would be a gross understatement, for it was accomplished with only $38,000 in cash. This was made possible by a number of factors, reflecting the overwhelming support of the practitioner of psychology. First and foremost, 250 psychologists volunteered to teach at least one class for the first 18 months of the school's existence. This constituted CSPP's founding endowment, and earned each member of the volunteer faculty the appellation of the founder. The first two campus deans, S. Don Schultz, Ph.D., in San Francisco and Arthur Kovacs, Ph.D., in Los Angeles, worked without remuneration for their first six months. After that, they became the first paid administrators of CSPP. I did not draw a salary for the first four of seven years I was founding president. In the fifth year, and at the insistence of the Board of Directors, I began to receive a modest salary, one that was far smaller than that paid to the campus deans.

This sacrifice on the part of the founding faculty and administration made it possible for a third of our student body to be on tuition-free scholarships. This was quite an accomplishment for a school that was supported entirely by tuition, but it contributed immensely to the incredible morale, dedication, and excitement that characterized the early years of CSPP.

The sites of the first two campuses were far more than just spartan. The Los Angeles campus was housed in a condemned Elks Club building, while San Francisco campus was above a machine shop. The hazard in Los Angeles was the frequency with which pieces of plaster fell from the ceiling, whereas in San Francisco, the huge machines below created a constant noise and vibration on the classroom floors. The faculty's commitment was infectious to the students, and neither seemed to mind the drawbacks of receiving an education under such conditions.

The Western Association of Schools and Colleges (WASC) required that the school have a formidable library before it could apply for provisional accreditation. Through the *California Psychologist*, I made an appeal to practitioners to donate books and journals. The response was electrifying, with several hundred boxes being received within a few weeks. It fulfilled our need for a journal library, provided a good start on psychology texts, and gave us over 200 sets of *American Psychologist*, most of which were complete sets spanning from 10 to 20 years each. I never had the heart to implore our benefactors to stop sending the *American Psychologist*, as the contributors would accompany that journal with books and other journals we needed. Nevertheless, libraries on both campuses were still woefully inadequate, and conservative estimates indicated we would need up to half a million dollars for library acquisitions before we could satisfy WASC. It was then I discovered an obscure state regulation that accorded any doctoral candidate in any college in the state a courtesy library card to any campus of the University of California system. When I applied for library cards for all our students, the UC librarians were stunned, but they were forthcoming when California's Superintendent of Public Instruction advised them that my request was valid. Thus, our library problem not only was solved, but our students and faculty had full access to one of the greatest libraries in the world. WASC was both impressed and satisfied.

THE STATE CHARTER:
MEETING WITH GOVERNOR REAGAN

California has, as most states do, a provision under which business, barber, and beauty schools, and other such institutions are chartered and allowed to solicit students, and to operate. I doubt if anyone had thought of applying this set of regulations to establishing an academic institution, and we frankly did not believe it would be a viable approach for us. Nonetheless, it was worth exploring. Our first inquiries brought the response that the University of California would never allow the chartering of a new college in this fashion. Such formidable opposition requires a drastic, and even brash, response. Through my association with Alex Sheriffs, Ph.D., a psychologist who had been dean of students at UC Berkeley and now was Governor Ronald Reagan's education adviser in Sacramento, I was granted an appointment with the governor himself. As Don Schultz, who had enthusiastically joined the effort to establish CSPP, and I drove to Sacramento, Don expressed trepidation. I had been president of CPA in 1968 and he had been the executive officer. Both of us had been outspoken on behalf of psychology in opposing Governor Reagan's decimation of the Department of Mental Health, and particularly his drastic reduction in the participation of psychology. Don fully expected that we would be chastised and then thrown out.

And the picture was actually even gloomier. On the day of our scheduled meeting with the governor, his newly appointed president of San Francisco State University mounted the sound truck in the midst of a student strike and disabled the loudspeaker. Sporting the tam that was to make him famous, and eventually follow him to the U.S. Senate, S.I. Hayakawa was the governor's hero. Our appointment was for 9:00 a.m., but we waited most of the day, talking with Alex Sheriffs. Occasionally, the governor would poke his head into the room and ask Dr. Sheriffs, "Shouldn't I order out the National Guard now?" With each new crisis on the campus, the question was repeated, and each time, Alex strongly recommended against the use of such force. Finally, at about 3:30 in the afternoon, the campus had quieted, and Don and I were ushered into the governor's office with the statement that we had only 15 minutes. I began the discussion with, "Your Excellency, we are here about a crisis in higher education." I had discovered in a book of political etiquette that this is the formal manner in which to address the governor of a state. Mr. Reagan smiled, added that this seemed to be the day for such crises, and asked me to go on. We explained the problems in educating professional psychologists in California, making much of the UC's role in almost eliminating such training, and then revealing its opposition to the founding of CSPP. What was to be a 15-minute meeting stretched to 2-1/2 hours, after which Governor Reagan pledged to facilitate the founding of CSPP if we demonstrated a first-class faculty, had a strong and appropriate curriculum, and set high admission standards. He fulfilled his pledge. Within a year, CSPP had a state charter for each of our first two campuses.

Many institutions have taken the state charter route since our initial success, and it now looks easy. It must be remembered that CSPP was the first to venture into "uncharted" territory, but in so doing we were committed to obtain full regional accreditation as soon as possible. A number of institutions operating in California today have no intention of going beyond the state charter, remanding their graduates to practice only in California, where a loophole allows them to take the licensing examination.

WHAT ABOUT THE LICENSING OF GRADUATES?

The state charters enabled us to operate and solicit students, but without regional accreditation, our credits were not transferable and our graduates would not be admitted to psychology licensing examinations. Later, the courts indicated that students from chartered but unaccredited programs had to be admitted to California licensing procedures, but we did not expect this to be the situation when we first began operations. Anticipating a long procedure before final recognition by state licensing boards, in the first two or three years, we accepted students who had received licenses on the master's level under the "grandfather" provisions included in the laws when the states enacted them. Thus, we were able to upgrade to the doctorate already licensed practicing psychologists, and without having to face the notion that our graduates would not be able to practice until sometime in the future.

We gambled that we would have the appropriate recognition within three years, so from the outset, we accepted beginning students in a four-year program, anticipating that by the time they graduated, they would be admitted to licensing procedures. Not only did we stake our credibility and reputations on such projections, but we were rewarded by the quality and intensity of the first wave of beginning students. They were eager, dedicated risk takers who shared our vision and made intense, believable interviewees during the difficult accreditation procedures that lay ahead. Half were women, and more than half were ethnic minorities, whose admission was made possible by our liberal tuition-free scholarships. No school ever had better spokespersons than CSPP's students. Every site-visit report spontaneously praised our students as the most dedicated the accrediting examiners had ever seen.

NORTON SIMON, JENNIFER JONES, AND CSPP'S ENDOWMENT

WASC was firm regarding the need for a sizable endowment, stressing that it was particularly important to establish the stability of a new school that essentially depended on tuition. This was our most formidable hurdle, as the figure of $1 million that was frequently mentioned was the equivalent in 1970 of $3 million or $4 million today. We hired a fund-raiser, who spent six months planning a campaign, and then presented me with research he had done on the 10 richest residents of California. This was to enable him to construct a letter for my signature that would be tailored to each of these individuals. To my surprise, however, he had written exactly the same letter to all 10. Then why all of the meticulous preparation? Receiving no answer that made sense, I fired him, and set about lamenting the wasting of precious dollars on this man who had come to us so highly touted.

After a time, I looked at his research, and found it to be excellent. I took the name at the top of the list, Norton Simon, who not only was the wealthiest man in California, but also one of the wealthiest in the world. Using the fundraiser's research, I constructed a letter that, without addressing the recent suicide of his psychology student son and the messy divorce from his wife, I attempted to tap his emotional needs, and to provide an outlet for them through his possible involvement with CSPP. It was a good letter, but it had to be better. It had to bear a message that would cause a succession of assistants who would be screening his mail not only to see to it that he personally got it, but to give it priority. It was a tall order, and I wrote and tore up dozens of versions during the ensuing several days. Finally, at 4:00 o'clock one morning, I typed the newest draft myself, for I knew that if I left it for my secretary to type, I would change my mind. At 5:00 in the morning, I drove to the post office and mailed the letter before I could lose my courage.

A month passed, and hearing nothing, I concluded that my letter had bombed. Then one day, while I was seeing a patient, my secretary interrupted me, which she was allowed to do only in an emergency. She sounded excited as she said, "This is either a joke or I have *the* Norton Simon on the line." Yes, indeed, it was Mr. Simon, who had been in the Bahamas for the past month and had just returned. "Dr. Cummings, my desk is loaded with mail and work. At the top of the pile was your letter, which I started to set aside. Then I wondered why my staff had put your letter for my attention above all else. I read it and I haven't been able to think of anything else since. When can we meet?" I was ready to drop everything and fly to Los Angeles from San Francisco the next morning, but he suggested that we meeting following the UC Board of Regents meeting in San Francisco the following week. Excited and terrified, I agreed.

Early on the day we were to meet in downtown San Francisco, I had my car washed and polished. But Simon had a stretch limo and a driver to take us both to the airport and he indicated disarmingly, "Dr. Cummings, you have the 20 minutes before we reach the airport to make your pitch." I made a gut-level decision at that moment to be brutally honest with this man. He liked my approach and what I had to say. He decided we would have dinner at the airport, and instructed his assistant to change his reservation. As we talked over dinner, he changed his reservation three more times, finally taking the last hourly flight to Los Angeles. It did not occur to me until the next day that the midnight plane had no first-class section. *The* Norton Simon had flown coach just so we could continue our discussion!

By 11:00 p.m., Simon had decided to consider my invitation to join our Board of Directors, and asked his final two questions. First, he demanded to know whether I wanted his knowledge, expertise, and influence or his money. Without hesitation, I replied that I wanted both his expertise and his money. He stiffened a bit, then asked, "For how long are you asking me to serve on the board?" When I said that I wanted him for just one year, he looked puzzled. "Why for such a short time?" I decided then and there that I could not abandon my brutal honesty, and replied with my heart in my mouth, "Mr. Simon, my office did not research you for six months without my learning that you are a very difficult man to get along with. In fact, you're known to be a control freak. Within a year, you would be telling me how to run the school. So I am giving myself one year to pick your brains, and also get a million dollars out of you." There was dead silence. Simon reddened noticeably, and was visibly angry. After about five minutes, he began to soften. Finally, he was both relaxed and amiable. "No one has talked to me like that in many years because they are either intimidated or they want something. In fact, I always wonder if anyone is really honest and frank with me anymore. If you promise to be the one man who always tells me the truth, no matter how bad, I'll come on your board." With that, he shook my hand, saying, "I'm with you, Nick. And from now on, I'm Norton." Within an amazingly short time, we became very good friends.

In spite of our relationship and his involvement in CSPP, there was no money forthcoming. I would ask about this from time to time, and he would put me off, "Not yet, if ever." I knew Norton was still depressed and unhappy over the loss of his son and his subsequent divorce. I decided to play Cupid. Another friend, Jennifer Jones, was one of the loveliest of filmdom's leading ladies during the late 1930s and early 1940s. She had had three tragic, highly publicized, Hollywood marriages, all of which had ended in the deaths of her husbands — one by suicide. This beautiful woman was still a frightened Oklahoma farm girl who was looking for a strong man. Her husbands all were strong men, but they had died. She now needed a man who was invincible, a man like Norton Simon. A homely man, he once confessed that he had always dreamed of falling in love with a beautiful and celebrated woman. To me, this was a marriage made in heaven, and my wife and I hosted an all-CSPP party on our campus above the machine ship. The not-so-hidden purpose was to introduce Norton to Jennifer.

It must be remembered that during the 1970s, psychologists and their students did not sit in chairs. Rather, we sat on pillows on the floor. So when Norton asked for a chair, it took almost 20 minutes to locate one on campus. This prompted Jennifer to ask who the stuffed shirt was with whom I had paired her off. In turn, he asked me what he was supposed to do with that spoiled Hollywood brat. The meeting was a disaster. Six weeks later, however, I was awakened in the middle of the night. It was Norton and Jennifer calling from Paris. They had run into each other three days earlier, had hit it off, and had just been married. "Nick," said Norton, "We wanted you to be the first to know. And we want to tell you that our wedding present to each other is the gift of CSPP's endowment."

Our highest hurdle had been vaulted. But then another set of troubles developed. Every idealist on campus, and CSPP had attracted some of the most dedicated, wanted to spend the money on student scholarships, especially for minority and underprivileged applicants. As lofty as this intent was, it was also impractical, as spending our endowment would jeopardize CSPP's desperately needed accreditation. I found myself having to guard our endowment with my very life.

THE STRUGGLE FOR FEDERAL STIPENDS

At the time, the person in charge of NIMH grants was Stanley Schneider, Ph.D., an affable psychologist who enjoyed his job of dispensing training stipends and other goodies. In fact, his position made him somewhat of a czar, with colleagues in APA-approved doctoral programs fawning over him at every opportunity. His ability to determine who received a grant and who did not gave him incredible power over the shaping of professional training in psychology. He favored the large, prestigious universities with rather traditional programs, and when he was approached on behalf of CSPP, he as much as indicated that our program was many years short of being eligible for consideration. Nonetheless, in our first year, we did apply for training stipends for both the San Francisco and Los Angeles campuses. Stan visited us, was amiable, and even sympathetic, but he was firm in discouraging our expectations. Of course, our applications went nowhere.

The following year, CSPP applied for four training grants, one for clinical and the other for community psychology, on each of our two campuses. This time, however, Norton Simon was on our board, and he announced that he was going to monitor progress of our applications. The following strategy was devised. At the beginning of each month, I would call Norton, who would then call his good friend Robert Finch, the Secretary of the Department of Health, Education and Welfare (DHEW). At that time, education had not been split off from DHEW into its own Cabinet, the Department of Education. Bob Finch would then send an inquiry as to the status of the CSPP applications through channels all the way to Stan Schneider, whereupon Stan was obligated to render a thorough report back through channels. Since the inquiry bore the letterhead of the Cabinet Secretary himself, Stan would have to take an inordinate amount of time to produce a meticulous report. I later learned that this would require about three days each month. In the eighth month, Stan notified CSPP that two grants, one for clinical psychology at CSPP-San Francisco and one for community psychology at CSPP-Los Angeles, had been approved. We, of course, were ecstatic. The important thing, however, is that subsequently all four of the CSPP campuses regularly applied for and received grants from NIMH. Another hurdle had been vaulted.

CSPP's Innovative Curriculum

The initial curriculum was a dramatic departure from anything that had gone before. The calendar was a trimester year, so that the students attended all year and earned 1-1/2 academic years annually. From entry to the doctorate, the program took six years. The first two earned the associate of arts (A.A.) degree and qualified the graduate to be a psychological paraprofessional. Such a person would serve as an employee of a psychologist, psychiatrist, or hospital, performing a number of duties that had historically been part of being a psychiatric technician. The next two years earned the master of arts (M.A.) degree and rendered the graduate eligible to work as a psychological assistant. CSPP was active in bringing about legislation that permitted each licensed doctoral-level psychologist to employ, supervise, and be responsible for two psychological assistants. Several other states followed California's lead and passed similar legislation. The duties paralleled those of a physician assistants (P.A.), thus giving our profession a psychologist extender. In creating these first two levels, it must be remembered that this was during the severe shortage of journey-level psychologists, and CSPP was responding to the recently enacted legislation establishing the category of psychological assistant. The final degree, culminating the fifth and sixth years, was the doctorate (Ph.D.) in clinical psychology.

There was considerable discussion at the time as to whether CSPP should grant the Ph.D., or the professional degree of doctor of psychology (Psy.D.) that had been established in the psychology program at the University of Illinois, headed by Don Peterson, Ph.D. Inwardly, I leaned toward the Psy.D., believing that the profession could best be served by having a professional degree, just as had every other health profession. But outwardly I opposed CSPP's conferring the Psy.D. degree because we had enough changes to legitimize without taking on the establishment of a brand-new degree. Furthermore, where many at the time wanted the scientist-professional model replaced by the purely professional model, I was strongly in favor of preserving within the highly trained clinician all the essentials of the science. I called this the professional-scientist model, and I found myself pretty much alone in its advocacy. Nonetheless, my views prevailed, and one of the demands of our program was a scholarly doctoral dissertation. This not only would be a contribution, but would teach the student to conduct research utilizing a wide variety of methods, from epidemiological studies to field testing of delivery systems, and everything in between. In other words, the dissertation was not limited to a controlled experiment per se. Furthermore, the dissertation had to be completed by the end of the sixth year, as all students moved in unison through the program, or they failed. There would be no so-called ABDs (all but dissertation), known as psychology's most prevalent "degree." The dissertation was always problematic on campus. There was considerable anti-intellectualism during the 1970s, and some faculty members were willing to sign off on almost any slipshod rendering. In the face of all this, I took seriously the dictum that as long as we were conferring the Ph.D. rather than the Psy.D., the dissertation had to meet stringent scholarly standards. This contention between me as the president and some of our less demanding faculty members never subsided below a crescendo, and was instrumental in my ultimate demise, as will be seen in a later section.

All faculty members held the rank of instructor, and were part-time, as they taught only the courses that reflected their vocation. In other words, psychotherapy was taught by persons in the practice of psychotherapy, statistics were taught by one who made a living as a statistician, and so forth. This was a radical departure from any faculty we knew, and it was made possible by the fact that during the first 18 months, all instructors were part-time unpaid volunteers. When the faculty began to be paid, we kept most of the volunteers, who were happy to continue their careers while teaching one or two courses at CSPP. At a later point, we required and got half-time commitments from each instructor.

Personal psychotherapy was required of each student each year in the program. The school had a long list of psychotherapists in the community who had agreed to see students either free, or for a very reduced fee. The student could choose the therapist, and although the school never intruded on the therapy, the psychotherapist was obligated to render regular reports that the student was keeping all appointments and was making progress. Each student was required to have two years of individual therapy, and the remainder of the therapy requirement could be met in group therapy, or the student could continue in individual treatment.

The architects of our innovative curriculum was a committee chaired by the late Hedda Bolgar, Ph.D., a Hungarian by birth, who was trained in the Chicago School of Psychoanalysis (founded by Franz Alexander, M.D., and his colleagues). She practiced psychoanalysis for many years in Southern California, and although those of us who knew her capacity for innovative thinking were not surprised, most psychologists were startled that a curriculum so radical emerged from a psychoanalyst. She was CSPP's first system-wide Dean of Academic Affairs, but remained with the school for only two years. She went on to found the Los Angeles branch of the Wright Institute.

PSYCHOPHARMACOLOGY

By 1970, psychotropic and antipsychotic medications had skyrocketed in importance, and the CSPP curriculum was the first to include mandatory courses in psychopharmacology, along with survey courses in neurology and neurophysiology that were requisite to an understanding of drug therapy. The courses were taught by a physician, usually a psychiatrist, and we experienced no difficulty in recruiting instructors who would teach on the same basis as all our instructors. The M.D. and Ph.D. instructors were paid exactly the same with no thought on anyone's part that is should be otherwise. The startling aspect is that physicians characteristically command higher salaries than psychologists, but the physicians who were attracted to CSPP were as infected with innovation and egalitarianism as all other faculty members.

It was the purpose of the psychopharmacology sequence to render the psychologist knowledgeable about medication so as to be able to help the physician in prescribing. This included awareness of which patients could best benefit from medication, as well as knowing which drugs were best for which kinds of patients, inasmuch as the prescribing physician would depend on the therapist's knowledge of the patient. Our experience with the psychopharmacology sequence in the first couple of years had such an impact that I prevailed upon the APA to appoint an ad hoc committee to study whether the profession of psychology should seek relevant prescription authority. At my suggestion, the late Karl Pottharst, Ph.D., of our CSPP-Los Angeles faculty was appointed chair of this committee. The committee met for two years and concluded that psychology had created so many effective new psychotherapies because it did not have the expediency of the prescription pad. To give the psychologist prescription authority might eliminate the one profession that was pioneering so many behavioral interventions. I was somewhat disappointed with this conclusion, empathized with its logic, and in looking back am satisfied that we anticipated by two decades the APA's current drive for psychologists' prescribing authority.

THE FOUNDING OF THE SAN DIEGO AND FRESNO CAMPUSES

Most persons affiliated with the CSPP today are unaware that the master plan called for eight campuses throughout California. This was somewhat grandiose and I used to present the plan tongue-in-cheek, but I was always convinced that CSPP should have at least four campuses, one of which would be a rural campus. The four proposed campuses that never were considered seriously were to be in Sacramento, Santa Barbara, Chico, and Monterey, although two additional campuses did come to fruition in San Diego and Fresno. They were established sooner than I had originally anticipated because two aggressive potential founders petitioned the Board of Directors.

The first of these leaders was Maurice J. Zemlick, Ph.D., who, after convincing me that he should do so, was encouraged to petition the Board of Directors. Subsequently, in 1973, CSPP-San Diego was founded. While Maury was in the process of assuring a rather skeptical board that the time for a third campus had arrived, I was besieged by the irrepressible I. M. Abou-Ghorra, Ph.D., a well-known Fresno psychologist who was eager to establish the fourth campus. The prospect of two additional campuses was frightening to a board that was struggling to keep the first two campuses viable, but I persuaded it to approve both new campuses by promising that I would abandon all plans for campuses five through eight. Secretly, I was relieved, as I had never seriously considered the eight-campus master plan, produced by an overly enthusiastic planning committee and consulting group. Thus, CSPP-Fresno was established in 1974.

From the outset, each campus had decidedly different character. CSPP-

San Francisco was our most far-out campus. It was here that the anti-intellectualism of the 1970s reached its epitome. Graduation was conducted outdoors, with the barefooted graduating class holding hands and chanting, preferably while stoned. It was this campus that constantly petitioned for strange classes, such as astrology, channeling, past lives, or Werner Ehrhart's EST, all of which were steadfastly refused. But it was our most vibrant campus, and secretly my favorite, as long as S. Don Schultz, Ph.D., a very capable administrator, was its campus dean. Don was able to allow enough of the "spirit of Aquarius," while preventing it from descending into the absurd. When, after four years, he was promoted to vice president, the campus experienced a series of campus deans who were unable to control the anti-intellectualism. The first of these, Zalmon Garfield, Ph.D., turned on me in order to preserve his standing on campus, and did not last a full year. His successor, Robert Morgan, Ph.D., to whom I shall always be grateful for stepping in when no one else dared, was a bit more far out than our student body. And the last, Theodore Dixon, Ph.D., who ostensibly had a strong hand that could bring order to the campus, barricaded himself in his office and let his subordinates deal with the daily problems. For almost his first week, he began to plot my demise as president.

CSPP-Los Angeles probably reflected what CSPP was intended to be more than did any other campus. Radical in its own right, it nonetheless was not surfeited by the anti-intellectualism that engulfed CSPP-San Francisco. Arthur Kovacs, Ph.D., was its first campus dean, and he continued in that role throughout my seven years as founding president. This campus was as much committed to social issues as CSPP-San Francisco, but was always aware that without accreditation, any progress would be negated. Los Angeles, however, had one propensity: the clash between the faculty and the campus dean. Art was a professional psychologist who reflected all of the aspirations and needs of our program, but he was just not a good administrator. Periodically, the faculty would "fire" him and I would fly down and, after obtaining the concurrence of the faculty, would reinstate him. It was of constant amazement to me how we could take the most empathic clinician, give her or him a faculty appointment, and within one week, that person would become contentious. Our Los Angeles faculty was typical: fiercely dedicated to CSPP, but constantly at odds with it.

Our most stable campus was CSPP-San Diego, which had only one campus dean while I was president. From the beginning, Maurice J. Zemlick, Ph.D. would have no slum school. He created a campus in a new industrial park where the students had access to a swimming pool and other niceties not known on the other campuses. He was a capable administrator, a bit heavy-handed at times, who, with his wife, Lucille Zemlick, as business manager, was very protective of the superior surroundings. He broached no nonsense in the curriculum or in teaching it. When the faculty and students squirmed because they did not have the same liberties as the other campuses, they would refer to CSPP-San Diego as the "mom-and-pop store." Twice they demanded the removal of Lu Zemlick, and twice I flew down and convinced the faculty that she was a valuable asset and that we needed her. CSPP-San Diego reflected the CSPP dream while, at the same time, remained our most solid campus.

CSPP-Fresno was always the low man on the totem pole. It would not have survived without the fierce promotion of founding campus dean I. M. Abou-Ghorra. Abou was a fanatic when it came to excellence, and a strong believer in training in rural community psychology if we were to reach underserved areas. To say he was irrepressible is a gross understatement. He just never could hear "No" in response to requests. I supported him throughout, especially in the never-ending attempts to shut down his campus, for which he was openly grateful. With his wife, Eva, he made that campus successful even though it was the least sought by student applicants. He fulfilled the CSPP dream without the constant turmoil and contentiousness found on other campuses. His faculty was completely loyal to him, and he is the only Egyptian I know who could introduce his Jewish deans as "three of my people." To this day I regard Abou and Eva as among my closest friends and as two of the finest people with whom I have ever worked.

THE VAIL CONFERENCE

There is no question but that the impact CSPP and the professional school movement had at the time convinced the APA and NIMH to mount a new conference on the education and training of clinical psychologists. Interestingly, Colorado was again chosen as the location, but with Vail the site rather than Boulder. All of us went to Vail with the greatest of expectations. It became the venue in which to discuss, debate, and advocate all of the issues that were to define psychology's new social conscience, but the real reason for the conference, the articulation of a new model of clinical training, was dwarfed in the process. There was only one small group assigned that task, and Don Peterson and I were both in it. There emerged within that committee the strictly professional model, and Don I were the only voices advocating the professional-scientist model.

A side issue that is little remembered is that the *National Register of Healthcare Providers in Psychology* was conceived in Vail. At that time, psychologists had obtained licensing and certification in many states, but the standards varied. For example, some states required two years of internship, one pre- and one postdoctoral, whereas other states required only one year. And there were still a number of states that had no statutory recognition of psychologists. These two factors, variability in licensing or the lack of it, were severely hampering the fight to obtain insurance reimbursement for psychological services. The insurers complained that the variability in standards was too great. In response, the *National Register* was conceived as a way of establishing one standard, so that anyone approved by that body was eligible for insurance reimbursement. The America Board of Professional Psychology (ABPP) was chosen to launch this organization while all of us were at Vail. The strategy worked, and it was very critical at the time in the struggle for recognition by third-party payers.

It is important that Vail, as the first assemblage of psychologists to address training since Boulder, grappled with the emerging social issues, and embedded them for all time in psychological education and training. It was disappointing, however, that the training of future professional psychologists was left far short of full articulation, and resulted in the lack of definition within the APA of what the Vail model constituted. To this day, the Vail model is whatever a professional school, which itself sometimes lacks definition, wants it to be. It is not a pleasant reflection that, in accordance with the parlance of the time, "the travail at Vail was of little avail."

SHOULD CSPP HAVE BEEN ON A UNIVERSITY CAMPUS?

From the beginning, it was apparent that much of the difficulty in founding the first professional school of psychology could have been avoided if it were founded as part of a university campus. I openly hoped that such an affiliation could be accomplished, but I was skeptical that any university would accept our new curriculum, the lack of faculty rank and tenure, and other radical ideas without diluting them considerably. The idea of a professional school of psychology attracted a number of suitors within a few months of its opening its doors. One university was in New York, and the distance was an insurmountable problem from the beginning, as were a number of other factors. The field was narrowed to two serious offers, and consideration of them was to occupy a great deal of my time for the next two years. One of these was from the chair of the department of psychology at the University of the Pacific (UOP) in Stockton, California. UOP had an APA-approved doctoral program, and John Preston, Ph.D., was serious about bringing CSPP to his campus as a semiautonomous professional school. The plan was scuttled after two years of extensive negotiations by a traditional faculty that was very nervous about the curriculum. Neither John nor I was willing to dilute the CSPP concept, so the faculty ultimately blocked the plan for merger by open revolt.

A second offer came from the University of California at Davis. The vice-chancellor of that campus was intensely interested in bringing CSPP into the UC system. After two years of active negotiations, however, it became apparent to both of us that it would take years to clear the hurdle posed by the world's largest academic bureaucracy if, indeed, it could be cleared at all. I had to accept the premise that the first professional school of psychology had to be autonomous so that it could showcase its very advanced curriculum and concepts. Other schools that were to follow could then be part of an existing university.

THE PROLIFERATION OF PROFESSIONAL SCHOOLS

Shortly after the launching of CSPP, Robert Weitz, Ph.D., a member of the Dirty Dozen, undertook to found a professional school in New Jersey. Within a year, Ronald Fox, Ph.D., now a former president of the APA, had mounted a similar effort in Ohio. I was privileged to serve on the advisory boards of both, as I was on the advisory board of the first of more than a dozen professional schools that came afterward. Bob's efforts resulted in the professional school at Rutgers University, with Don Peterson as its first dean, whereas Ron's work brought about the professional school at Wright State University, with Ron, himself, as the first dean. After he retired and moved to Florida, the indefatigable Bob Weitz founded a professional school there.

A historical note is important here. There has been confusion over the last 25 years as to which professional school was the first. The late Gordon Derner, Ph.D., after whom the Institute for Advanced Psychological Studies at Adelphi University is named, referred to CSPP as the first autonomous professional school, whereas Adelphi was the first professional school. I have remained silent because of my profound respect for, and debt to, Gordon Derner, my mentor. He founded the first professional *program* in psychology, which I attended and from which I graduated with a Ph.D. degree. It was a remarkable program, and sowed the seeds in my head that flowered during the founding of CSPP. But the program at Adelphi was part of the psychology department and was not a professional school. I remember during CSPP's first year Gordon's coming to me and saying, "You have shown us the way. We should have professional schools." He then asked for my help in persuading the trustees of Adelphi University to make his professional program a professional school, and to elevate him to dean. I wrote an eight-page letter, which I still have, and shortly thereafter the trustees acceded to Gordon's request. Therefore, it is more accurate to say that Adelphi was the first professional school on a university campus, whereas CSPP was the first professional school of any kind. There is another reason why I had remained silent during Gordon's lifetime. He had always wanted to become president of the APA. The fourth time he ran successfully was my first run, and I was put in the uncomfortable position of having defeated my esteemed mentor to whom I owed such a debt. Probably it was he, in the first place, who instilled in me the idea of becoming APA president, although I had never thought of such a possibility until just before it happened.

CSPP's GOVERNANCE SYSTEM: IDEALISM RUN AMOK

The 1970s were a period in American history during which rules were to be broken, standards were to be ignored, and love would triumph over all. In this spirit, a governance system was created for CSPP that defied all probability of success. First, in keeping with my own strong, but displaced, belief that the profession of psychology should always evolve its own education and training, half of the CSPP Board of Directors was elected by the Board of Directors of the California Psychological Association (CPA). In turn, the president of CSPP was ex-officio with a vote on the CPA board. Reflecting the egalitarianism of the time, one-fourth of the CSPP board was elected by the faculty, another one-fourth elected by the students, apportioned among the four campuses. This was in keeping with the tone of the times that the students should have a deciding stake in the training enterprise.

From the outset, this governance system was a nightmare. At the monthly Board of Directors meetings, a frequent concern of the CPA directors would be the closing of one of the four campuses, usually identified as Fresno. The faculty and student directors often would have caucused and would demand the raising of faculty salaries and the lowering of tuition. At best, there would be a standoff, and after hours of haggling, I would declare a presidential consensus. This meant that since the board did not come to a decision, the president would make that decision. At worst, one of a large number of possible destructive motions would pass and I would have to argue why I, as president, in the best interest of the school, could not implement it.

The architects of this well-intentioned governance systems were Hedda Bolgar, Ph.D., who sincerely believed it would work, and Irwin Leff, the school's attorney and board secretary, who wanted to demonstrate his pet theory of political dynamic tensions. Dynamic tension is one thing, but this was built-in warfare. I must admit that I was as enthusiastic as they when the system was first conceived, but when early on it was obviously nonworkable, my pleas that we reconsider it were staunchly rebuffed.

Fortunately, there were some wise heads on the CSPP Board of Directors, usually from the CPA, but occasionally from the faculty and the students. Among these were Dirty Dozen members Rogers Wright, Ph.D., and Ernest Lawrence, Ph.D. At a time when things were really falling apart, George Hoff, Ph.D. (a CPA-elected board member) was elected chair. For the next three years, George devoted countless hours to making the potentially destructive governance system workable, and had to shoulder with the president the angry fallout when the persistent demands for campus autonomy were once again thwarted. Another very helpful board member was an alumnus, James Anderson, Ph.D., whose devotion to his alma mater never wavered. When things got so bad that some board members would not speak to one another, he volunteered his Lake Arrowhead mountain home for board retreats.

These were turbulent times, but in the end, everything seemed to work out and reason prevailed. Two things were of immense help. The board members shared a commitment to ensuring that CSPP would survive and prosper, and they evinced a welcomed sense of humor. For example, a very troublesome faculty board member who was disgruntled because the CSPP would not adopt his system of multiple therapists (two or more therapists in each individual session with one patient) came to the meeting in a bizarre costume. As best as I can describe it, it was from the 17th century, complete with satin breeches and jacket, plumed hat, and silk hose. He assumed a position on the floor behind the president's chair, and for the entire morning, silently performed yoga exercises. The board members totally ignored him, and he grew more and more agitated over the neglect. When we broke for lunch, he tendered his resignation and left in a huff, never to be seen again. But, this was not the strangest thing that occurred with this board, nor was it the last.

The Board of Overseers

The CSPP had an extensive community board and borrowed its name, the Board of Overseers, from Harvard. It was initially chaired by Charles Thomas, Ph.D., the founder of the Association of Black Psychologists, and had among its members some of the top business and community leaders in California. As just a few examples, there was Stanley Langsdorf, the senior vice president and controller of the Bank of America; Bruce Woolpert, the president of GranitRock; Carl Frederick, senior vice president of FiberBoard; Judge Creed of the Superior Court; and Patricia Costello, president of the California Association for Mental Health. This Board of Overseers participated in our Board of Directors' meetings and provided much-needed ballast. The Board of Directors would have bogged down much earlier had not the Overseers, individually and collectively, captured the vision of CSPP and been committed to its success. When the campus deans staged their "palace coup" (see below), the Overseers, more than any segment of the community, felt betrayed.

Exit Nick Cummings

In retrospect, I realize that I very much enjoyed all of the currents and subcurrents that swirled around this new school, as this turmoil also reflected the excitement and enthusiasm that made it work. I enjoy start-ups, and when a new organization reaches a certain level, I lose interest because I am not an institution builder. My life has been characterized by a succession of start-ups, leaving the institution builders to pick up where I left off. After five years as president, I knew CSPP was far from mature. But I am also a realist who knew that every time I had to declare "presidential consensus," I had spent another chit from my depleting arsenal of good will. It was getting close to the time I should leave, and in the last two years of my tenure, I resigned every six months, four times in all.

Each time, the board refused my resignation, dunning me with guilt feelings because the job had not yet been completed. So I stayed, only to be fired by that same board just a month after I tendered my fourth resignation.

It is not surprising that the initial volunteers who stampeded to be a part of this new school brought with them a variety of social, political, and personal agendas, which often seemed to override the main purpose of CSPP to redefine graduate education and training in psychology. I empathized with most of these, having been an early part of the civil rights movement, and every movement thereafter, through the feminist revolution to gay liberation. As each member of CSPP had an individual axe to grind, sometimes I felt as if I were the only one who remained focused on the need for accreditation and our subsequent survival. But I was not alone in this concern; psychologists on the board who were not faculty and thus not caught up in the idealism run amok were alarmed by the poor quality of the dissertations. Among them was Rogers Wright, who headed a special commission to investigate and advise the school on the dissertations. His commission concentrated on the Los Angeles campus as a start, where the dissertations were described in the commission's preliminary report as "appalling." Reforms would have prevailed at that time were it not for Campus Dean Kovacs and prominent faculty member, Karl Pottharst, who actively undermined the work of the commission. The Wright Commission was disbanded, leaving the dissertations to range from about 10% good, and even excellent to 50% unacceptable.

Actually, the overwhelming consensus even among the faculty and student body was that the school had to achieve standing, but there were unrealistic expectations of the president and those who were helping me to achieve the goal of recognition for CSPP. The prevailing attitude was that we had pulled so many rabbits out of the hat, and would continue to do so. WASC said we needed an endowment, admissions standards (rather than open enrollment), doctoral-level faculty (instead of good people without higher degrees, but with their hearts in the right place), solid doctoral dissertations, and a myriad of other requirements. Yet much of the well-intentioned CSPP community believed we could ignore these and still "wiggle the system" to accredit us. After all, "Nick will do it."

I was under constant assault to declare open enrollment, spend the endowment, rehire ineligible faculty, approve slipshod dissertations, and declare each campus autonomous, free to pursue its own designs. Any one of these would prevent the school's success; together, they spelled disaster. The CSPP was coming to the end of its provisional accreditation and we had to step up to the plate. Under particular scrutiny were our disserta-tions, about which we had been warned: "If you insist on the Ph.D. rath-er than the Psy.D., the dissertations must be of academic quality." I knew most were not just substandard, but outrageously inadequate. In one, for example, the student wandered about the mountains behind Big Sur for three days without a watch and wrote about his "disorientation." Others were even worse, yet the faculty had signed off on them, justifying their behavior that it was in the spirit of the anti-intellectualism of the 1970s. I had to take drastic steps, and I informed the campuses that 58 of 73 doc-toral dissertations would not warrant graduation. The reply was that the faculty approves dissertations, not the president, to which I responded that it is the president who signs the diplomas. At that moment, I knew I had cashed in my last chit.

Coupled with the faculty dissatisfaction was the rebelliousness of three of the four campus deans, who knew they were on their way out because they could not maintain the necessary academic standards. Dixon had no control of his campus, and Zemlick was on probation. Kovacs announced at the last meeting I had with all the campus deans, "There will be no cabal against the president." Then he immediately set out to lead the other two rebellious campus deans in a "palace coup," omitting Abou-Ghorra, who would have none of it. The strategy was very simple. The three campus deans would declare at the next board meeting that they no longer would follow the president, whereupon the school counsel and board secretary, Irwin Leff, who was also on his way out, would declare the president "incapacitated" under the bylaws. The board members were lobbied aggressively by the students and faculty. Under the tutelage of the deans, well-meaning faculty and students convinced them that getting rid of the president would be the only way to save the CSPP. Actually, the campus deans were convinced that they would, without presidents, be autonomous, ruling their own fiefdoms. All of this was accomplished se-cretly and launched within the month preceding the February 1976 board meeting.

That board meeting began in a circus atmosphere and concluded as a massacre. The campuses had chartered buses to bring in students by the hundreds. They could not be seated in the relatively small boardroom, so the grand ballroom of the hotel was rented to accommodate them, while in the boardroom a student with a walkie-talkie (cellular phones had not yet been invented) described everything occurring there. As I walked into the room, I heard him utter into the walkie-talkie, "The president and the vice president just walked into the room. Nick has a stunned look on his face." When the board was called to order, in preplanned motions, the chair George Hoff, was removed without thanks. I demanded time to call for a vote of thanks for his three years of service, but was gaveled down by the newly installed puppet chair. Wright, Lawrence, Anderson, and other board members who were not privy to the plot objected loudly, and threatened to walk out. Had they done so, the meeting would have lost its quorum, so the campus deans quickly brought the circus atmosphere into some semblance of order. I was allowed to make a motion thanking Dr. Hoff for his three years of dedicated service, and the motion was perfunctorily passed without any real thanks. The massacre continued as the cooler heads on the board were outvoted. That day, they resigned from the board, and I resigned the presidency effective the first of July.

In large measure, I was relieved as I was ready to move on. However, I was startled by the vehemence and treachery of those who ostensibly had been my friends long before the founding of CSPP. Not only was I bitterly attacked, but so was my family. The intensity of the attack on my wife and two teenage children, bystanders at best, left them with a feeling of distaste for CSPP and a disdain for the perpetrators. It was as if I had to be assassinated several times over, and I had to be crippled further by attacks on my family; otherwise, I would rise from the dead and retaliate. The legal counsel I sought was adamant that Leff's fabricated "incapacitation" of the president would not hold up in court, and that I had excellent recourse. My being elected to the APA presidency just one year later convinced many at CSPP that now I would retaliate. But a father does not destroy his own child, and I chose to withdraw quietly and forever. Furthermore, I was already convinced that I had accomplished all I could for CSPP.

Only one last task remained to conclude my work for the professional school movement, and for that reason, I demanded the title of president for six more months. In exchange for this, I even accepted the indignity of suffering under the authority of a preselected puppet president who would be running the school in the interim.

NCSPP

My last task relating to the professional school movement was to establish the National Council of Professional Schools of Psychology (NCSPP). I had been working on this for some time, and in mid-1976, I convened the first meeting. By this time, the professional school movement had blossomed, and more than 20 such schools were represented at the organizational meeting. I informed them that the way had been prepared with the Council of Professional Accreditation (COPA) in Washington, which had been advised that the NCSPP would be applying to become the accrediting body for the professional schools of psychology, and that COPA was congenial to the idea. The group then passed the bylaws and elected Gordon Derner, Ph.D., dean of the professional school at Adelphi, its first chair.

The NCSPP did not seek accrediting status, as I had hoped. The reasons were complex, but of importance was that Gordon, as he explained to me years later, had just made his third unsuccessful bid for the APA presidency and was interested in increasing his credibility with the APA when he made a fourth run. In looking back, I am convinced that many compromises had to be made in seeking APA approval, and that the professional schools would have been farther ahead without it. In addition, the emergence of so many professional schools on university campuses dictated that many of the innovations, such as part-time faculty who also had concurrent careers doing what they taught, as well as the absence of tenure, had to be discarded in an established academic environment.

Nonetheless, many of the main thrusts of a professional program, with clinicians being eligible for faculty appointments, survived and thrived. The Psy.D. degree has become the professional degree of the professional schools, and there are probably more Psy.D.s graduating today than there are Ph.D.s in professional psychology.

EPILOGUE ON CSPP: ENTER JOHN O'NEIL

My successor as CSPP president, John O'Neil, was far from the pushover the rebellious campus deans had envisioned. John is an institutional builder, and he set about doing just that. Through a series of lawsuits, he dismantled the unworkable governance system and divested the school from CPA "ownership." The faculty and students no longer controlled the board, and he immediately got rid of the disloyal attorney. Leff, however, refused to step down, insisting that his appointment as counsel was by the board rather than the president. The board would have none of this, and when it fired him, he removed his shoe and pounded it on the table as Nikita Krushchev had done years before at the United Nations. Then, in rapid succession, John fired the rebellious campus deans, beginning with Dixon, then Kovacs, and finally Zemlick. The last refused to leave, and he had to be forcibly carried off the premises and locks replaced.

We built CSPP to be very strong, making it impossible for the four campuses to break away into fiefdoms as the rebellious deans had planned. They surely would not have survived competing against each other. Then John made sure that CSPP would survive well into the future by divesting it, through a series of lawsuits, of its well-meaning romantic and fanciful governance system. He served as president for 21 years, three times as long as I had. Such is in keeping with our respective roles, I doing the start-up and he building the institution. I am grateful to him for this. And I look forward with excitement to the continuing presidency of Judith Albino, Ph.D., who assumed that role in 1998. She shows promise of being an outstanding institutional builder as she begins expanding CSPP as one school within Alliant International University.

WHAT WENT RIGHT AND WHAT WENT WRONG?

Once and for all, professional education was established within psychology, and even the traditional programs brought clinicians to the campus as faculty. It established the Psy.D. as a legitimate professional degree, but it fell short of establishing it as *the* professional degree in the same way that the M.D., R.N., D.D.S., D.P.M., and other such degrees immediately define who is the professional in the healthcare arena.

Perhaps the greatest failing is that the profession did not solve the master's-level problem. I predicated in the *APA Monitor* in 1975 that if we did not find a place in the scheme of things for the master's-level practitioners, eventually these individuals would form an independent profession and become our successful competitors. Unfortunately, this has come to pass, and it is not the glut of doctorates that suppresses doctoral-level incomes, but the horde of master's-level practitioners who undercut us in the marketplace.

One of the outgrowths of seeking APA approval rather than making the NCSPP our own accrediting body is that professional schools became too closely identified with the APA, and failed, along with it, to adapt to the swiftly changing marketplace. Consequently, the curricula of the professional schools are only slightly ahead, if at all, of the traditional schools in having failed to evolve education and training relevant to the present era of the industrialization of healthcare. And finally, we have yet to adequately define what a professional school is and to ensure its proper place in the scheme of things. It is 26 years since Vail, and the Vail Model still has not been satisfactorily articulated. Consequently, in too many instances, a professional school is whatever a particular school wants it to be. The public is not adequately protected from the fly-by-night programs, or even the outright diploma mills, that masquerade as professional schools.

Finally, as has all psychology, professional schools have the obligation to inform students of the stark realities of employment in our field. Unfortunately, most professional school faculties are as ignorant of what is demanded by the new behavioral healthcare marketplace as are traditional programs. The current and continued decline in applications should be a warning. The programs that survive are the ones that prepare the graduate for the new healthcare environment.

{ 4 }

How the APA Became
An Advocacy Organization:
The Founding of CAPPS

AT THE TURN OF THE MILLENNIUM, the American Psychological Association is one of the most politicized membership organizations in America. Not only is it engaged in extensive lobbying of the Congress, state legislatures, and the executive branch, but it has spawned and supported a series of lawsuits and threats of lawsuits. No wonder that in the year 2000, the APA had to spinoff part of itself into a new 501(c)(6) organization in order to cease jeopardizing its 501(c)(3) tax-exempt status. In the light of today's flurry of activity aimed at shaping public policy, it is difficult for psychologists to remember that not too long ago, the APA would have nothing to do with professional advocacy.

For several years, practitioner activists had been trying to move the APA toward taking a stance on federal legislation that would have an impact on the practice of psychology. It was a difficult uphill fight, and even the Dirty Dozen tactically recognized the futility when it adopted the establishment of psychology as an autonomous profession as a priority. Patience and waiting for a better day seemed to be the strategy employed to make the APA an advocacy organization. The flash point, however, came suddenly in 1965 with Medicare.

PSYCHOLOGY AND THE 1965 MEDICARE HEARINGS

For months, several of us had been urging the APA to participate in the Medicare hearings that were underway prior to the implementation of the newly enacted amendments to the Social Security Act known as Title 18 (Medicare) and Title 19 (Medicaid). We believed, and subsequent experience confirmed, that these two entitlements eventually would be the largest healthcare programs in the world. By 2000, Medicare and Medicaid represented 40% of the $1.2 trillion in U.S. annual health expenditures. Not only was it important that practicing psychologists participate as independent practitioners in providing services in Medicare, but also that the inclusion of our profession would constitute a model to be emulated by the private insurance sector. Much was at stake in 1965.

The resistance by the APA Board of Directors was fierce. This was long before the first professional psychologists were elected to the board, and one board member prided himself on being quoted that he would "not lift a finger to put one more dollar in the pocket of any private practitioner." The time allotted to the Medicare hearings was nearing an end, and it was obvious the APA was not going to participate. Several of us sought an appointment with Wilbur Cohen, the newly appointed Medicare administrator. To our surprise, Secretary Cohen readily responded to our request and received us on a Friday afternoon, just a few days after we had contacted his office in desperation.

It is important, in putting the meeting with Cohen in context, to recall the mood in Washington in 1965. It was the early years of the Lyndon Johnson Administration, during which a blizzard of social legislation was enacted by the Congress and signed by the president. Medicare and Medicaid were only two of many programs, but the political leaders in Washington believed these heralded the beginning of government-sponsored universal healthcare. Furthermore, the expansive mood was inclined toward inclusion rather than exclusion. In this vein, Cohen was happy to see us, as he believed firmly that psychologists should be recognized providers of Medicare.

He explained that the hearings would be ending at noon on the upcoming Monday, and that any profession that had not participated by that time could not be recognized. He agreed to make an exception, and if the APA would submit a letter requesting that psychologists be recognized as Medicare providers, and that letter was received by noon three days hence, our profession would be included. We were stunned and delighted, but then we realized that we had less than 70 hours to convince the APA board to reverse its opposition. The letter obviously had to come from no less than the president of the APA.

Fortunately, the board was meeting that weekend. We spent all day Saturday pleading to have our cause heard by the board, but to no avail. APA President Jerome Bruner, with the support of his board, steadfastly refused to give us even 20 minutes. Finally, in the early afternoon of Sunday, President-Elect Nicholas Hobbs stepped out of the boardroom to speak with us in the vestibule. He asked naively, but quite earnestly, what the matter was about, and in a half-hour we described the issue as well as we could. Nick Hobbs, who later was to become a close personal friend, was surprisingly sympathetic, and he promised to go back into the board meeting and attempt to secure us a hearing. We had been cooling our heels for more than an hour when Hobbs emerged from the boardroom smiling. We were ushered in and told we had only 20 minutes. We had anticipated being allotted little time, and had our presentation prepared accordingly. Our articulate spokesperson was Rogers Wright, the spiritual leader of what became to be known as the Dirty Dozen (Wright & Cummings, 2001). At the end of his presentation, the board agreed that if we could have a letter for President Bruner's signature in the morning, he would sign it before leaving for Harvard. Arthur Brayfield, the executive officer, would see to it that it reached Secretary Cohen before noon. We were ecstatic.

I was chosen to write the letter, while others took late afternoon flights home. I was up all night in my room at the Gramercy Hotel composing a three-page letter. It had to strike just the right note. Finally satisfied that I had written the best letter I knew how to write, at 4:00 a.m., I went to into the APA building by prior arrangement and typed the letter on official letterhead. When the staff arrived at 8:00, I had the letter on Brayfield's desk for Bruner's signature. Assured that all was well, I caught a cab to Dulles Airport and flew home to San Francisco, too excited to sleep on the plane, even though I had been up all night.

About a month later, I received a phone call from Bruner's secretary at Harvard. She advised me that Dr. Bruner was in Europe, and asked what I wanted her to do with the letter on his desk. My heart sank, and I was speechless. We had missed the deadline. I immediately called Wilbur Cohen's office and was told what I was certain would be the case: it was much too late for psychology to be considered, and there was no mechanism for a reconsideration. At this point, we decided to begin thinking about an advocacy organization outside of the APA.

FAST-FORWARD TO 1990

Psychology was to be excluded as a Medicare provider for 25 years. Ironically, when, in 1990, the APA made the successful presentation to Representative Fortney (Pete) Stark's Congressional health committee that resulted in psychology's inclusion, I gave one of the two presentations, along with Bryant Welch, head of the Practice Directorate of the APA. This was a day to celebrate the fulfillment of our goal, in spite of the painful awareness that were it not for the APA's bungling, by this time we could have enjoyed a quarter of a century as Medicare providers. Much of the satisfaction was seeing the commitment the APA now had to the advocacy of professional issues. This was brought about not by persuasion, but by founding a successful organization, in this case, the Council for the Advancement of the Psychological Professions and Sciences (CAPPS), which did the job without the cooperation of the APA, and thereby cajoled the APA into action.

I can attest to the fact that none of us involved in the 1965 fiasco held Jerry Bruner personally responsible for our having to wait 25 years for this victory. How the passive-aggressive course to dropping the ball was decided, whether it was Jerry's or Art's idea, or who actually dropped it, are irrelevant questions. They were only reflecting the fierce resistance to advocacy that pervaded the APA at that time. Not only did it take another organization to bring about the APA's own advocacy arm, but there is the untold story that another organization I later founded was instrumental in providing the data that favorably impressed the Congress. That was American Biodyne, which had received the first Medicare behavioral-care carve-out contract in 1986, in Florida. The highly successful programs for older adults that we instituted there were delivered by psychologists by virtue of their being part of a managed behavioral-care organization (MBCO), rather than because psychologists were eligible to do so, which they were not. I shall never forget Representative Pete Stark's questions to me, which reflected his having been impressed by the uniqueness and relevance of our programs for the aged, and also by the fact that they were designed and implemented by psychologists, not psychiatrists. Before the hearing was over, Bryant and I knew we would soon be included as recognized providers in Medicare.

THE UNLIKELY FOUNDING OF CAPPS

Even though in 1965, Rog Wright and I realized that we had to found an advocacy organization soon, we did not get around to it until 1972. The APA's Committee on Health Insurance (COHI) had been formed (see previous chapter), and because I was chairing it, we hoped it could be that advocacy organization. The COHI was instrumental in devising the free-dom-of-choice legislation and took the leadership in advocating its passage in the states. This in itself was a full plate. In addition, as COHI was an arm of the APA, it could not serve the purpose we had in mind. I re-signed from COHI to found the California School of Professional Psy-chology (CSPP) in 1969, and it was three years before I could come up for air from that arduous task. It was then we agreed that the time had come.

On a Friday shortly after noon, Ernest Lawrence, Rogers Wright, and I gathered at Rog's home in Long Beach, California, vowing not to emerge until we had formed an advocacy organization. It was an early spring weekend in 1972, and a wonderful time to be on the beach instead of indoors. We were more determined than we were informed on how to do this, but by early Friday evening, we were unanimous that the organi-zation we formed should have no official or unofficial connection whatso-ever with the APA. By early Saturday afternoon, we had an organization well conceptualized, along with its governance system, and we even had the first draft of the bylaws. We named the organization the Council for the Advancement of the Psychological Professions and Sciences (CAPPS), not to be confused with the modern Council for the Advancement of Professional Psychology (CAPP without the "s") that is currently a part of the APA governance structure. Ernie and I were adamant that we should include the psychological sciences, and Rog agreed with us that it would be ironic, but effective, if we lobbied Capitol Hill on behalf of academic/research funding, as well as professional issues.

We constructed a list of 500 prominent practitioners throughout the United States by using the *APA Directory*. We divided the list among us and began calling them early Saturday afternoon. We described CAPPS and invited them to join the Board of Governors for $500. By Sunday night, over 100 had signed on. We had raised $50,000 in two days, a for-midable sum in 1972. From the beginning, practitioners flocked to CAPPS, and we soon had over 500 psychologists on the Board of Gover-nors. Within that first year, we had raised half a million dollars, enabling us to hire an executive officer, as well as an administrative assistant, and to rent office space.

Obviously, an organization run by a 500-member Board of Governors would be unwieldy, so we formed an executive committee, called Ex-Comm, of less than a dozen members. Ernie and I served on the Ex-Comm, and it was agreed that Rog should be president. He served CAPPS superbly for its brief three years of existence. The Ex-Comm also included Ted Blau, Jack Wiggins, and the late Max Siegel, who, along with me, were all to become presidents of the APA. Soon we were joined by Helen Senukian of Illinois, and the late Herb Freudenberger of New York. Later, we added Suzanne Sobel, who lived in Washington, D.C., and was able to give us a daily presence there. A capable young man named Jack Donohue was hired as the executive officer, and after CAPPS was dissolved, he accepted an invitation to join the APA staff.

OUR FIRST YEAR

CAPPS held its first open meeting at the 1973 APA convention. I was chosen to give our first annual report to an audience that filled the hotel auditorium. Proudly, I was able to state that in its first year, CAPPS had made more representations on Capitol Hill than the APA had done in its previous 80 years. This would not have been difficult given the APA's refusal to be an advocacy organization, but the amount of direct lobbying we had done would be impressive for a mature organization, to say nothing of the fledgling CAPPS. We expected to be challenged by the academic community, but it had not yet caught up with what we were doing. We were blind-sided from an unexpected source.

In the middle of my presentation, several women came down the aisle waving banners, and after mounting the podium, they demanded to know what CAPPS had done on behalf of the ERA (Equal Rights Amendment). I cannot recall most of their names, but one was Hannah Lerman, who worked for me as dean of students at CSPP-Los Angeles. The answer to their question, of course, was that we had done nothing. The public-interest constituency of the APA, and particularly the feminist movement, was just getting underway. In our haste to form an advocacy organization, we had overlooked their concerns. We began that day to include public-interest concerns along with academic/research and professional issues, and although this was important to do, the fact is that CAPPS' financial base for its three years was 95% composed of the practitioner community. In fairness, it must be said that we spent 80% of our resources on matters related to practice, so there were no further complaints from any of the three constituencies until the scientific community awakened to our success and demanded that we never again intercede on its behalf.

EXTERNAL VERSUS INTERNAL LOBBYING

No one can question that professional psychology, thanks to CAPPS, suddenly had a presence on Capitol Hill. We continued to lobby when and where we deemed it important and without regard to the APA's increasing uneasiness that CAPPS, and not the APA, had become the perceived voice for psychology in Washington. As concerned as the APA establishment was with this external lobbying, it was the internal lobbying that worried it the most.

During the mid-1970s, CAPPS was able to get four of its Ex-Comm members on the APA Board of Directors. In the order of their being elected, they were Ted Blau, Rogers Wright, myself, and Max Siegel. When staunch professional activist Don Schultz was subsequently elected to the board, seemingly overnight five of the 11 board members were professional psychologists.

As active as CAPPS was on Capitol Hill, there is no question but that we spent as much, if not more, time lobbying the APA. The Council of Representatives, thanks to a number of new Divisions that were primarily identified with practice, was steadily adding professional psychologists to its membership. These early Divisions were 13 (Consulting), 27 (Counseling), 29 (Psychotherapy), and 31 (State Association Affairs). The academic/scientific community began to strike back, objecting mostly to the internal activism. A committee was formed to reach some kind of accommodation between CAPPS and the APA as to when and where each organization would be authorized to represent psychology.

CRAPACAPPS: ENTER THE AAP

The Committee on Relations between the APA and CAPPS (CRAPA-CAPPS, known among sympathetic professionals as "the committee to crap-on-CAPPS), was appointed with Wilse (Bernie) Webb as the chair, while CAPPS was represented in the ensuing negotiations by Rog Wright and Ernie Lawrence. Although a staunch member of the academic community, Bernie understood and was accepting of the needs of professional psychologists for advocacy. The outspoken opponent was CRAPACAPPS member Norman Garmezy of Minnesota. From the very beginning, his dislike of CAPPS and its leadership inadvertently played into our overarching strategy.

CAPPS was formed to force the APA into advocacy. This avowed strategy was kept under wraps in the Ex-Comm, and was particularly the dirty little secret of the three founders. When CRAPACAPPS, responding to the cries of Garmezy, demanded that CAPPS disband, we refused. When Norm softened his demand to say that if the APA formed an advocacy arm, then CAPPS should agree to disband, we loudly cried "foul." In the ensuing negotiations, it was agreed that a new organization would be formed, nominally at arm's length from the APA so as not to jeopardize the APA's tax-exempt status, and that half of the board members would be from CAPPS, with the other half appointed by the APA. The new organization would be called the Association for the Advancement of Psychology (AAP), which exists to this day. We agreed to the plan, moaning, groaning, and complaining bitterly all the way.

The night after the agreement forming the AAP and disbanding CAPPS was signed, the former Ex-Comm members held a celebration to express their jubilation. It was kept secret, as we maintained the facade that we were pained to see CAPPS dissolve. All along, our plan had been to move the APA into advocacy, and that CAPPS would be a temporary organization whose success would prod the APA by proclaiming, "If you don't do it, we will." This entire sequence spanned only three years from the founding of CAPPS to its disbanding, making it one of the most successful organizations established solely for the purpose of moving the policy/decision makers in American psychology. In retrospect, I marvel that all of us at Ex-Comm never lost sight of the goal to disband after success. We had seen too many groups refuse to dissolve after achieving the goals for which they had been organized.

Appendix 4A

Mental Health and National Health Insurance: A Case History of the Struggle for Professional Autonomy[2]

Nicholas A. Cummings[3]

This article traces the history of the struggle to gain professional and insurance carrier recognition for psychology. Psychology's future under various national health insurance plans being considered by Congress, NIMH, and private organizations is examined, and several models of mental health service delivery are analyzed.

Paradoxically, the nation that was first to put a man on the moon may be the last major Western power to enact a universal, government-sponsored health system. The reasons for this are varied and complex, and only the highlights can be touched on in an overview. But placing the issue of mental health coverage within the overall perspective of the general issue of national health care is essential to its understanding. Psychology is a relatively recent arrival to the debate on national health insurance. Beginning with a trickle of dedicated interest nearly 20 years ago,

[2] Reprinted with permission from Cummings, N. A. (1979). Mental Health and national health insurance: A case history of the struggle for professional autonomy. In C. A. Kiesler, N. A. Cummings, & G. R. VandenBos, *Psychology and national health insurance: A sourcebook* (pp. 5–16). Washington, D.C.: American Psychological Association.

[3] Nicholas A. Cummings is currently President, American Psychological Association; Director, Mental Research Institute, Palo Alto, California; and Clinical Director, Biodyne Institute.

the American Psychological Association (APA) now expends a significant portion of its total resources on matters relating to the issue of national health insurance. The way in which the APA became deeply involved in the matter is essentially a case study of one profession's struggle for professional autonomy and recognition.

General History

A universal, government-sponsored health system has been under discussion in the United States for several decades, but not until recently has a majority conceded that national health insurance is imminent, and perhaps even overdue. The concept has its modern roots in the latter half of the 19th century, but the present overview begins with the economically depressed years of the 1930s when the possible provision of health services by the government to its citizens was a concept that began to intrigue proponents of the New Deal. The idea was then termed socialized medicine. It was only one of many ideological proposals proffered within the first two Roosevelt administrations, but it was the one that organized medicine was to attack openly and vigorously during the next three decades. Whether or not Congress would have enacted a comprehensive, government-sponsored health system during those years had not a rigorous battle been waged against it by the American Medical Association (AMA) can be left only to conjecture. But the AMA campaign resulted in a negative connotation to the term *socialized medicine* — a phrase that has all but disappeared from the American vocabulary. However, the concept, replaced in the lexicon by the current term *national health insurance*, received new life in the blizzard of social legislation that characterized the Great Society of the Johnson administration.

In the mid-1960s, Congress amended the appropriate 30-year-old Social Security Act to give a sizable portion of citizens, principally the elderly and the poor, a new kind of federally financed health care in the form of two new programs. These programs, Medicare and Medicaid (Titles 18 and 19) of the Social Security Act, were stridently opposed by the AMA. Following the defeat in the legislative arena, AMA acquired, almost immediately, a more realistic and enlightened posture under the slogan, "don't oppose, but propose." Accepting federal and state intervention as inevitable, organized medicine now strives to guarantee medicine's control, or at least its preeminence, in whatever legislation is enacted. The strong resistance to outside interference can be at least partially justified by professional and scientific considerations. However, medicine's strident opposition to incursions from the government, and more recently from consumer advocates, has its roots in the manner in which medicine began to flourish in the United States.

American medicine grew from a small entrepreneurial system relying heavily upon the apprenticeship model to a giant industry incongruously retaining much of its horse-and-buggy philosophy in the face of modern medical technology and runaway health costs. The image of the benevolent country doctor making calls by horse and buggy is the one that organized medicine would like to maintain in the minds of the public. To a surprising extent, it has been successful; television's Marcus Welby is that benevolent country doctor, updated by present and futuristic science and technology and the elimination of house calls. Within the giant healthcare industry, the small-business individualism of the nation's physicians was safeguarded by an extensive system of medical-practices acts designed to prevent medical practice from falling into the employ or control of nonmedical forces. Small-business individualism, however, had the inadvertent effect of encouraging 19th century entrepreneurialism. In order to care for the poor, the rich were "soaked." This medical Robin Hoodism never really worked from its inception. It had to be supplemented by a system of private charities, which, in turn, had to be supplemented by county hospitals and clinics. This situation resulted in a two-tiered system of healthcare in which those who had the means visited the private practitioner, while the indigent were relegated to charity or county hospitals and clinics. Even within the private sector, two levels of fees emerged, one for the middle class and the other for the carriage trade, with the middle class not infrequently and ignominiously falling into the charity tier in the face of catastrophic illness that could wipe out a family's entire resources. The incomes of private-practicing physicians were maintained at a high level, while the hospitals balanced their budgets by including the training model within the two-tiered system. Thus, interns and residents struggled to get by on poverty-level salaries. In the public, or charity, sector, care could be excellent for patients in teaching hospitals who were fortunate enough to have an exotic illness considered helpful in the training of physicians. Those suffering from illnesses having little or no teaching value, no matter how serious, were often subjected to overextended stays and overcrowded conditions in substandard settings. The two-tiered system of medicine has survived a series of challenges, not the least of which has been the development of health insurance, and it is with us today in a form perhaps even more pervasive than ever.

The birth of the private health insurance industry was characterized throughout the thirties and forties more by exclusions, limitations, coin-surances, and deductions than by benefits. Encouraged by organized medicine as an acceptable alternative to socialized medicine, the health insurance industry grew in coverage and extensiveness to the point where most working Americans now have some kind of health insurance.

During this same era, various health care schemes have gradually been adopted so that an uncoordinated nonsystem of national health care somewhat like a giant patchwork quilt has evolved. Much of this has been accomplished by successive redefinitions of the concept of "medically needy" beyond the original eligibility of the indigent. Thus, a partial, unplanned national health care system is being created from the welfare model, which is gradually and inadvertently being turned into an unworkable nonmodel characterized by inefficiency and duplication and threatening to survive as an establishment within whatever national health insurance structure is eventually adopted. Interestingly, often those social planners who most decry the waste, duplication, and inefficiency of our current system of private-public care are those who become the most vigorous proponents of the next patch on the quilt.

The first large-scale thrust to promote national health insurance was made in the early 1960s by the labor unions, principally the United Auto Workers (UAW) under the leadership of the late Walter Reuther. Calling together prominent proponents from a widely representative segment of our society, Reuther established the Committee of 100 whose sole purpose was to promote the concept of a universal health care system in the United States. Today this effort is continued by the Committee for National Health Insurance, directed by Max Fine. Although it would be difficult to assess to direct impact of this group, there is virtually no question that the UAW conception of a national health insurance system has emerged in several Congressional bills, particularly those introduced by Senator Edward Kennedy and Representative Martha Griffiths.

National Health Insurance Versus National Healthcare

Although national health insurance and national health care are often used interchangeably, it is important to point out that they are essentially two distinct national health schemes. *National health insurance* conceives of health services delivered within a variety of public and private institutions and financed by the Social Security system or by a method similar to the Social Security system (i.e., employer/employee contributions). Within *national health care*, on the other hand, the government would own all of the delivery systems in a manner similar to Veterans Administration medical service delivery. Some leadership within the Department of Health, Education, and Welfare and organized labor share a distrust of the private sector and favor national health care. The opposite is true within the majority of the Congress and certainly within the health insurance industry, which inherently resists government interference.

The last several years have seen over three dozen national health bills introduced into Congress, each reflecting the views of sponsors at several points along the continuum from national health insurance to national health care. Table 1 presents a sample of these bills to illustrate some of the similarities and differences. At one extreme, the UAW approach proposes complete healthcare provided under total government auspices. At the other extreme, the insurance-industry-sponsored bills suggest a system of delivery with minimum disturbance of the private sector. Predictably, most bills reflect an amalgam of these two disparate views.

How the APA Became Involved

The struggle to alert the American Psychological Association to the potential impact and implications of an inevitable national health system has spanned two decades and has literally reshaped the face of American psychology. Often bitter, sometimes comical, but always colorful, the movement to involve the APA in national health insurance advocacy demonstrates the dedication of a handful of early activists.

In the late 1950s, through a mechanism he called the National Clinical Liaison Committee, Leonard Small of New York began to circulate a mimeographed sheet warning clinical psychologists that it would not be long before most, if not all, psychotherapy in the United States would be finance by third-party payment. He argued that if psychology were not recognized as a primary mental health provider by insurance carriers and the government, who would compromise the third-party payers, the profession of psychology would suffer economic extinction. One of the first to heed Small's exhortation was Rogers Wright. Wright has spent his professional lifetime insisting that only organized psychology operating within an advocacy stance can assure autonomy of the science and profession of psychology. He attracted a small number of activists who operated totally outside the APA governance structure for years but who began to be listened to by the state psychological associations, particularly in New York and California. Their objective was to energize the APA.

The first concession to these clinicians' demands came in 1963 when the APA sponsored the Ad Hoc Committee on Insurance and Related Social Developments (AHCIRSD, which was acronymed a-curse-ed). The name derived from the conviction held at the time on the part of APA's Board of Professional Affairs that the subject of insurance was neither respectable enough for a standing committee nor important enough to occupy an ad hoc committee's entire attention. The committee's chair, Milton Theaman, not only had the task of persuading insurance companies to recognize the services of psychologists but also had to constantly defend the activities of AHCIRSD as a legitimate APA endeavor. The demand by clinical psychologists for parity with psychiatrists tended to be viewed as an attempt to line the pockets of private practitioners, and it was difficult to keep the critics focused on the major issue of the professional autonomy of psychologists. If psychology were ever to provide alternative delivery modalities to the medical model, it first had to achieve recognition and independence.

During its first five years of existence AHCIRSD did, against overwhelming odds, persuade a handful of insurance carriers (representing an almost infinitesimal percentage of the insured) to recognize psychologists. This very modest achievement was offset by the success in persuading the APA to establish, in 1968, the standing Committee on Health Insurance (COHI). The first COHI chair, Nicholas Cummings, who had also served on AHCIRSD, immediately abandoned the previous strategy and devised the so-called freedom-of-choice legislation, which by 1978 amended the insurance codes of 29 states. This amendment provided that any health insurance that reimburses for the services of a psychiatrist must also reimburse for those of a qualified psychologist. Thus the consumer was granted, for the first time, the freedom to choose between the two professions. Predictably, as with licensure or certification for psychologists, most or all states will eventually adopt such freedom-of-choice insurance legislation. The legislative struggle for recognition could stop here were it not for the implications of national health insurance. Should a redefinition under national health insurance exclude psychologists as independent providers (as was originally the case in Medicare and Medicaid), the successes won by this freedom-of-choice legislation would become irrelevant.

Indeed, it was the exclusion of psychologists as providers under Medicare and Medicaid that prompted professional psychologists to renew their efforts to move the APA into a legislative advocacy role in the early 1970s. Professionals, finding the APA unresponsive, were motivated to create the Council for the Advancement of the Psychological Professions and Sciences (CAPPS). The founding of CAPPS makes an interesting study in social process. Vowing not to emerge until there was a national advocacy structure, Wright (who was to serve for four years as the CAPPS president), Cummings, and Ernest Lawrence sequestered themselves on a Friday afternoon. By Saturday they had devised a structure for CAPPS and were contacting leading professional psychologists across the country with the goal of obtaining at least 500 persons to serve as the Board of Governors and to underwrite CAPPS by contributing $100 each. That same Sunday CAPPS was enthusiastically launched.

From its inception, professional psychologists flocked to CAPPS and made it an effective, self-sustained advocacy organization. The demise of CAPPS stemmed from its unfortunate embroilment in APA internal politics, for it was still the goal of the clinical activists to move the APA into the arena of advocacy. This goal was realized with the creation of CAPP's successor, the Association for the Advancement of Psychology (AAP), which represents not only professional psychology, as did its predecessor, but also scientific and academic psychology. Federal cuts in research and training funds and other untoward events during this time convinced all facets of psychology of the need for advocacy on the federal level. By 1977 it became apparent that the legislative office previously maintained by the APA (and which had been eliminated with the formation of the AAP) had to be reestablished. Through this legislative office, not only does the APA contribute to the AAP, but it also provides the guidance, leadership, direction, and position papers that only organized psychology, speaking thoughtfully and with careful deliberation, can provide.

Simultaneously, and under the leadership of many of the same professional-psychologist activists, two other forces were operating to further change the face of American psychology: the professional school movement and the politicization of the APA. The establishment in 1968 of the first two of the four campuses of the California School of Professional Psychology led the profession of psychology to see how it could have significant control in the training of its own practitioners. Once the imagination of professionals was captured, events moved quickly. The Vail Conference on Levels and Patterns of Training occurred within five years. Within 10 years, 28 professional schools, conceived as semiautonomous units of a university campus, were either operative or about to become so.

The political transformation of the APA had its roots in the late 1950s under the thrust of the New York State Psychological Association and its skillful executive officer Allen Williams. Later, this group being eclipsed by the more strident voices in California and, to a lesser extent, New Jersey, the activists became embroiled in bitter quarrels with three successive APA executive officers. These activists did succeed, however, in achieving a greater professional balance within the Council of Representatives, only to witness that body's new attention to professional issues relegated to low priority by an academician-dominated Board of Directors. In 1972 a formal political structure was launched called the Committee of Concerned Psychologists (CCP), whose avowed aim was to capture the APA presidency and to elect professional-oriented members to the Board of Directors in relative proportion to the number of professional psychologists within the APA. The inordinate success of the CCP is attested to by the fact that three out of the last four individuals elected as presidents were clinicians and that a balanced Board of Directors has been achieved that no longer ignores the importance of national health insurance to the future autonomy of the profession. By 1978 social psychologists and finally academicians had also formed their own political coalitions, and the APA was thoroughly politicized.

At the present time the APA expends a significant portion of its resources and energy toward involvement in issues pertaining to national health insurance. This does not mean mere attention to guild issues at the expense of the consumer and the public welfare. There are three major groups of psychologists who have a substantial interest in national health insurance. Professional psychologists see it as an opportunity to deliver services and to develop their subfield of psychology. Other psychologists are concerned that our role in national health insurance be socially responsible and that it emphasize the needs of the consumer of such services. Scientific psychologists are concerned about a tough-minded approach to evaluation of national health insurance outcomes and evaluation of social programs in general. These three groups of psychologists have quite different views of national health insurance and the potential role of psychology in its development and implementation.

These three sets of beliefs and approaches logically imply a specific range of general outcomes. First, they imply that the APA should support national health insurance with specific constraints. One aspect of these constraints should be a tough-minded approach to evaluation and specific accounting of how the money is spent. Such a system of evaluation should provide feedback for future decisions about services. In 1976 the APA Board of Directors sponsored an ad hoc task force to develop such mechanisms of accountability and evaluation for both legislation and regulation within national health insurance.

Second, the program should be oriented toward social concerns and the problems of the individual as perceived by the individual. National health insurance should regularly solicit systematic consumer input regarding the nature and progress of the program. The planning of the delivery of services should be done in a socially responsible manner.

Finally, psychologists should actively work toward a concept of the experimenting society, in which science helps society to ask the right questions and to gather information that allows thoughtful decisions. The APA hopes to provide the core ingredients to focus various contingencies within psychology on the important professional and societal issue of providing useful services to society.

Systems of Mental Health Care

The two-tiered structure and patchwork nature of general health care delivery accurately reflect the manner in which mental health care is dispensed within the medical model. Psychologists aped psychiatric practice and rode the crest of the tremendous "overnight" demand for individual psychotherapy that swept the United States following World War II. Americans who could afford private fees were assured of care in well-appointed offices, while the care of the poor was relegated to the states (rather than the counties, as was the case with general medical care). As the state hospitals grew beyond all predicted proportions, they experienced difficulty in attracting qualified professionals away from the equally burgeoning but more lucrative and socially prestigious area of private practice. With the increase in third-party payment, the efforts of psychologists were directed toward changing the system that denied them parity with psychiatrists. This battle was aided by the shortage of psychiatrists in the face of what appeared to be an ever-growing public demand for psychotherapeutic services. However, not until recently have psychologists shown definite signs of shifting from demanding to be allowed into an outmoded system to proposing alternate delivery modalities based upon empirical research and clinical experience.

Modern clinical psychology was not born in the university but in the military during World War II. Quick, decisive, short-term psychotherapeutic intervention as close to the combat situation as possible was needed. Faced with a relatively tiny pool of trained psychiatrists, the military was forced to resort to the transforming of young physicians and clinically naive psychologists into "90-day psychiatrists and clinical psychologists." In this way, the military gave birth to the new breed of clinical psychologist, and the Veterans Administration (VA) gave them their first home. In the VA there was an early recognition of clinical psychology, and although the control of mental health in the VA remained and continues to remain with medicine, professional psychologists have flourished there on as large a scale as anywhere, with the probable exception of private practice.

Originally, the VA was intended as part of the two-tiered system in which care could be accorded needy veterans with service-connected disabilities or illnesses. Through a series of Congressional acts, eligibility has been extended beyond service connection and beyond original need. With the eventual extension of care to dependents of veterans, there are now 40 to 50 million Americans potentially eligible for VA care. If such a concept were to be implemented, the VA would become the largest patch in the quilt. Such a prediction is not so farfetched. One out of every 20 physicians currently practicing in the United States is employed by the VA. Should the proponents of national health care (as opposed to national health insurance) have their way in Washington, the VA would be the only viable government-owned health establishment able to undertake delivery of care. The VA has much to commend it, but the stretching of one of the nation's largest and most unwieldy bureaucracies to cover the health needs of all Americans is not likely to produce the best possible universal health delivery system.

Whereas VA psychologists have essentially fought their own internal struggle for recognition within their system, the private practitioner implored the help of the APA as soon as rules governing third-party payment threatened to encroach on the professional psychologist's autonomy. The demands on the APA by the private practitioner were in direct proportion to the severity of the threat. The government-employed psychologist who is not accorded recognition as an autonomous provider still has a job, albeit not exactly as desired. On the other hand, under a universal health care system, any profession not recognized as a provider will soon vanish into economic extinction. When the insurance industry began to offer mental health coverage 10 years ago in response to growing consumer demands, the same timidity that once characterized health coverage in general surfaced again in the area of mental health coverage, resulting in the numerous exclusions and limitations that now plague most benefits packages.

Demands by psychologists for parity with psychiatrists evoked responses that psychology has not yet identified its own journeyman-level health provider, and, indeed, psychology had not yet clearly declared itself to be a health profession. The publishing of the *National Register for*

Health Service Providers in Psychology answered these challenges, but continued insurance-industry resistance reflected the fear that psychologists would push benefits beyond insurable "medical" definitions. Basically, insurance carriers respond to what has been axiomatic in the insurance industry: Adding a new profession as a provider increases costs. Finally, medically dominated plans, such as those offered by Blue Cross and Blue Shield, suffer from medicine's determination to maintain its preeminence.

Although psychologists have achieved considerable success in their fight for inclusion, the present accommodation is threatened by the possibility that psychologists will not be included as independent providers within national health insurance despite the report of the President's Commission on Mental Health, which respects the autonomy of the four major mental health professions: psychiatry, psychology, psychiatric social work, and psychiatric nursing. Lending credence to this threat are the documented practices of Medicare and Medicaid that accord psychologists spotty and limited participation primarily as providers in public or semipublic agencies.

With the spawning of a nationwide system of community mental health centers (CMHC) beginning with the Kennedy and Johnson administrations, an appropriate deemphasis of long-term state hospitalization and a dismantling of our gargantuan state hospitals have taken place. The interplay among the CMHCs, the state hospitals, and Medicaid has been many faceted. As the community model gained momentum, there was a shift of focus away from the state to the community level, but this also brought a shift from the back ward to the street. Many of the chronically emotionally disturbed now line the park benches instead of the back wards, and Medicaid provides for their health care. Not only have medical costs for these persons escalated inordinately, but the cost of providing outpatient psychotherapy can account for as much as 15% of a multibillion dollar expenditure. There is a growing uneasiness, as these chronic patients fill the streets and parks, that the more costly approach may have only slightly, if at all, bettered the situation.

The National Institute of Mental Health (NIMH) proposes that the CMHCs become the mainstay mental health delivery system under national health insurance. This is not surprising inasmuch as NIMH spawned the CMHC movement. Recently, NIMH has been accused of wanting to slow down enactment of national health insurance until it can be assured of the survival of the centers it created. The Congress seems to have retrenched from the original overly ambitious Kennedy plan for developing a center in every community in the United States. And the

CMHCs have come under attack, one criticism of them being their inordinate costs. Although the CMHCs have a meaningful role, especially in underserved areas where even inordinate costs can be justified, most authorities would not regard their preemption of mental health delivery under national health insurance as desirable.

Responding to increasing mental health costs, CHAMPUS (the Civilian Health and Medical Program of the Uniformed Services) provided grants to psychology and psychiatry to seek methods of controlling costs. Rising to the challenge, psychology, under the auspices of the APA, has defined proper, customary, and effective practice and has provided methods of controlling it, thus taking a unique leadership position in innovating cost-therapeutic, effective techniques.

Probably the most unique and totally innovative mode of health care delivery to emerge within recent decades is the Health Maintenance Organization (HMO). Under the traditional system of third-party payment, the practitioner is reimbursed for services rendered, while under the HMO model, a group of practitioners are given a monthly capitation, or a relatively small fee each month for every subscriber insured regardless of whether they seek services or not. Services are then provided the subscribers at no further cost to either the patient or the third-party payer (insurance carrier). Whereas in the traditional system, the provider is compensated for services rendered to sick persons, under the HMO model, the practitioner succeeds by keeping the insured healthy.

The prototype for the HMO model is the Kaiser Permanente Health System, which began under the direction of Henry J. Kaiser as a service to his shipyard employees during World War II. Following the war, it offered health coverage to the public and spread from the San Francisco Bay Area to Portland (Oregon), Southern California, Hawaii, Cleveland, and Denver. Several years ago, HMO legislation was passed by the Congress, and Washington began to encourage the development of this concept. In addition to providing development, or startup monies, these laws have boosted HMOs by requiring employers who offer their employees insurance benefits to offer them the additional choice of one HMO along with the traditional choices.

To qualify as a Health Maintenance Organization, a group must file a complicated application to the Department of Health, Education, and Welfare and comply with a maze of regulations. Kaiser Permanente, as the prototype, regarded these criteria as destructive to the very concept they were designed to promote. Not until a series of waivers from these regulations were obtained did Kaiser Permanente agree to qualify as an

HMO under the law. In the meantime, there have been a number of scandals and bankruptcies among HMOs. Kaiser Permanente, however, flourishes as the original system that almost alone continues to make the HMO concept work successfully, at least on the large scale of several million insureds.

The HMO model has become the prototype image to many individuals of what national health insurance might be like. Historically, however, organized, private-sector medicine opposed the Kaiser Permanente plan in its early years and regarded it as "encroaching socialized medicine." In the Northern California Region of Kaiser Permanente, the first of the series of semiautonomous regions of that health system, psychologists have flourished as the mainstay system of mental health delivery. It is here that the field research on the effects of psychotherapy, within a comprehensive health system, was conducted over a period of 18 years.

While learning from the successful experiences of Kaiser Permanente, it is also possible to learn valuable lessons from unsuccessful experiences. Although labor unions provide the bulk of the millions of Kaiser Health Plan subscribers, Kaiser Permanente has carefully avoided becoming directly and overly dependent upon any one segment of subscribers. The bitter consequences of such dependence were dramatically demonstrated with the demise of the excellent mental health system sponsored entirely by the Retail Clerks Los Angeles local. This system, which employed a wide variety of successful techniques, including outreach, suddenly collapsed when an overly zealous union leadership mandated to the professionals involved that various forms of intervention be supplanted by mega-vitamin therapy and other questionable forms of treatment. Similarly, the UAW's attempt to create a showcase health service in Detroit resulted in near disaster. In that system, mental health services by professionals were mostly superseded by the utilization of co-workers, particularly shop stewards, trained as paraprofessionals. It was found that automobile workers failed to avail themselves of these services, *but the investigators missed the implication of this resistance.* The often-cited contention that blue-collar workers will not utilize mental health services when they are made available is a misinterpretation of the Detroit experience. The study really demonstrated that workers will not utilize shop stewards and fellow workers functioning as mental health counselors. When mental health services provided by professionals with full confidentiality are made available, blue-collar workers do utilize such services.

An interesting experiment that has avoided some of these pitfalls is the Group Health Cooperative of Puget Sound (in the state of Washington), where a subscription to the health plan is literally a share of ownership in the health system. Certainly this demonstration of shared control between professionals and consumers can yield a great deal of information, both good and bad, and suggests directions for future health plans.

Psychology, because of its research base and its concern for human welfare, is in a unique position to evaluate existing health systems, to formulate directions for innovative systems, and to provide continuing development and reevaluation of both systems and modes of practice that will define cost-therapeutic effectiveness. To do so, psychology must continue to insist upon its rightful autonomy, it must free itself from outmoded medical concepts, and it must persist in its concern for the consumer.

Table 1: *A Comparison of Major National Health Insurance Bills in the 94th Congress (as of June 1975). Prepared by the Committee for National Health Insurance.*

Legislative Proposal	Concept	Coverage	Benefit Structure	Financing
Health Security Act S.3 HR 21	Universal, federalized comprehensive health insurance plan with provisions for reorganization of the health care system and development of health resources.	Covers all U.S. residents. Medicare repealed; Medicaid retained in part to cover services beyond benefits provided.	Benefits cover the entire range of personal health care services including prevention and early detection of disease without coinsurance, deductibles or waiting period. Some limitations on adult dental care, psychiatric care, long-term nursing home care and drugs. Grants to develop social care services to aid chronically ill, aged and other homebound patients.	50% from general tax revenue and 50% from a 3½% tax on employer payroll, a 1% tax on the first $21,150 a year in wages and a 2½% tax on the first $21,150 a year of self-employment income and non-earned income all to be administered through a Health Security Trust Fund.
Principal Congressional Sponsors & Endorsements Representative Corman (D-Calif.) Senator Kennedy (D-Mass.) Committee for National Health Insurance AFL–CIO Church Groups Senior Citizens Consumer Groups Health Professionals				

Table 1: *(Continued)*

Legislative Proposal	Cost Control Reimbursement of Providers	Quality Control	Health Delivery and Resources	Administration
Health Security Act S.3 HR 21	Operates on annual national budget, regional budget, prospective budgets for hospitals and other institutions, negotiated budgets for prepaid group practices and negotiated payments to physicians in solo practice charging on a fee-for-service basis. Providers barred from making additional charges to individuals for services performed within the system.	Establishes quality control commission and national standards for participating professional and institutional providers. Regulation of major surgery and certain other specialist services; national licensure standards and requirements for continuing education.	Health Resources Development Fund established for improving delivery and increasing resources with emphasis on development of various forms of prepaid group practice plans. Provisions for encouraging more efficient organization of existing health manpower, and of training and retraining of health professionals.	Publicly administered program in Department of HEW, five-member, full-time Health Security Board appointed by the President. Ten HEW regions, 200 sub-regions. Advisory councils at all levels with majority of members representing consumers.
Principal Congressional Sponsors & Endorsements				
Representative Corman (D-Calif.) Senator Kennedy (D-Mass.)				
Committee for National Health Insurance AFL–CIO Church Groups Senior Citizens Consumer Groups Health Professionals				

Table 1: *(Continued)*

Legislative Proposal	Concept	Coverage	Benefit Structure (cont.)	Financing (cont.)
National Healthcare Services, Financing & Reorganization Act HR 1	Federally approved comprehensive private health insurance through (1) a plan requiring employers to provide private health insurance for employees, (2) a plan for individuals, (3) federally contracted coverage for the poor, the medically needy and the aged. Promotes non-profit Health Care Corporation (HCC).	Available to all U.S. residents except federal employees. Employers must provide plan for employees; self-employed covered through private purchase; the poor, medically needy and aged by federal government; those eligible, under unemployment compensation. Medicare replaced; Medicaid federalized, covers services beyond benefits provided.	professionals; medical appliances; outpatient prescription drugs; laboratory and x-ray services; home health services; in- and outpatient mental health services; and ambulance services (Reduced limits for inpatient mental health, alcoholism, and drug abuse services for Health Care corporation [HCC] registrants.) Outpatient health maintenance services, such as periodic health evaluations; well-baby care; and vision and dental services through age 12 – all without limits or copayments. Catastrophic coverage after out-of-pocket expenditures reach specified levels, related to family size and income.	and employee premium payments for purchase of private insurance, federal premium subsidy for low income workers. Self-employed pay own premiums at group rates. Low wage employers and self employed eligible for tax credits. Federal subsidies for full or partial purchase of private insurance from general tax revenues for the poor and medically needy, enrollee contributions based on income and family size, with lowest group paying nothing. Medicare, with part A and B merged, financed through present payroll tax and general federal revenues. 10% federal subsidy for HCC registrants. Deductibles and coinsurance for most services.
Principal Congressional Sponsors & Endorsements				
Representative Ullman (D-Ore.)		**Benefit Structure**		
American Hospital Association		Phased in over 5-year period, with limits and/or copayments on: hospital in- and outpatient services; skilled nursing facility and nursing home care; services of physicians and other health	**Financing** Employer (minimum of 75%)	

Table 1: *(Continued)*

Legislative Proposal	Cost Control Reimbursement of Providers	Quality Control	Health Delivery and Resources	Administration
National Healthcare Services, Financing & Reorganization Act HR 1	Payment to institutional providers and HCCs on prospectively approved budgets; to physicians on basis of reasonable charges. Both require State Health Commission (SHC) approval, under federal guidelines.	Department of Health sets standards of quality and establishes regulations for all providers with Medicare standards as minimum; SHCs implement regulations and monitor providers.	Federal funds for development and operation of SHCs. Emphasis on formation of HCCs and outpatient care facilities, with incentives, through payment mechanisms, federal grants and loans. Requires establishment of SHCs and HCCs. Funds for development of paramedical personnel.	Establishes a Cabinet-level Department of Health to set standards for and coordinate all federal health programs. National Health Services Advisory Council at federal level, with consumer representation, reviews all regulations.
Principal Congressional Sponsors & Endorsements			SHCs responsible for all state health planning, certification of need, licensure and approval of provider operations.	State Health Commissions (SHCs) implement federal standards and regulate all providers and insurance carriers at state level, including approval of carrier rates and provider charges.
Representative Ullman (D-Ore.)			National Health Services Advisory Council to study need for establishment of federal trust fund for resources development.	Non-profit private or governmental HCCs to coordinate delivery of health services with designated geographic areas.
American Hospital Association				Coverage provided through approved private insurance carriers; federal government contracts with private carriers for subsidized coverage.

Table 1: *(Continued)*

Legislative Proposal	Concept	Coverage	Benefit Structure	Financing
The National Health Care Act of 1975 HR 5990 S 1438 **Principal Congressional Sponsors & Endorsements** Representative Burleson (D-Texas) Senator McIntyre (D-N.H.) Health Insurance Industry of America	A voluntary approach based on federal income tax incentives for employees and employers to encourage purchase of a minimum package of approved private health insurance, through (1) employer or (2) individual (private) plans, and (3) grants to states to buy insurance for the poor and the uninsurable through a state insurance pool (state plan). Includes minimal provisions to improve health care delivery.	Voluntary for all U.S. residents. Medicare continued; Medicaid covers services beyond benefits provided. Consumer could refuse to purchase. non-citizen residents would not be eligible.	To be phased-in in two stages with maximum deductible of $100 and coinsurance of 20% with a maximum annual out-of-pocket expense per family per year of $1,000 with exceptions of mental health and dental benefits. In 1977 benefits would include unlimited hospital inpatient and outpatient physical and psychiatric care; physicians' services; 20 outpatient mental health visits; prescription drugs and contraceptive devices; 180 days of skilled nursing and 270 days home health care; certain oral surgery; well-child care. In 1985 coverage for very specific dental care, physical and speech therapy, eyeglasses and periodical physical examinations would be covered.	Complex provisions for purchase of private insurance based on three categories of beneficiaries: (1) employees, (2) individuals, and (3) state health care plans for the poor and near poor. A beneficiary can fall into one of 27 categories. Employer-plan: shared premiums for purchase of private policies; low income employee contributions limited according to wage level. Individual plan: enrollee pays full premium. Federal income tax deduction for employers and enrollees equal to full cost of premium payments for approved insurance; no tax deductions for unapproved plans. State plans: enrollee premium contributions based on income and family size; balance paid with state and

Table 1: *(Continued)*

Legislative Proposal	Financing (cont.)	Quality Control	Health Delivery and Resources	Administration
The National Health Care Act of 1975 HR 5990 S 1438	federal general revenues through a state insurance pool. Federal share ranges from 70% to 90%.	Except for meeting Medicare standards and regulations to be established for HMOs, no provision for quality control.	Emphasis on creation of outpatient care centers through grants, loans, and loan guarantees. Loans and grants for health manpower development, with priority to shortage areas. Option to join HMOs to be available under all plans. Provisions to strengthen health planning, with increased funds and authority to state and local planning agencies. Presidential Health Policy Board set up to advise on planning and conduct research.	For the private plans, state insurance departments approve policies and monitor financial operations of private carriers. Treasury Department rules on tax status of plan. For state plans, HEW sets standards for operation of plans; state insurance departments supervise the operations. Thus, state insurance departments become the administrators.
Principal Congressional Sponsors & Endorsements Representative Burleson (D-Texas) Senator McIntyre (D-N.H.) Health Insurance Industry of America	**Cost Control Reimbursement of Providers** Payments to institutions based on prospectively approved rates, by category of institution. State commission approves budgets and charge schedules on basis of reasonable charges, subject to HEW review. HMOs paid on per capita basis. Physicians paid on reasonable charges not exceeding customary and prevailing rates.			

Table 1: *(Continued)*

Legislative Proposal	Concept	Coverage	Benefit Structure	Financing
Comprehensive Health Care Insurance Act of 1975 HR 6222	Mandates employers to offer qualified private health insurance to employees and families. Federal cash subsidies or tax credits to employers if program increases total payroll costs by 3% or more. Federal assistance via tax credits for non-employed and self-employed.	Voluntary acceptance of coverage by employees, non-employed and self-employed. Medicare population eligible for benefits equal to those for the general population. Health Insurance for the unemployed.	Inpatient and outpatient hospital care services, 100 days in skilled nursing facility, diagnostic, therapeutic and preventive medical services, home health services, dental care for children 2 through 6, and emergency dental services and oral surgery for all. 20% coinsurance for all services with limits based on family income and ceilings of not more than $1,500 per individual and $2,000 per family.	Premium payments of at least 65% by employers and the rest by employees if they chose to participate. Federal assistance to employers whose payroll costs increased more than 3% because of the program, ranging from 80% of the excessive increase during the first year to 40% in the fifth year. Federal assistance in the form of tax credits for health care insurance for non-employed and self-employed individuals and their families. Amount of federal assistance scaled according to tax liability.
Principal Congressional Sponsors & Endorsements				
Representative Fulton (D-Tenn.)				
Representative Duncan (R-Tenn.)				
American Medical Association				

Table 1: *(Continued)*

Legislative Proposal	Cost Control Reimbursement of Providers	Quality Control	Health Delivery and Resources	Administration
Comprehensive Health Care Insurance Act of 1975 HR 6222	NONE	Amendments to Professional Standards Review Organizations (PSROs) to make them more responsive to Medical Societies.	Establishes Offices of Rural Health within HEW to award grants, contracts, loans and loan guarantees for projects pertaining to rural health care delivery. Otherwise, no changes in present system.	A 15-member Health Insurance Advisory Board consisting of the Secretary of HEW, the Commissioner of Internal Revenue, six M.D.s, 1 D.O, 1 D.D.S., and the remaining five appointed by the President from the general public to prescribe regulations and federal standards for States' Insurance Departments and review effectiveness of the programs.
Principal Congressional Sponsors & Endorsements				
Representative Fulton (D-Tenn.) Representative Duncan (R-Tenn.)				
American Medical Association				

Table 1: (Continued)

Legislative Proposal	Concept	Coverage	Benefit Structure	Benefit Structure (cont.)
Long–Ribicoff (as introduced in the 93rd Congress) **Principal Congressional Sponsors & Endorsements** Senator Long (D-La.) Senator Ribicoff (D-Conn.)	Three-part federal program providing (1) catastrophic coverage for all, (2) a medical assistance plan with basic benefits for the poor and medically needy, and (3) voluntary program for certification of private insurance to cover basic benefits.	Catastrophic coverage; all U.S. residents covered by Social Security. Medical assistance plan: all persons now receiving Medicaid plus others meeting certain income limits, varying according to family size, who are considered medically needy. Medicare continued; Medicaid federalized.	Catastrophic plan: all medical bills after out-of-pocket expenses reach $2,000 per family; all hospital costs over 60 days per person; additional co-payments limited to $1,000 per family. Medical assistance plan: Hospital, skilled nursing, and intermediate facility care; home health services; physicians services; x-ray and laboratory medical appliances; prenatal and well-baby care; family planning; periodic screening, diagnosis and treatment to age 18; inpatient mental health care in community health centers. Copayments of $3 for each of first 10 visits to doctor per family. Certified private plans must	provide coverage for pre-catastrophic costs with limits on cost sharing. **Financing** Catastrophic: .3% increase in Social Security payroll taxes on employees and employers. Medical assistance plan: general federal revenues with state contributions.

Table 1: *(Continued)*

Legislative Proposal	Cost Control Reimbursement of Providers	Quality Control	Health Delivery and Resources	Administration
Long–Ribicoff (as introduced in the 93rd Congress)	Same as under Medicare. Payments must be accepted as payment in full under medical assistance program.	Same as under Medicare, including Professional Standards Review Organizations (PSROs).	Same as Medicare; provides for HMO option.	Through Social Security Administration. HEW Secretary certifies private plans in voluntary program, based on adequacy of coverage, conditions of eligibility, and availability. Insurers not offering certified policies ineligible to serve as Medicare carriers or intermediaries.
Principal Congressional Sponsors & Endorsements				
Senator Long (D-La.) Senator Ribicoff (D-Conn.)				

FOUNDING THE
NATIONAL COUNCIL OF SCHOOLS OF
PROFESSIONAL PSYCHOLOGY:
FROM INNOVATION TO CONSTERNATION

A NATIONAL ASSOCIATION of the rapidly proliferating professional schools was necessary if these programs, a number of which were free-standing and with no prospect of affiliating with established universities, were to survive. There was general agreement by early 1976 that setting up such an organization was imperative, not only among the more than a dozen and a half of such schools that were already in operation, but surprisingly, also within the APA governance. The Vail Conference had dramatically heralded the era of the professional school movement, and there was such excitement among rank-and-file practitioners that even the APA was caught up in its impact. I sought, and was quickly granted, the authority to convene a meeting at the 1976 APA Convention of the leadership of all of the professional schools with the avowed purpose of founding what I had tentatively named the National Council of Professional Schools of Psychology (NCSPP, later renamed National Council of Schools and Programs of Professional Psychology). This had already been accomplished before I was fired by CSPP in February 1976, and in spite of the pain I was feeling at the time, I was determined to proceed with the planned meeting. This is why I informed the CSPP Board of

Directors that I would voluntarily relinquish the management of CSPP if I were allowed to retain the title of president until September 1, 1976. In this way, I could convene the organizational meeting at the August APA meeting with my title intact, giving me the right to attend and participate. Also, the CSPP was not to challenge my authority to do so. They agreed, knowing that the alternative was a lawsuit they could not win. The "ruling" by board secretary and school general counsel Irwin Leff that I was incapacitated by virtue of the fact that three of the four campus deans had refused to respect my authority was so contrived that it probably would have been thrown out of court. Emotionally bleeding from every pore, I moved steadily ahead to found the NCSPP, having decided this would be my final contribution to the professional school movement.

During the months preceding the APA convention, I labored feverishly to achieve consensus on a set of bylaws, working informally with the schools that were operating successfully. These included freestanding professional schools in Florida, Massachusetts, Illinois, and Oregon, and additional programs in California, as well as university-based professional schools, such as Adelphi, Rutgers, Wright State, Baylor, and Denver. There had already emerged a trend in which existing schools that were religiously identified were establishing professional schools of psychology. Among these were Fuller Theological Seminary, Rosemead, and Yeshiva. I was able to open the August meeting with such a consensus on the bylaws and other documents that ratification came within the first 10 minutes after convening. I had introduced myself as chair *pro tem*, to serve only until the body had adopted the bylaws and elected its first chair. I also made it clear that this was to be my last contribution to the professional school movement, as I was going on to other things. It was important to clarify this, as I would be the logical choice for the first elected chair. This was impossible, for once I was no longer president of CSPP, a fact that was only two weeks away, I would not be eligible to be a part of NCSPP.

Before opening the nominations process for permanent chair, I explained to those assembled that the purpose of NCSPP was to be *the* organization of the professional schools of psychology, and would be creating its own accrediting structure and mechanisms. I had been in extensive dialog with the Council of Professional Accreditation (COPA) in Washington, which accredits the "accreditors," and it was agreed that NCSPP would preempt the APA approvals process by becoming the accrediting body for the professional schools. I emphasized that it was important that the professional schools never seek APA approval, as to do so would dilute their innovation and threaten their viability as alternatives to the usual APA-approved doctoral programs. Everyone nodded assent, leaving the erroneous impression that these principles were widely accepted within the group as convened. I conducted the election process by voice nomination and vote. Gordon Derner, the dean of the professional school at Adelphi University that, after his death, was to be renamed the Gordon F. Derner Institute for Advanced Psychological Studies, was the only nominee. He was elected unanimously.

The choice of Derner was, in many respects, the logical one. Twenty years earlier, he had won a pitched battle to obtain the approval of the APA for the program he had founded at Adelphi University. As a part of the psychology department, it was part of the college of arts and sciences, and, therefore, was not a professional school, but it was profoundly a professional program, and the first of its kinds. By the time of the NCSPP organizational meeting, Derner had become a full-fledge dean of a bona fide professional school within its university, and with his historical credentials, he was undoubtedly the logical choice once I had eliminated myself.

In spite of my profound respect, admiration, and love for Gordon Derner, I realize in hindsight, that he was also an unfortunate selection. By the time of his election, he had been an establishment university administrator for more than a quarter of a century, and was no longer the firebrand who had taken on the APA two decades earlier. He had also run unsuccessfully three times for the presidency of the APA and was planning to run again the following year. He courted the respectability that he thought would win him his coveted APA presidency, and he could never conceive that the new professional schools of psychology would not seek APA approval. Those who remained after I departed told me I had hardly left the room before Gordon was strategizing with the participants on ways to win APA program approval. The irony is that in the following year (1977), Gordon lost his final bid for the APA presidency to me on my first attempt. I was troubled by this far more than he was, as he was gracious, and even reveled in the fact that his student had become an APA president.

In its early years, the NCSPP leadership was predominantly from university-based professional schools. These, of course, had never experienced the intellectual freedom and the potential for innovation accorded by virtue of being freestanding. They also had not experienced the burden of having to earn credibility and acceptance in the intellectual community. The NCSPP expended an enormous amount of time and resources over many years in courting the favor of the APA, instead of defining the Vail Model, developing its own criteria for accreditation, and creating the platforms that would guide continued professional innovation through outcomes research, consumer feedback, and the evolution of the science of psychology. Indeed, the Vail Model has yet to be defined after over a quarter of a century.

The innovations that exemplified the vitality of CSPP disappeared in rapid succession. The first to be jettisoned was the concept of the part-time, nontenured faculty. This was undoubtedly the provision most hated by academics, and its abolition was a giant step toward making the professional schools more like the traditional environment they had once eschewed. Bringing clinicians on the faculty with full credentials was retained, and this spread to the traditional APA-approved doctoral programs. But the requirement that the half-time faculty members be doers devoting the rest of their time to performing successfully that which they were teaching, not only disappeared, but is hardly remembered today. This original model of faculty doers included not only those who taught psychotherapy, but also those who taught statistics, research, child development, gerontology, and every other class. In other words, each teacher had to be doing off campus that which was being taught on campus. In one fell swoop, CSPP had obliterated the old saying, "If you can't do, teach," and the NCSPP, in another fell swoop, brought it back.

A QUARTER-CENTURY RETROSPECTIVE

It has now been over 25 years since the founding of the NCSPP and it boasts many accomplishments. Frequently, it valiantly had to defend the very existence of professional schools of psychology, especially if they were freestanding. The early roster of persons who served the NCSPP and the professional school movement includes a number of legendary leaders, such as Gordon Derner of Adelphi; Don Petersen, who became the first dean of the school at Rutgers; Ron Fox, who was the founding dean of the school at Wright State, and who later became president of the APA; Robert Weitz, who was instrumental in founding the Rutgers school and later repeated this feat in Florida; Eugene Walker of Baylor; Nelson Jones of Denver; and Gene Shapiro of Nova, who continues to be an outstanding champion of the professional schools and the doctor of psychology (Psy.D.) degree. These are only a few of the leaders, and psychology owes much to them. What Charles Kiesler, the executive officer of the APA, predicted in 1979 became true very quickly: the vast majority of clinical psychologists are graduates of the professional schools. My own disappointment is apart from the successful struggle they waged for a quarter of a century, for I can only reflect on what would have been if the original intent of the NCSPP had been implemented. As the old saying goes, "Once you get on the road to Glocamorah, there is no way you can get to Killarney."

It would be useful to look at some of the consequences following the failure of the NCSPP to implement its initial purpose and potential.

Accreditation

Once the organized professional school movement ignored the opportunity to develop its own accrediting process, it became solely dependent on the APA approvals process, and it lost control over its own destiny. In the 25 years since the founding of the NCSPP, so much time and energy have been devoted to vaulting the many roadblocks to approval by the APA that the effort sapped its vitality and its vision. It is ironic that a movement that was launched against the antiprofessionalism of the Education and Training Board agreed to compromise after compromise until the professional schools looked more and more like those against which they had rebelled. They all sought APA-approved doctoral programs, they continued to graduate good clinicians for the 1980s, and they overlooked the need for education and training reform to meet the demands of the new behavioral-care marketplace.

Built into the professional-school concept was the mechanism for ongoing change that would occur through a part-time, nontenured faculty that would be spending most of its time in the real world and would bring this reality to the campus. Building ivy-covered walls unfortunately often has a consequence that is not intended; in addition to protecting academic freedom from outside assault, they insulate academia from the real world. When the concept of a "doer" faculty was rejected, access to the outside world, which would have constituted a steady, unrelenting impetus for ongoing professional progress and change, was severely curtailed. The professional schools were no more inclined to revise their curricula in accordance with the new health economy than were the more traditional clinical programs. They were too busy complying with APA approvals requirements to survey the consumer world and its needs in order to translate these into the curricula of today and the future.

The Vail Model

The professional school movement gave rise to the Vail Model, and one would think that the NCSPP would have become an outspoken force for its definition and promulgation. Instead, it paid lip service to the Vail Model, and a professional school of psychology became whatever each professional school of psychology happened to be. This was unacceptable, and it gave the APA approvals process legitimate ammunition to go after this loose, often anti-intellectual configuration. While this was going on, the totally nonaccredited "professional schools" that took advantage of loopholes, especially in California, proliferated. Had the NCSPP become the voice of the professional school movement, it could have defined the Vail Model and its accreditation process, and silenced the fly-by-night school. Instead, it was in a struggle with the APA, which had no jurisdiction or interest whatsoever in the less legitimate programs that were giving professional education and training a bad name.

Many of the professional schools have overly emphasized professional training to the detriment of research training. In its disdain for the Boulder scientist–professional model, Vail championed a less-than-defined professional model and rejected the professional-scientist model that I had hoped to proffer. Paradoxically, as the APA puts more and more pressure on the professional schools, the psycho-religions (sometimes known as schools of psychotherapy) persist. A number of the original professional schools, some on university campuses, such as at Adelphi, remain strongly psychoanalytic in an era in which psychoanalysis is an economic atavism.

A Culmination

Born off campus where it had the freedom to innovate, CSPP flourished and succeeded because it rejected overtures to become part of an established university structure with its attendant bureaucratic obstacles to change. Now, over 30 years since the founding of CSPP, the APA has enunciated what many hope will become doctrine: there should be no freestanding professional schools of psychology. Even CSPP had expanded to university status and has merged with United States International University (USIU) to form Alliant International University. With consternation, I have watched us go full circle.

Undoubtedly the APA hopes to reduce the number of professional schools that are graduating far more clinical doctorates than we need. The professional schools are graduating the majority of our clinicians. To be sure, during this era of glut, there is little need for cookie-cutter programs training more and more outmoded clinicians who are having difficulty finding internships, to say nothing about the near impossibility of finding well-paying jobs. During his term of office, former APA president Richard Suinn would ask the tongue-in-cheek question, "What is the difference between a newly minted Ph.D. in clinical psychology and a pizza?" The answer is that a pizza will feed a family of four.

One would suspect another motive. With applications to doctoral programs significantly decreasing over the past few years, the elimination of a number of professional schools would reduce the competition for student applicants and avoid the lowering of admission standards that is already beginning to occur.

Although there are far too many programs in clinical psychology, there is a glaring absence of programs that are graduating professional psychologists well prepared for the new millennium. The NCSPP is too busy fighting a rear-guard battle to make this imperative its primary priority.

{ 6 }

THE NATIONAL ACADEMIES OF PRACTICE:
AN ORGANIZATION TO BRING THE
HEALTH PROFESSIONS TOGETHER

IN THE EARLY PART OF 1977, I was privileged to testify before the Congress of the United States on matters of health reform and on behalf of the American Psychological Association. All of the professional societies had been invited to submit testimony, and each of us was limited to 10 minutes. The startling aspect of the combined testimonies was that more time seemed to be devoted to criticizing other professions than to making constructive, interdisciplinary suggestions for health reform. As the Congressional committee was to hear from consumer groups the following day, most of the professional society representatives stayed over that night. Several of us had dinner together. All were leaders in our respective professions, including W. Walter Menninger, who represented the American Psychiatric Association (APA).

After the perfunctory polite pleasantries and platitudes that always preceded serious discussion whenever the competing disciplines got together, I expressed my dismay at our collective failure to go beyond turf interests in our testimonies. My dinner companions agreed that this was unfortunate, but the friction among the various professions was a fact of life and there was nothing that could be done about it. I disagreed, pointing out that what was needed was an overarching organization composed of all the health professions, an organization that could overcome its myopia in the interest of national health. Everyone responded with jocular skepticism, the consensus being that the various health professions could not live together at a national disciplinary meeting of *all* the disciplines for two days. By the middle of the second day, open warfare would surely erupt. I persisted, arguing against a conclusion that would have been unanimous among us had it not been for my demurer. It was Dr. Menninger who finally ended the discussion: "Well, Nick, it's your idea. Why don't you figure out a way to do it?" I must admit that at that moment I had not even the beginning of a solution. Later that same year, I was elected to the presidency of the APA, to take office as president-elect, president, and finally past president from 1978 to 1981.

I took my responsibilities seriously and I embarked on four years of parochial activism on behalf of the APA, during which I testified before the Congress several more times. The antagonism among the members of the various professions, such as between psychologists and psychiatrists, optometrists and opthamologists, podiatrists and orthopedic surgeons, nurses and physicians assistants, to mention only a few of the most blatant, seemed to be escalating. I was more determined than ever to tackle the problem of an interdisciplinary organization once my tenure at the APA was concluded. I did so promptly after my past-presidential year ended in 1981.

CONCEPTUALIZING THE DISTINGUISHED PRACTITIONER

My decision following my completion of my APA presidency was never to seek elected or appointed APA office again. There were several reasons: (1) It is unseemly to use the name recognition of a past president to keep running for offices that are far less prestigious and important than that of president, as many past APA presidents do. (2) The APA needed to cultivate, encourage, and then elect younger people, and the presence of an "old guard" tends to stifle the emergence of new blood. (3) As an elder statesperson, I had an obligation to go beyond psychology and to look at the general issue of healthcare in America. This became a guiding principle for me, and I hypothesized that a group of elder statespersons from all the professions might be as ready as I to transcend turf issues in the interest of national health. I thus conceived of an organization of persons of such stature that their colleagues would unanimously regard them as Distinguished Practitioners. These person would have been awarded all the honors their peers could heap on them, and they could well be ready to pledge themselves to the higher purpose of defining the best in healthcare for Americans. There would be eight (later nine, and still later, ten) Academies of Practice, limited to 100 Distinguished Practitioners in each, so that election to a particular Academy was a matter of supreme recognition. The Academies would be as follows, and collectively they would be known as the National Academy of Practices (sic), or NAP, a title corrected as noted later.

National Academy of Practice in Dentistry
National Academy of Practice in Medicine
National Academy of Practice in Nursing
National Academy of Practice in Optometry
National Academy of Practice in Osteopathic Medicine
National Academy of Practice in Podiatric Medicine
National Academy of Practice in Psychology
National Academy of Practice in Social Work

One year later:
National Academy of Practice in Veterinary Medicine

And 15 years later:
National Academy of Practice in Pharmacy

The original eight organizations were chosen because they represented healthcare professions that were authorized by the federal government to receive direct reimbursements for their work with patients. This decision eliminated ancillary professions, such as x-ray technicians, occupational therapists, and such other "paraprofessionals" who were not eligible for direct reimbursement. In addition, no matter how high a person's academic rank or how great his or her research accomplishments, an electee would have to be a *practitioner* with at least 20 years of hands-on treatment of patients.

The structure of the NAP would allow for both standing committees and ad hoc committees, the latter to be appointed as needed. No committees, however, could deliberate unless the representatives of five different Academies were present. This would guarantee the interdisciplinary nature of every committee meeting.

The organization would position itself as a nonpartisan, nonparochial (i.e., above the self-interests of one's own profession) advisor to the Congress. To facilitate this, it would petition for a Congressional Charter not unlike those held by the National Academy of Sciences (NAS) and the Institute of Medicine (IOM). The National Academy of Practice in Medicine would differ from the IOM, which elects members on the basis of their research accomplishments, not their contributions to practice.

I discussed this general structure with colleagues I admired and got a mixed bag of responses. For example, Ted Blau, at the time the only other practitioner past president of the APA, suggested that I conduct a needs assessment, a response I had learned to expect from Dr. Blau whenever he did not want to do something. Dr. Menninger questioned whether medicine would settle for just 100 Distinguished Practitioners as representatives of all the specialties the in the field. He further doubted that medicine would accept being limited to the same number of Distinguished Practitioners accorded the other Academies. Most psychologists who responded would agree with Dr. Menninger, as they voiced their own low expectations of interdisciplinary cooperation from medicine. On the other hand, my early mentor, Gordon Derner, applauded the concept, and Rogers Wright said, "Nick, this is one of your best ideas." Both thought my concept of Distinguished Practitioner would bring medicine on board. Surprisingly, the response was even more positive and optimistic from leaders in medicine, as will be discussed below. The ability to found the National Academy of Practice in Medicine was a prerequisite to founding a successful NAP, for without medicine, it would never be regarded as a viable interdisciplinary organization.

SCOUTING THE CONGRESS

After testing the somewhat tepid waters among professionals, there remained the question as to how the proposal for the NAP would be viewed by the Congress. I first consulted with the late Alan Cranston, then the senior U.S. senator from California, as both a constituent and a good friend. He doubted that I could pull all of these warring healthcare professions into on organization, but he thought the concept of Distinguished Practitioner was a probable avenue and he encouraged me to go ahead. I then spoke with Senator Edward Kennedy, to whose Senate Health Subcommittee I had consulted years earlier. He liked the idea and urged me to proceed with it, promising to support the Congressional Charter petition. I then consulted his opposite number, Senator Orrin Hatch, who was the leading health advocate among Republicans. Little did I realize that many years later such a liberal and conservative, respectively, as Kennedy and Hatch would be cosponsoring health and antismoking legislation. Senator Hatch always had a medical doctor on his staff, and he arranged for me to meet with him. My idea of the NAP received a very enthusiastic reception from his health staff officer, who pledged, and later delivered, his personal help and support. A number of the U.S. representatives from California were positive from the beginning, notably Representatives Tony Coelho and Vic Fazio. Undoubtedly, the leading supporter was Senator Dan Inouye, who literally was to become the "patron" of the NAP within the Senate. He brought on board Senator Joseph Biden and several other Senate supporters, and he remained our champion throughout.

INCORPORATION

The next step was to incorporate in the District of Columbia as a nonprofit 501(c)(3) educational and professional organization, and papers were filed as the National Academy of Practices (sic). We had received our corporate charter when my erudite colleague, Robert Perloff of the Katz School of Business at the University of Pittsburgh, informed me that whereas there were sciences, as in the National Academy of Sciences, there was only practice. The exception was the use of good versus bad practices, a connotation we would want to avoid. Therefore, our name should be National Academies of Practice, *not* National Academy of Practices. We immediately set out to correct the name with the District of Columbia, a feat that required 11 years of constant petitioning before the incredibly inefficient bureaucracy responded. We would know each year that the name had not been corrected when we received a delinquency notice that the National Academy of Practices had not paid its annual fee. It made no difference that the National Academies of Practice was on time with its filing each year; the District of Columbia government simply could not put the two together during more than a decade of our pleas. We continued to do business under our corrected name starting in 1981, even though it was not official until 1992. We finally got action when we bypassed the Washington bureaucracy and went to the Congressional committee that oversees the District's self-rule.

GOVERNANCE STRUCTURE

Each Academy has a chair and a co-chair elected by the Distinguished Practitioners of that Academy. These chairs and co-chairs are part of the NAP Council, as are also the three officers elected from the Council: president, secretary, and treasurer. The bylaws specify the length of terms, and since these are staggered, overlap is always experienced as some NAP Council members rotate off. The officers are elected from the NAP Council, have been chairs and/or co-chairs, and if still in one of those offices, must resign to assume one of the three Council positions. The bylaws were later amended to add a fourth officer with the title of founding president. This was a kind gesture by the NAP to keep me as its founder on the NAP Council for as long as I am willing and able to participate.

After my marathon tenure of 12 years, NAP presidents were limited to three-year terms without the possibility of reelection. To date, there have been five presidents of the NAP as follows, demonstrating the interdisciplinary nature of leadership.

Nicholas A. Cummings, Ph.D., Sc.D.
> NAP in Psychology   1981–1993

William Felts, M.D.
> NAP in Medicine   1993–1996

Ron G. Fair, O.D.
> NAP in Optometry   1996–1999

Hurdis Griffith, Ph.D., R.N.
> NAP in Nursing   1999–2002

Daniel M. Laskin, D.D.S., M.S.
> NAP in Dentistry   2002–2005

There is no rule that states that a president must be elected from an Academy that has not yet contributed a president, and the choices up until now have been spontaneous.

CRITERIA FOR DISTINGUISHED PRACTITIONER

If the right persons who could address the interdisciplinary and consumer goals of the NAP were to be chosen, it was important that the bylaws establish clear and strict standards for their selection. The following criteria were adopted by a working committee that I had appointed, and they

stood for many years. Recently, however, they have been somewhat eroded for the reasons described later. The standards for election to Distinguished Practitioner were as follows:

1. Nominations would be made by the Academy representing the nominee's profession. Such nominations would first be approved by the
   Academy, and would then be presented to the NAP Council for final
   approval (election).
2. A nominee must have made significant and enduring contributions to
   practice as determined by his or her peers, who would also readily recognize these contributions on a national level.
3. A nominee must have no fewer than 20 years of successful hands-on
   practice with patients.
4. A nominee must be free of malpractice judgments, felonies, suspension
   of state license to practice, or other blemishes that would detract from
   the status of Distinguished Practitioner.
5. The NAP Council is the final determiner of eligibility or disqual-
   ification.
6. Once elected to the status of a Distinguished Practitioner of the National Academies of Practice, the appellation remains for life, unless
   the person is disqualified by subsequent conviction for a felony or
   other judgments as defined in the bylaws.

LAUNCHING THE FIRST ACADEMY

The logical place to start, since I knew psychology best, was with the
NAP in Psychology. I approached Dr. Derner, who enthusiastically accepted the position of founding chair. We developed the procedure, to be
followed by every Academy thereafter, of organizing a nucleus of 10
founders, themselves Distinguished Practitioners, who would nominate
the next group of Distinguished Practitioners. Along with Dr. Derner,
Dr. Blau, and myself as founders were such well-known psychologists as
Ron Fox, Herb Freudenberger, Robert Reiff, Max Siegel, Joan Willens,
Rogers Wright, and Carl Zimet. Among these were two APA past presidents (Blau and myself) and a future APA president (Siegel). Dr. Derner
died shortly thereafter, and was succeeded by Dr. Fox as chair and Dr.
Willens as cochair. Dr. Freudenberger served for several years as secretary
of the entire NAP, and Robert Harper and Jules Barron, who were
among the first group named as Distinguished Practitioners in Psycholo-

gy, served, respectively, as treasurer of the entire NAP and as founding editor of *The Bulletin of the National Academies of Practice.*

In these early years, the NAP in Psychology was the driving force for all the NAP, holding the offices of president, secretary, treasurer, and newsletter editor. In later years, psychology unfortunately began to play a lessor role in the governance of the NAP.

LAUNCHING THE SECOND ACADEMY

It was my intent to establish the NAP in Medicine next, for if medicine were not an integral part, the NAP would never be a viable force. Medicine still dominates the health field, but in 1981, this was doubly so. This was the era before the American Medical Association modified many of its near-monopolistic stances, capitulating to the threat of prosecution under the restraint-of-trade laws and regulations. This followed the passage of a series of bills by the Congress, and the subsequent decision of the U.S. Department of Justice that health organizations were subject to lawsuits and/or prosecution under the restraint-of-trade and antimonopolistic statutes. Thus, the government made possible the elevation of the other health professions to their current status.

I was sidetracked in my intent that medicine should constitute the second Academy by a remarkable clinical social worker, Florence Lieberman. She phoned from New York on behalf of the Federation of Clinical Social Work Societies to invite me to its board meeting in Washington, two weeks hence. Dr. Lieberman said she had read about the formation of the NAP, and had immediately grasped the implications and potential of such an organization for all practitioners. The Federation members were troubled by the disinterest on the part of the National Association of Social Work (NASW) in private-practice issues and had thus formed their own clinical consortium of local, grass-roots groups of independently practicing social workers. She had already formulated in her mind that the NAP in Social Work should be the second Academy, and that the Federation could be the launching platform. I confided that it was the plan that the NAP in Medicine be formed next, and in doing so, I completely underestimated Dr. Lieberman's determination and talent. When I attended the Washington meeting, she had already marshaled her forces and was ready to leap forward.

Under Florence Lieberman's leadership, the NAP in Social Work was established early in 1982. She became the founding chair, and chose as her

10 founders a stellar array of social workers that included Drs. Florence Hollis and Helen Harris Perlman, both giants in their field. Betty Synar, her cochair, would assume the chair some years later when Dr. Lieberman concluded her term. Although Academy chairs currently are limited to three-year terms, in the beginning, the terms could be extended for the sake of continuity. From its inception, the NAP in Social Work was a vital force in the NAP. I could always rely on Dr. Lieberman's support and wisdom, and she was undoubtedly a power that fueled the progress of the NAP. Twenty years later, she remains a dear and respected friend, along with Dr. Edna Roth, who served as NAP secretary, as well as chair of the NAP in Social Work, and is still very active in the organization. I never regretted delaying the formation of the NAP in Medicine in response to the irrepressible Florence Lieberman; it was fortunate that the NAP in Social Work came on line early, and so was able to exert its invaluable influence almost from the beginning.

LAUNCHING THE THIRD ACADEMY

Now it certainly was time to form the NAP in Medicine, or so I thought. Again, I was sidetracked, this time by a phone call from a man in Seattle who had just completed his presidency of the Washington State Podiatric Medical Association. His name was Chris Vance, and he, too, had read an article about the formation of the NAP. He offered his services in helping to found the NAP in Podiatric Medicine. Since I was about to visit my brother in Bellevue, a suburb of Seattle, I made arrangements to meet him there.

Dr. Vance was an energetic young man whose determination to establish the next Academy was irresistible. We went to work immediately, and in no time, he had organized the group of founders of the NAP in Podiatric Medicine. After doing so, he refused to serve as its chair, stating that someone of greater stature than he should lead the Academy. He nominated Ron Valmassey, who was at the San Francisco Podiatric Medical College. Although he accepted, Dr. Valmassey proved a disappointment as he never really grasped the reins. His co-chair, Charles Brantingham, did take hold, and in time became the chair. Dr. Brantingham was a delightful man, the father of environmental podiatric medicine. One of the first commissioned podiatrists in the military, he was also a cofounder of the Reserve Officers Association in Washington. He and I bonded almost immediately, and several years later, I mourned his death. But he left a legacy of wonderful podiatrists, among them Joe Addante, Charles Bradley, Darrell Darby, and Arthur Helfand. The latter three served as chairs of the NAP in Podiatric Medicine, and as of this writing (2001), Dr. Bradley is in his second term as secretary of the entire NAP, and remains a dear friend. Dr. Darby was a friend and confidant of Senator Byrd of West Virginia, one of the most powerful members of the U.S. Senate, who helped us immensely with the bills we were later to introduce into the Congress. Dr. Darby is the only podiatrist ever to be nominated for the post of Surgeon General of the United States, and he may be the only nonmedical doctor to make the short list of candidates presented to the White House. It is no disgrace that he was passed over in favor of the now legendary C. Everett Koop, and Dr. Darby remained a hardworking practitioner, an astute politician, and a dedicated supporter of the NAP. As president of the NAP, and with the enthusiastic backing of the NAP Council, I wrote a letter of support for Dr. Darby to President Reagan, and later learned that he was on the final list of three considered by the president.

The interactions with our Distinguished Practitioners of the NAP in Podiatric Medicine were unexpectedly delightful, and learning of the contributions to healthcare of an allied profession was exciting. It was interesting to see how podiatric medicine, in its struggle for recognition and third-party reimbursement, preceded psychology as it overcame the same obstacles. And now that psychology is striving to gain prescription authority, we could learn much from these colleagues who succeeded in winning this battle several decades ago.

FINALLY, THE NAP IN MEDICINE

The forming of the three previous Academies were not discrete events, as there was much overlap. Once Dr. Lieberman and Dr. Vance were well on their way, I immediately turned my attention to medicine, while continuing to work with the NAPs in Psychology, Podiatric Medicine, and Social Work. I sought out my friend and mentor, Morris F. Collen, cofounder with Sidney Garfield of Kaiser Permanente, the nation's first HMO. Over lunch, I explained the purpose, mission, and structure of the NAP and solicited his help in forming the much-needed NAP in Medicine. What was scheduled to be a luncheon meeting took the entire afternoon as we retired to Dr. Collen's office and plunged into the task. Dr. Collen was quick to grasp the importance of such an interdisciplinary health organization, and although he foresaw difficulty regarding some of medicine's potential demands, he suggested a way to move the formation rapidly. He went one step beyond my conceptualization of the Distinguished Practitioner model, insisting that the 10 founders be *the* most prominent physicians in America, without exception. First, each should be a Fellow of the Institute of Medicine (as was Dr. Collen), and he began calling them on the phone. We followed up with a letter over both of our signatures that explained the NAP and invited them to join in the endeavor. Dr. Collen's own stature and reputation in medicine inspired immediate attention and interest.

It should be mentioned here that not only were we inviting these physicians to be Distinguished Practitioners of the NAP in Medicine, but we also were requiring a written pledge to transcend self-interest in favor of the goals of the NAP, and to send in the first annual $100 dues payment. Furthermore, we were asking the premier health profession (medicine) to accept a role equal to that played by a number of other health professions, none of which society regarded as being in the same league with medicine. This was a tall order, and it is a tribute to Dr. Collen's persuasiveness that the founders of the Academy included, along with himself, Herbert Abrams, Michael DeBakey, William Felch, William Felts, Stanley Lesse, Donald Lindberg, W. Walter Menninger, Robert Moser, Kenneth Platt, William Roy, and William Spencer. These household names were soon joined by an additional array of household names — Marsden Blois, Lonnie Bristow, Harvey Estes, Margaret Heagerty, Bernard Lown, Judd Marmor, Samuel Sherman, Norman Shumway, Carlos Vallbona, and Malcolm Watts, among many others. Dr. Collen served as the founding chair, and Dr. Watts of the UC San Francisco School of Medicine was the founding co-chair. Dr. Watts died not too long thereafter, and Dr. Lesse, an energetic psychiatrist and the editor of the *American Journal of Psychotherapy*, succeeded him as co-chair. One of the founders, Dr. Felts of the George Washington University School of Medicine, succeeded me as NAP president in 1992.

From the outset, the Distinguished Practitioners of the NAP in Medicine were committed to obtaining a Congressional Charter. They liked the idea of practitioners having the same clout with the Congress as the IOM, and they were distressed that practice issues were often assigned to the IOM for recommendation, even though the matters were beyond the experience and expertise of these members. The furthering of practice, in contrast to academic medicine, was a driving interest and they saw the Congressional Charter as the avenue. These were exciting times, working with the NAP in Medicine, and never did I experience any feeling other than that all of us in the NAP were coequals striving for the same goal. The issue of a larger membership for the NAP in Medicine than that of the other Academies never even came up.

THE NAPs IN OPTOMETRY AND NURSING

Dr. Collen took such complete command of the NAP in Medicine that I was able to tackle the formation of the next two Academies, Optometry and Nursing, concurrently. I never ceased to marvel at the caliber of colleagues from other health disciplines that the NAP brought together, and each time I told myself that there would never be another professional like this one, several more would appear as Distinguished Practitioners and founders.

To most readers who are psychologists, the name Richard Hopping may mean nothing, but it is a name admired and respected throughout the field of optometry. As the president of the Southern California College of Optometry, he raised the funds to move the physical facility from an aging building in central Los Angeles to a beautiful new campus in Orange County, California. He also raised the standing of the school so that it became the gold standard in the field. His office was an architectural triumph and a technological wonder. This was my introduction to Dr. Hopping as we met in his office to discuss the formation of the NAP in Optometry. His impeccable attire matched his meticulous thinking, and whenever I met Dr. Hopping thereafter I could not help but admire both his sartorial and intellectual brilliance. As chair of the NAP in Optometry, he formed it in record time, as one would have predicted from his organizational acumen. His co-chair, William Ludlam from the College of Optometry at Pacific University in Oregon, was a pioneer in the prescription of contact lenses in which one lens is adjusted for near vision and the other for distance. Dr. Ludlam became the chair when Dr. Hopping was no longer able to continue in that post. An early Distinguished Practitioner in Optometry was Ron Fair, who later was to become not only the chair of the NAP in Optometry, but also the third president of the NAP. Actually, Dr. Fair might well have become the second president, but he deferred to Dr. Felts, stating that my immediate successor should be a medical doctor to ensure the prestige and maturation of the NAP.

Along with meeting Dr. Hopping, I also met a world-renowned nurse, Luther P. Christman, who had been dean of several nursing schools, and was celebrated in both nursing and sociology. When I visited with the president of the American Nursing Association (ANA) at its headquarters in St. Louis, she told me that a proposed NAP in Nursing would best be discussed with Dr. Christman. I traveled to Chicago to meet with him, and found someone who not only enthusiastically endorsed the concept of an interdisciplinary health organization, but also was eager to establish an NAP in Nursing. While we were still exploring the establishing of this Academy, he made a list of potential founders and began calling them. All were nurses of stature, several were or had been deans, and all but one held a doctorate, as well as an R.N. degree. Rachel Zonnelle Booth, the dean of the Duke University School of Nursing, became his co-chair, and one of the founders, Dr. Thelma Wells, would eventually succeed Dr. Christman as chair. Much later, Dr. Hurdis Griffith became the chair of the NAP in Nursing, and still later she was elected the fourth president of the NAP.

Among his many accomplishments, Dr. Christman founded the American Men's Nursing Association (AMNA), I am proud to be a recipient of the AMNA's highest Honor, the Luther P. Christman Award, and my picture hangs in a special room, along with that of fellow recipient, President Gerald Ford, at the Nursing Museum in Indianapolis.

THE NAP COUNCIL

We now had five Academies and we held our first official NAP Council meeting early in 1983 in my office in San Francisco. Up until this time, I had been meeting separately with the leaders of the individual Academies, and everyone was anxious to see how we would interact as an interdisciplinary group. Present were Drs. Brantingham (Podiatric Medicine), Christman (Nursing), Collen (Medicine), Fox (Psychology), Hopping (Optometry), and Lieberman (Social Work), together with the NAP officers, myself (president), Dr. Freudenberger (secretary), and Dr. Harper (treasurer). Everyone was responsible for paying his or her own travel and lodging expenses, and it was expected that if the meeting were less than worthwhile, there could well be some grumbling, and even defections. The meeting was an incredible success. Within the first two hours of the all-day and evening discussions, the participants achieved a profound respect for each other and their respective disciplines. A number of decisions were made, not the least of which was that the members of the Council would always take care of their own travel and lodging. The

NAP was a small organization, and with membership limited to 100 Distinguished Practitioners for each Academy, it would never exceed a total of 800 members for the eight Academies (later to be nine, and much later, 10 for a ceiling of 1,000 members). Thus, until the NAP received its Congressional Charter, there would be annual dues and self-subsidy for travel/lodging, whether to a Council meeting or a general membership forum.

Several months later, the NAP Council's second meeting was hosted by Dr. Hopping. It had been decided that the various Academies would rotate the hosting of the Council, and the meeting in Fullerton, California, set a standard difficult to emulate. Dr. Hopping and his wife not only were gracious hosts, but they also had mobilized the campus into helping with arrangements. Everyone was met at the airport by a student who acted as chauffeur and man/woman "Friday" throughout the two-day meeting. This was a hard act to follow, but Dr. Lieberman, in turn, hosted a spectacular meeting at Hunter College in New York City. There was one more Council meeting under this rotating plan, this time by the NAP in Podiatric Medicine, and it was held at the Ritz Carlton Hotel in Atlanta. All subsequent Council meetings were held in the Washington, D.C. area, under the auspices of the entire NAP, rather than a particular Academy. How was this amazing ambiance possible and sustainable, with renowned practitioners volunteering both their time and their money?

OUR AMAZING AMBIANCE

For the 12 years that I was president, the Distinguished Practitioners of the NAP paid not only $100, and then $150, in annual dues, but also their own expenses to attend the Council and various committee and task force meetings. Even further, they supported the organization with voluntary contributions whenever there was a need. And to top it all off, I had no difficulty in regularly getting 50, and often as many as 80, of them to volunteer two days of their time whenever we did our frequent legislative forays into the Congress, while paying their own expenses. I marveled at the dedication of our Distinguished Practitioners, as I expressed my gratitude to them. One of our founding psychologists replied on one such occasion, "Never underestimate the narcissism of this group." I pondered this seemingly flip response and felt ashamed that it reflected the kind of armchair psychoanalysis of which we, as psychologists, are often guilty in our conversations with each other. The atmosphere at the NAP was much more profound and complex.

First of all, the Distinguished Practitioners were having a good time working with peers from the other disciplines. After each get-together, whether large or small, my mail would be flooded with letters of appreciation for the opportunity to interact with such remarkable practitioners, and to learn about contributions the other professions had made to healthcare. Second, they were excited by the idea that as members of such an outstanding group, they could collectively make a contribution to the national health. They were dedicating their time and efforts toward attaining that interdisciplinary goal, and they would clamor to be assigned tasks on behalf of our mission. The fact that we were a small, elite group in a vast political arena only added to the fervor. They had received all the honors their professions could bestow on them, and they were not looking for more recognition. Rather, by rising above self-interests, they could, as an interdisciplinary group, clearly see for the first time that our health system was in trouble, and they could finally admit that their own professions had contributed to the mess. Internecine warfare in the field of health was apparent to all of us, and our vision was to rectify it.

As for myself, it was probably one of my busiest times professionally. While founding the NAP, scurrying from Academy to Academy, meeting with the Congress, and answering hundreds of letters, I was commuting every other week to Hawaii, where I was conducting the HCFA-Biodyne-Medical Project that altered the way in which Medicaid was to be financed and delivered. I was also the founding CEO of American Biodyne, the first practitioner-driven national behavioral healthcare delivery system, which grew to 14.5 million enrollees in 39 states during seven of the 12 years I was founding president of the NAP. I was putting in 90-hour weeks, flying half a million miles a year, and devoting a considerable portion of my personal staff's clerical time to the NAP. I mention this only in the context of the vitality of the NAP, as many colleagues confided that they were inspired by my vision, as well as by my dedication.

THE NAPS IN DENTISTRY AND OSTEOPATHIC MEDICINE:
A SUCCESS AND A NEAR FAILURE

There remained the founding of the NAPs in Dentistry and Osteopathic Medicine. For each, I received strong recommendations as to who the founding chair should be. For the NAP in Dentistry, I was referred to D. Walter Cohen, president of the Medical College of Pennsylvania, whose father was widely considered the "father of American dentistry" because of his profound influence in establishing the standards for modern dental schools in the early part of the 20th century. I met with Dr. Cohen several times, first in Pennsylvania and then at airports where both of us were changing plans. He was so busy and overextended that I was almost embarrassed to lay before him the formidable task of organizing the NAP in Dentistry. He obviously was intrigued by the concept of the NAP and excited that there would be an NAP in Dentistry, but his heavy schedule caused him to pause. I had an ally, his daughter, who wanted to be a psychologist and subsequently did receive her doctorate. I was as assiduous as I could be in helping her to select and apply to graduate programs, and if Dr. Cohen needed a final nudge, his daughter provided it. He agreed to be the founding chair, and chose as his co-chair the retired, venerable, and charming I. Lawrence Kerr.

The two made a dynamite team; Dr. Cohen brought to the Council his years of organizational experience and business acumen, and Dr. Kerr brought his lifetime of political experience gained on behalf of the dental profession. As for his charm, I shall never forget when several of us were meeting with Hillary Rodham Clinton early in 1993, after she had begun her ill-fated health task force. While the rest of us were extolling the value of interdisciplinary health, Dr. Kerr interjected, "Mrs. Clinton, you not only have a beautiful smile, you also have perfect teeth." She smiled one of her best smiles, and at that moment, Dr. Kerr won for the NAP a voice on her task force.

The NAP in Dentistry remained a significant force in the early affairs of the NAP, and we all felt the loss when Dr. Kerr died. Drs. Cohen and Kerr were succeeded as chair and co-chair by Daniel Laskin and Harold Black, respectively, and in 1999, Dr. Laskin was chosen president-elect to succeed Dr. Griffith to the NAP presidency in 2002.

Establishing the NAP in Osteopathic Medicine was quite another matter. At the outset, I was referred to two prominent osteopathic physicians, both on the faculty of the University of Osteopathic Medicine and Health Sciences in Des Moines, Iowa. We met and discussed the formation of the NAP in Osteopathic Medicine and they enthusiastically agreed. Phyllis Cotrille became the chair, and David Leopold the co-chair. They pointed out that as colleagues in the same building they could work efficiently together, and at first they did. Within three weeks, they had assembled their group of 10 founders, one of whom was Kenneth Riland of New York. Then all activity came to a halt. Not only had they stopped working, but Drs. Cotrille and Leopold seemed to have fallen off the face of the earth. For nearly a year, they did not return phone calls or answer correspondence, and I did not have an inkling of what had gone wrong. While the other Academies were in full swing, the NAP in Osteopathic Medicine languished. Finally, I wrote a letter and left a phone message to the effect that I was planning a trip to Des Moines, and that brought a telephone response from Dr. Leopold. He apologized saying that he and Dr. Cotrille had been overwhelmed with work, but would now become active in choosing the first group of Distinguished Practitioners. Then communications went dead again. Both Dr. Cotrille and Dr. Leopold had attended an early meeting of the NAP Council in Chicago shortly after selecting the 10 founders, but there had not been a person from their Academy at a meeting since, now over two years. Then Dr. Riland, one of the original 10 founders, attended a meeting and was distressed to find that the Academy to which he belonged was inactive. We helped him poll the other seven founders (Dr. Cotrille and Leopold did not respond, of course) and he was named the new chair of the NAP in Osteopathic Medicine. He enjoyed reactivating his Academy, and he brought to it a number of prominent osteopathic physicians, including J. Jerry Rodos of Chicago and Edward Stiles of Kentucky. Dr. Rodos was named co-chair, and he succeeded Dr. Riland within less than a year, when the latter passed away.

Dr. Rodos is an osteopathic psychiatrist and a dedicated leader in the NAP. From the beginning, he became, and has remained, a good friend. Along with his many accomplishments, he has been a leader in conceptualizing and advocating the training of physicians assistants, and in this regard, he has served as an advisor to the office of the U.S. Surgeon General.

WHOOPS! WHAT HAPPENED TO THE NAP IN VETERINARY MEDICINE?

By 1985, there were eight Academies of the NAP and the Congress received a bill sponsored by Senator Inouye to grant the organization its Congressional Charter. This initial bill was intended as a trial balloon, to test the mood of Congress in this regard, and we were not pushing its passage. It contained the mission and structure of the NAP and listed its eight Academies. By way of getting feedback, Robert Juliano, our legislative advocate, and I were visiting various members of the Congress known to be interested in health issues. One was a veterinarian from Montana, and he immediately asked, "Why isn't veterinary medicine one of your academies?" He went on to explain how much of what is known about human diseases was first discovered in animals by veterinarians, and he noted that lupus, an autoimmune disorder, was first described and treated in canines. This was our last Congressional visit of the day, and when Bob Juliano and I got into our cab, we both exclaimed, "Whoops." We immediately went to Senator Inouye's office and asked him to amend the bill to include a ninth Academy, the NAP in Veterinary Medicine. This was subsequently ratified by the Council, which amended the by-laws to reflect this, at its next meeting. Our working relationship was so cohesive that the Council trusted the president to have the bill amended in advance of its approval. None of us wanted to wait several months until the Council met, at which time the NAP would have been ingrained in Congressional staffers' minds as having only eight Academies.

Bob Juliano was also instrumental in bringing in William Kay, the head of the New York Veterinary Hospital, to be founding chair of the NAP in Veterinary Medicine. Within minutes after hearing the concept described, Dr. Kay became one of its most enthusiastic supporters. An energetic, persuasive, and sometimes volatile man, he often had to be exhorted to tone it down, or he would have attempted to dominate the Council. When focused on target, Dr. Kay was one of the most effective NAP Council members. His co-chair was William F. Jackson, and among his 10 founders was William McCarthy, who not only would succeed him as chair, but would become executive secretary of the NAP a number of years later. William Carlson, a Distinguished Practitioner of Veterinary Medicine who worked at the U.S. Department of Agriculture and was a university president-emeritus, was soon to succeed Dr. Harper as treasurer of the NAP. Although an afterthought and the last Academy to be formed as part of the original sequence, the NAP in Veterinary Medicine immediately set about becoming an influential part of the NAP.

While we were in the midst of our Congressional legislative campaign, Senator Robert Dole's office called the NAP to tell us that the senator's dog, Leader, seemed to be seriously ill. His office wanted to know if there were a Distinguished Practitioner who might treat Mr. Dole's pet. We immediately arranged to have Dr. Kay fly down from New York to look at Leader, which so impressed the senator that from that day on, and until he retired from the Senate, he remained a strong advocate for the NAP.

INDIVIDUAL ACADEMY MEETINGS AND
OUR FIRST NATIONAL FORUM

As each Academy came into being, it held meetings of its own at its respective professional society's annual convention, and each also held one meeting annually that was an installation banquet for its newly elected Distinguished Practitioners. To celebrate the importance of these installations, the dinners were formal, which added to the exciting ambiance that was characteristic of the NAP, as well as to the solemnity of the occasion. I went to all of these individual Academy installation banquets until the NAP began having its own annual meetings. The four annual banquets for the NAP in Psychology were held in conjunction with the yearly conventions of the APA, and so it was relatively easy for me to be there. But the installation dinners for the other Academies required that I make special trips. Thus, the NAP in Social Work, as the second formed, held three annual banquets at the National Press Club in Washington, all of which I attended. To provide some insight into the heavy travel schedule required of the president, in addition to these, there were banquets for the NAP in Podiatric Medicine in Nashville and Miami; the NAP in Dentistry in Atlanta and Philadelphia; the NAP in Optometry in Los Angeles, Denver, and New York; the NAP in Nursing in Chicago, Washington, and Atlanta; and the NAP in Veterinary Medicine in Las Vegas. In 1985, these individual installations were superseded by one annual black-tie installation banquet for the entire NAP. Since that year, with one exception (Denver in 1996), all have been held in the Washington, D.C., area.

By 1985, all nine Academies were functioning, and we conceived of the annual meeting as being a forum on a chosen topic, alternating each year with a general membership meeting at which the goals and mission of the NAP would be reviewed, renewed, or revised with feedback from the attending membership. The first national meeting in 1985 was held at the Marriott Hotel in Washington, with the first national installation being held that same weekend at a black tie banquet in the National Press Club next door. This formal tradition has been continued at every national installation banquet since, but the initial idea of including a prominent speaker has been discontinued as it takes almost two hours following dinner just to introduce the new Distinguished Practitioners, Academy by Academy, and to take group photographs and those of the individual Academy chairs and co-chairs.

The 1985 national meeting was a test to see whether the nine interdisciplinary professions could get along with each other for the first time, and for two days. Many had predicted that this was impossible, or at least unlikely. The nine professions not only got along, the attendees enjoyed the interaction immensely and gave the meeting, and the plan to repeat it annually, a resounding endorsement. The next year established the concept of a forum at which a topic (such as diabetes) would be chosen, and each Academy would contribute a speaker who would address the contribution each profession could make to defeating that disease while working in a collaborative model. The results of each forum were published as a position paper that could be distributed to the Congress and the relevant government agencies.

THE NAP MEDALLION

In 1985, in time for our first national installation banquet, the NAP had a bronze medallion struck with the NAP logo imprinted on one side and the list of the nine Academies on the other. The medallion was designed to be worn on a red, white, and blue ribbon around the neck and with formal dress or academic robes. Each Distinguished Practitioner was entitled to a medallion, but had to attend the installation banquet to receive it. If circumstances prevented attendance, the Distinguished Practitioner could ask for the presentation at a subsequent installation banquet.

With all nine Academies in place, the NAP began to publish a directory that not only was distributed among the membership, but also was given to the members of Congress or their staffs. In this way, we could showcase the outstanding Distinguished Practitioners who made up the NAP, and each member of Congress could ascertain who among these Distinguished Practitioners were also constituents. During his presidency, Dr. Fair had designed a new full-color NAP logo that shows the overlap of the by-then 10 Academies, and the area of the health field common to all disciplines. It adorns the cover of the most recent directories.

From the very beginning, the medallion was a hit with the Distinguished Practitioners, who wore it proudly at other formal and academic functions aside from those of the NAP. It contributed to the cohesiveness of the organization, and increased the feeling that we were on a special mission. I never told of the fiasco that had occurred during the striking of the medallion. After the design was approved, the manufacturer translated it to a stamp, but in doing so, misspelled the name of one of the Academies. Of course, it had to be that of the NAP in Medicine, which appeared on 1,000 medallions as "Medecine." I refused to pay the bill unless the manufacturer could strike 1,000 more medallions with the correct spelling in time for our April national meeting in Washington. The manufacturer completed the task on time, but in order to cut its losses, did not supply new ribbons. For over a week, I had two persons in my office removing ribbons from the discarded medallions and attaching them to the new ones, an arduous task that had to be done by hand. I insisted that the first set of medallions be destroyed, as I did not want one to fall into the hands of someone who might accuse the NAP of not knowing how to spell medicine.

THE NAP LEGISLATIVE AGENDA

The long-range mission of the NAP was defined as working to influence proposed healthcare legislation in the direction of collaborative care. In this mission, we would remain nonpartisan, championing the collaborative model in bills introduced by either Democrats or Republicans. If opposing bills were introduced into the Congress, we would make recommendations to both. In this way, we maintained working relations with both sides of the aisle, without being branded either liberal or conservative. Thus, we had just as good a working relationship with Senator Kennedy's staff as we did with Senator Hatch's.

Our immediate legislative task was to obtain the Congressional Charter, naming the NAP as an advisor and resource to the Congress. In this regard, it was doubly important that we be seen as nonpartisan and, in the initial years while we were still seeking the Charter, to retain a low profile.

In 1985, Senator Inouye introduced for the first time a bill to grant the NAP a Congressional Charter. During that session, our thrust was to educate the Congress, and to obtain feedback and support for the reformulated bill that would be introduced in the following Congressional session (it must be remembered that a Congressional session is two years long, beginning in January and coinciding with the seating of the members elected the previous November). Throughout our work with Senator Inouye, we were fortunate to have as a Distinguished Practitioner in Psychology the senator's aide, Dr. Patrick H. DeLeon, who provided an avenue for constant communication. Senator Inouye liked the idea of a Congressionally Chartered NAP and was generous with his support and his guidance. He recommended the lobbyist for the petroleum industry, stating that we could never afford him, but I persuaded him that the NAP would be an excellent pro bono endeavor. I flew to Oklahoma City, spent most of one day with the lobbyist, and in the end got a flat refusal.

Senator Inouye told me not to be disappointed. He wanted the NAP to have one of the most influential lobbyists in Washington, and the oil lobby was powerful, indeed. He then recommended Robert Juliano, who represented the Hotel and Culinary Workers Union, another powerful lobby. In contrast to my first attempt, I found Mr. Juliano to be affable and eager to work with our group. He had heard Senator Inouye describe the NAP as "the creme de la creme of healthcare," a frequent comment in the senator's speeches. When I told him what we could pay him, I saw the most incredulous look I would ever see on Bob Juliano's face. With a pained expression, he replied, "I don't mind doing something pro bono, but you are asking me not just to do something free, but actually to lose money." I fully expected another refusal, and was delighted when Bob agreed to join us. He was respected enough on Capitol Hill that he was able to get access to the senators and representatives themselves, not just with their staff officers. He would arrange two full days of appointments, for which several dozen Distinguished Practitioners would volunteer to fly to Washington at their own expense. We would deploy in groups of four or five, making certain that each Distinguished Practitioner was from a different Academy, and we would go from appointment to appointment, seeing as many as 50 or 60 members of Congress in two days. These forays were frequent, well organized, and productive. Bob was our grand marshal and our teacher, giving us an inordinate amount of time. Occasionally, while I was thanking him, I would say, "Bob, please don't tell me how much time and money you are losing on us, as I would not sleep nights." He would laugh and respond, "I can't tell you because I'm afraid to add it up." Then he would wax eloquent as he told me how much he was enjoying working with the NAP. "You have brought into my life the most incredible and brilliant people, and I thank you for it." Bob was having a good time. I was having a ball, and after a year and a half of our trial legislative endeavor, I was on a first-name basis with most of the members of the U.S. Senate and about half of those of the House of Representatives.

In 1986, Senator Inouye introduced a refined bill to grant the NAP its Congressional Charter, and we went to work in earnest. Our teams of Distinguished Practitioners became a familiar sight in the halls of the Capitol. Most Americans have never seen the underground train provided for the members of Congress, which runs between the Senate and House sides. Our NAP advocates became regular commuters. Our success midway through the Congressional session astounded us. We had passed the Senate with unanimous consent (100 to 0), and we had 254 representatives who had signed on as cosponsors. Since over half of the House of Representatives were cosponsors, we were assured of passage once the bill came to a floor vote. We were so certain of victory that we began to meet with the White House to assure that once the bill was passed by both Houses, the president would sign it.

One of the reasons we were so successful in obtaining this remarkable level of support was that the societies representing the various healthcare professions either endorsed the concept of a Congressional Charter for the NAP, or took a neutral stance. At first, the IOM opposed it, stating that it was an interdisciplinary body and another one was not needed. We met with the IOM several times, during which we pointed out that although the IOM members come from various disciplines, they are chosen for scientific, not practice, contributions. The IOM then agreed to remove its expressed opposition and to remain neutral. Similarly, the American Medical Association (AMA) opposed our Charter, and after several trips to its headquarters in Chicago, the AMA also agreed to remain neutral. Of the remaining eight professions, seven wrote strong letters of endorsement. To the end, however, Clarence Martin, the executive director of the Association for the Advancement of Psychology (AAP), tried to undercut our effort. Apparently his public attacks on the NAP got so bad that Johnny Carson, the lobbyist for the American Podiatric Medical Association (APMA), felt compelled to warn me that, as a psychologist, I had an enemy in my own ranks. I spent time with Mr. Martin, who was disgruntled because the NAP was not taking guidance from him. I tried to explain that it was by design that the respective professional societies not take an instrumental role, as the day could well come when the direction of the NAP might be at odds with a particular "home" professional society. He tried to appear affable, but I was never confident that he did not continue to subtly undercut us in Washington politics. Eventually I stopped worrying about it, as he was quite ineffective as a lobbyist. He would astound psychologists with apocryphal stories of his political acumen, but eventually others saw through him and he was replaced by the AAP.

Before his departure, however, Mr. Martin caused me considerable embarrassment. I was spending a great deal of time consulting with Jay Constantine, the chief clerk of the U.S. Senate Finance Committee, who was a lawyer and was especially interested in matters of health. Clarence Martin was quoted in a story in the *Washington Post* as implying that there was a conspiracy between Jay Constantine and "a certain powerful health lobbyist" (ostensibly me, of all things). Jay hit the ceiling, as the word conspiracy has a very serious connotation in Washington politics. He blamed me for Mr. Martin's indiscretion and did not speak to me for several weeks. Finally, I was able to impose on the friendship we had developed, and got the opportunity to explain to him why Mr. Martin was doing a number on us, and particularly on me. I continue to be amazed in retrospect at how I was able to get every lobbyist either on board or neutralized, except the one from my own profession.

ENTER BARNEY FRANK

According to folklore, everyone is destined to meet at least one villain in his or her life. To the extent that this might be true, it would have been ordained that mine hold the rank of archvillain and be named Representative Barney Frank (D–Mass.). As ranking member of the House Judiciary Committee, Representative Frank had decided that there would be no more Congressional Charters or Commemoratives. It had become a personal obsession with him, and he bottled up our bill in committee, preventing its ever coming to the floor vote we certainly would have won. When the Congressional session adjourned, our bill died. Before that time, we had met with him repeatedly, but he would not budge. Neither would he give a believable reason, except that he thought the practice should stop.

Senator Inouye and his Congressional colleagues introduced the bill again in 1987. We had hired Judy Brotman, a former employee of the Department of Health and Human Services, who meticulously went back to all our previous cosponsors. In addition, our teams reinforced her activity, as well as making calls on new members of Congress. The results were as impressive as they had been in the previous Congressional session. For the second time, our bill passed the Senate 100 to 0, and over 60% of the House signed on as cosponsors. Again Representative Frank bottled the bill in committee, where it died a second time just as soon as the session adjourned. Visibly distressed, Senator Inouye had leaders in the House, such as the now retired Representative Vic Fazio, who was a ranking Democrat at the time, put pressure on Mr. Frank, but to no avail.

The bill was introduced again at the next Congressional session beginning in 1989, with identical results: the Senate passed it unanimously, two thirds of the House signed on as cosponsors, and Representative Frank bottled it up in committee, where it died a third time. During this session, an enormous amount of pressure was put on Mr. Frank. We paid him several visits to plead our cause. Leading Democrats (his own party) talked to him several times. Senator Inouye failed to convince Mr. Frank, and he enlisted the help of Senator Joseph Biden, who, as chair of the Senate Judiciary Committee, was Representative Frank's counterpart in the upper chamber. Senator Biden spoke with me at length after our third defeat, stating that he had called Representative Frank twice, and finally had walked over to the House side and said to him, "Barney, you don't understand; I want this bill." In accordance with the sense of noblesse oblige that unofficially governs the Congress, this is all a colleague has to say and a bill is released. Senator Biden was shocked when Mr. Frank refused, and was at a loss to explain it.

In subsequent conversations on Capitol Hill, I learned that a ranking member not only has the power to bottle up a bill, but also that Representative Frank has a reputation for arrogance that stems from his holding a safe seat. He has survived at least one scandal of outrageous proportions, but the story goes that as long as he gives his constituents what they want, they will reelect him no matter what. And although my Democrat friends in the Congress would be reluctant to admit it, there is the further arrogance that can only come from the fact that the House of Representatives had been at the time under single-party rule for 40 years.

When Representative Frank killed our bill for the third time, he issued a press release that said, in part, "At least we have killed this snake in the garden." This was a curious remark, especially since there are so many burning issues confronting our nation, and it is especially curious as it implies that there are other snakes in his garden. For a long time, I wondered why Representative Frank would expend so much time, effort, and political capital on this minor matter. I finally learned what I believe is the answer, but I have not been able to verify it, and until I do, I am more comfortable leaving the dead snake lie where Mr. Frank killed it.

In 1992, the Republicans captured both the House and Senate for the first time in 40 years, and Representative Frank, now a member of the minority party, lost the clout that he had held so long. At our Charter's postmortem meeting with him, I found him to be less arrogant, but probably no more honest. He promised that if the NAP did not continue to pursue a Congressional Charter, he would see to it that the NAP would be able to accomplish many of its goals through Congressional funding. Later, when the NAP did decide not to try to attain a Charter again, he never granted me, or any other NAP member, another meeting.

THE CONGRESSIONAL CHARTER: R.I.P.

When the new Congress convened in 1993, Senator Inouye offered once again to introduce the bill to grant the NAP a Congressional Charter. He pointed out that the relevant committee was now in Republican hands, and that it would be unlikely to share Representative Frank's obsession for "killing his snake in the garden" a fourth time. In fact, Senator Inouye urged us to try again, as finally success seemed probable. I had just turned over the NAP presidency to Dr. Felts, who shared the view of the majority of the physicians in the NAP in Medicine that the Congressional Charter was necessary if the NAP were to be an effective force in healthcare policy. Unfortunately, Dr. Felt's energy was drained by his wife's protracted illness and her death during his term in office. This was followed by a series of health problems of his own. There were many in the NAP who did not want to tackle the mountain of work that it took to get our bill to the point it had reached on each of the three previous tries. Prominent among those saying No were both the current and previous executive secretaries, Dr. McCarthy and Beverly Carlson, in addition to those Distinguished Practitioners who had come to the NAP later, and were not dedicated to obtaining a Congressional Charter as the founders were. They believed that the NAP should redefine itself and move forward in new directions. In the end, they prevailed and the pursuit of the Charter was discontinued.

I took a minor role in this debate, for having led the Council as president for 12 years, I thought it was time for me to shut up and let the newcomers have their say. Nonetheless, after getting to know the new Republican Congress, there is no doubt in my mind that the fourth try would have given us the coveted Congressional Charter. In fact, since Representative Barney Frank lost control of the process, a number of Congressional Charters and Commemoratives have been approved.

It was distressing for me to see the NAP in Medicine, out of disappointment, quickly lose its vitality and feeling of involvement. More than any other Academy, the NAP in Medicine believed the granting of a Charter to be imperative, and saw the discontinuation of its pursuit as a broken promise. By this time, the firebrands who supplied the energy to the NAP in Medicine, Dr. Collen and Dr. Lesse, had left the Council: Dr. Collen's term had expired, and Dr. Lesse had met an untimely death due to a heart attack. During their active years on the Council, they would join with Dr. Vallbona and other physicians, creating a force that inspired the NAP toward the repeated efforts to obtain a Congressional Charter.

As of this writing (2001), only now has the NAP successfully begun to redefine itself. President Fair began the process, secured some private foundation funding, and now President Griffith is well on her way to completing the transformation. At this moment in time, however, it has not coalesced to the point where its future is well defined.

SIGNIFICANT ACCOMPLISHMENTS

Although two decades later interdisciplinary cohesiveness seems a minor achievement because it has already been attained by the NAP, our first accomplishment was bringing all the health professions under one umbrella organization, and without having to concede special numbers or preeminence to medicine. Not only did the professions get along well together, they relished the interdisciplinary interrelations. The opportunity to get to know persons of stature from other professions, and to meet and discuss issues with them as equals, had not been afforded on a national level across the major health professions until the NAP.

It should be noted here, as the reader may have noticed, chiropractics was not invited to join the NAP, even though it is a health profession widely accorded direct third-party payment. During the era of its formation, had the NAP included chiropractors, it would have lost most of the other Academies and created a storm of opposition. For years, I was concerned that chiropractors, who are very active politically, would come to us one day demanding involvement. I would rehearse in my mind what I would do in that case. Finally, I quit worrying; they never came. This is one battle we did not have to fight. I have subsequently learned that chiropractors like to go it alone, eschewing collaboration with most of the professions in the NAP, and especially with medical doctors, with whom there seems to be perpetual conflict.

In 1997, the NAP appointed a special commission to study the desires of several additional healthcare professions to become Academies of the NAP. After considerable deliberation, it was determined that the requirement of federal recognition for direct third-party reimbursement should be respected and continued. Based on this decision, only one other profession qualified to receive Academy status, and the NAP in Pharmacy was founded in 1998.

The NAP prepared and distributed to the Congress and the relevant federal agencies a number of position papers on collaborative care that were well received. Some of these emerged as proceedings from our forums, whereas others were topics assigned to specific task forces. One of the most successful outgrowths of a forum was the book, *Aging in Health*, edited by Florence Lieberman, D.S.W. This followed the forum devoted to the interdisciplinary care of older adults.

A unique publication of the NAP was an extensive project headed by Herbert Dorken, Ph.D., a psychologist who spent a lifetime in the administration and financing of healthcare. His task force devoted months to preparing a complex but workable plan to finance healthcare for all Americans. This followed the forum at which a number of experts on health economics and managed care, as well as those from the Rodham Clinton Task Force, debated the economic and practice issues. *The Financing of Healthcare in America*, written by Dr. Dorken, was distributed to the Congress. In the wake of the Rodham Clinton Task Force's inability to deal with the financing of its plan, the NAP publication created considerable interest and we were inundated by requests from Congressional staffers for copies. Shortly thereafter, the Rodham Clinton plan met its demise and the interest in universal healthcare waned once again.

In 1999, one of our most energetic and dedicated Distinguished Practitioners, Judith Lewis of the NAP in Nursing, received Council approval and founded the official journal of the NAP. Known as *Issues in Collaborative Care*, it is published by Sage, and is a refereed journal under the auspices of a multidisciplinary editorial board headed by Dr. Lewis as editor.

One of our most successful forums was *Healthy Children 2000: Obstacles and Opportunities*, held in 1992, and resulting in a publication by the same name, again edited by Dr. Lieberman. These are just some examples of the kinds of contributions that can be made by a dedicated interdisciplinary national organization of Distinguished Practitioners. As the NAP reinvents itself for the future, it is anticipated that it will find ways to be an effective voice in collaborative care, even without a Congressional Charter.

During its years of activity, the NAP established several awards, the leading one being the Daniel K. Inouye Award for Contributions to Health in the Public Interest. Its first recipient was the man for whom the award was named, and other recipients include the late Senator Claude Pepper, an outstanding advocate for the healthcare of the elderly, who received it on his 92nd birthday; Surgeon General C. Everett Koop; and Senator Jay Rockefeller. More recently, under a generous grant from two donors, the NAP established the Nicholas Andrew Cummings Annual Award, given to the nominee who made the most unique contribution to collaborative care in the previous year.

Although most of the original founders have died or no longer participate in the day-to-day activities of the NAP, there are notable exceptions,
such as Distinguished Practitioners Edna Roth (Social Work) and Dr.
Charles Bradley (Podiatric Medicine). I am appreciative that the NAP
Council has amended the bylaws to establish a lifetime position for me
called founding president. In this way, I can continue to take part in one
of the most exciting endeavors of my career.

APPENDIX 6A

OUR NATION'S FIRST INTERDISCIPLINARY
HEALTH POLICY JOURNAL[1]

With the publication of this first issue of the *National Academies of Practice Forum*, the National Academies of Practice (NAP) has achieved another landmark in the history of interdisciplinary healthcare in America. Almost anything the NAP has done in its relatively brief 17-year history has set a precedent, but the publication of its own refereed journal establishes our nation's only interdisciplinary health policy forum as a true scholarly, scientific, and professional society.

The *National Academies of Practice Forum* is the result of the vision and dedication of its editor, Judith A. Lewis, Ph.D., R.N.C., FAAN, who is also the current cochair of the National Academy of Practice in Nursing. Dr. Lewis was the first to recognize the need for interdisciplinary health care to have its own scholarly journal, and she worked skillfully and tirelessly toward that goal as she forged a cooperative relationship between the NAP and a prestigious publisher. By providing a vehicle through which the need for interdisciplinary collaboration and the attendant findings from research and practice could be disseminated to the public, the federal and state governments, the private health sector, and the broader practice community, the NAP has come of age.

The NAP was founded in 1981 in recognition of the need for interdisciplinary collaboration in healthcare. The age of specialization has created

[1] Reprinted with permission from the *National Academies of Practice Forum*, 1(1), January 1999.

stellar advances in treatment, but it also has resulted in the fragmentation of our health system, with isolation of the professions from one another. It inadvertently has fostered duplication, although discouraging other potential treatment advances that could result from cross-fertilization. Initially, the NAP was composed of eight Academies representing the disciplines recognized by the federal government as independent providers: the National Academies of Practice in Dentistry, Medicine, Nursing, Optometry, Osteopathic Medicine, Podiatric Medicine, Psychology, and Social Work. That National Academy of Practice in Veterinary Medicine was added in 1983, and the National Academy of Practice in Pharmacy was added in 1998.

Prior to 1981, the various health professions were characterized by their inability to get along with each other. Skeptics doubted if they could sit in the same room with one another without falling into contentious competition, a view that quickly was dispelled by the collegiality present in the early meetings of the Academies with one another. The concept was a simple one: A body of Distinguished Practitioners from all of the primary-care professions might well rise above interdisciplinary distrust and isolation. Such individuals who had made significant and enduring contributions to healthcare practice and who had received all of the honors and recognition their respective professions could accord them may well be ready to set aside turf interests and address in concert what would be the best in healthcare for the American people. The next several years were spent in establishing the nine National Academies of Practice with a limit of 100 Distinguished Practitioners in each Academy as nationally recognized by their peers. During that time, we learned about each other's unique perspectives and contributions, and we established a working relationship dedicated to the national health rather than to our respective turf interests.

By 1985, the NAP was well on its way, and a series of interdisciplinary national health policy Forums was initiated during which timely and often controversial healthcare topics were discussed, examined, and debated toward consensus in the interest of the national health. In its role, the NAP remained nonpartisan, not only from the parochial endeavors of its parent organizations, but also from political ideology. The NAP defined its mission to examine all health legislation and regulations to ensure their basis in interdisciplinary collaboration. As a result of these interdisciplinary health policy Forums, a series of books and monographs were published on such diverse interdisciplinary topics as aging and the financing of healthcare. The latter was distributed widely to all members of the Congress and to the White House.

As a unique organization, the NAP bears heavy responsibility, as well as great potential. Its primary resource is the dedication of the nation's Distinguished Practitioners to a national health policy of interdisciplinary collaboration. They now have at their disposal a scholarly journal dedicated to that mission. It is with pride that we launch the *National Academies of Practice Forum* and with gratitude that we recognize Dr. Judith Lewis, its visionary and dedicated editor.

Nicholas A. Cummings
Founding President,
National Academies of Practice

APPENDIX 6B
HISTORY OF THE NAP[2]

The National Academies of Practice was founded in 1981 in recognition of the need for interdisciplinary collaboration in healthcare. The age of specialization has created unprecedented advances, but it has also resulted in the fragmentation of our health system, with isolation of the professions from one another, duplication, and the loss of other potential advances because cross fertilization is lacking.

The need for interdisciplinary collaboration became painfully apparent in the Congressional Medicare Reform hearings of the late 1970's. All of the health professions were invited to testify, giving their views on how healthcare for the elderly might be improved. This mission was all but forgotten as the various professions defined and carefully guarded their respective turfs, which often required taking antagonistic aim at other professions. Subsequent discussions with leaders in the United States Senate revealed a need for an interdisciplinary body that could transcend guild issues and address the interest of the national health. All were pessimistic that this could be done, however necessary, in view of the fact that the entire history of the world, the healthcare professions had never been able to get along with each other. In ancient Egypt, specialization had developed to the point that the physician who treated the right eye was not allowed to look at the left eye, and neither specialist would collaborate with the other.

After some deliberation, it was conceived that a body of Distinguished

---

[2] Reprinted from the *National Academies of Practice Membership Directory*, 1997–1998.

Practitioners from all of the primary health professions could provide the vehicle for interdisciplinary collaboration. These individuals who had made significant and enduring contributions to healthcare practice, and who had received all of the honors and recognition their respective professions could accord them, might well be ready to set aside turf considerations and address in concert what would be the best healthcare for the American people. The next four years were spent in founding the nine National Academies of Practice (Dentistry, Medicine, Nursing, Optometry, Osteopathic Medicine, Podiatric Medicine, Psychology, Social Work, and Veterinary Medicine), with each Academy limited to 100 Distinguished Practitioners as recognized nationally by their peers.

The first of a series of forums was convened in September of 1985. The goal of this initial gathering was to determine whether the healthcare professions could get along together for an entire weekend of interdisciplinary meetings and dialogues. There were many skeptics carefully watching the proceedings. Not only did the nine health professions get along, they were unanimously enthusiastic about the process, and had plans to continue and intensify the interdisciplinary collaboration. That weekend there was rekindled a respect for each other's profession, and there were several discoveries that for problems in one profession, there were solutions in another profession.

The NAP remains as our nation's only truly interdisciplinary health policy forum. It is the only body where interdisciplinary issues can be examined and debated toward a consensus, and in the interest of the national health. In this endeavor, Distinguished Practitioners not only must set aside the turf interest of their parent profession, but they must also suspend political allegations and ideology. Interdisciplinary collaboration is nonpartisan. It is neither conservative or liberal, Democrat nor Republican. It is the responsibility of the NAP to examine legislation, regulations, or health policy as it is being fashioned, and to assure that it is based on interdisciplinary collaboration.

As a unique organization, the NAP bears heavy responsibility, as well as great potential. Its primary resource is the dedication of the nation's Distinguished Practitioners toward a national health policy of interdisciplinary collaboration.

Nicholas A. Cummings, Ph.D., Sc.D.
Founding President, 1981–1993
Past President, 1993–1996

APPENDIX 6C

THE NATIONAL ACADEMIES OF PRACTICE:

BACKGROUND INFORMATION[3]

Purposes and Goals

The National Academies of Practice was founded in 1981 based on the desires of its members to provide a realistic advisory function to Congress and the Executive Branch of our government. It was then, as it is today, the only interdisciplinary group of healthcare practitioners dedicated to addressing the problems of healthcare. The stated mission of the National Academies of Practice is as follows:

The National Academies of Practice is dedicated to quality healthcare for all, by serving as the nation's distinguished interdisciplinary policy forum that addresses public policy, education, research, and inquiry.

Membership

Membership in the National Academies of Practice (NAP) is contingent upon election as a Distinguished Practitioner in one of 10 Academies. Those Academies are:

The National Academy of Practice in Dentistry
The National Academy of Practice in Medicine

[3] Reprinted from the *National Academies of Practice Membership Directory*, 1997–1998.

The National Academy of Practice in Nursing
The National Academy of Practice in Optometry
The National Academy of Practice in Osteopathic Medicine
The National Academy of Practice in Pharmacy
The National Academy of Practice in Podiatric Medicine
The National Academy of Practice in Psychology
The National Academy of Practice in Social Work
The National Academy of Practice in Veterinary Medicine

Distinguished Practitioners are chosen by their peers and are individuals who have spent a significant portion of their professional career as practitioners in the practice of healthcare delivery and its consumer; and who have been judged by the Academy to which they pertain to have made significant and enduring contributions to the advancement of professional practice. Nine Academies were created between the years of 1981 and 1985. In 1997, the 10th Academy, the National Academy in Pharmacy, was created by the NAP Council. Founding and charter members of the new Academy were inducted as Distinguished Practitioners in 1998. Each of the 10 Academies is limited to 100 active Distinguished Practitioners. Distinguished Practitioners who have retired may choose to become Emeritus Members, who do not count against the limit.

Interdisciplinary Health Policy Forums

To date, seven Interdisciplinary Health Policy Forums have been developed and implemented by the National Academies of Practice. They are as follows:

First Forum, September 1985. Explored for the first time the ways in which nine healthcare professions could work together to benefit both the patients and the providers.

Second Forum, September 1987. Developed interdisciplinary workshops to discuss such issues as Long-Term Care, Families of the Elderly, Environmental Changes, The Future of the Healthcare Professional in Cybernated Healthcare, Diagnostic Systems, and Design of the Future Healthcare Industry.

Third Forum, April 1990. Discussed Quality Healthcare for the Elderly and the unique contributions made by each of the nine healthcare professions. The Proceedings of this Forum were presented in a book entitled, *Aging in Good Health*, published by the Plenum Publishing Corp., New York, N.Y.

Fourth Forum, April 1992. "Healthy Children 2000: Obstacles and Opportunities." Interdisciplinary panels discussed Abuse, Better Health, Learning Disabilities, and Social Problems, all related to the health of children. Proceedings of this forum were published by the NAP and copies were distributed to selected members of Congress. Additional copies are available.

Fifth Forum, April 1994. "The Dollars and Sense of Healthcare." Concentrated on the proposed changes in healthcare financing and delivery that were then being considered by the Congress. Speakers included representatives from the Clinton Health Care Task Force; the American Medical Association; Richard Lamm, former governor of Colorado, who was chairman of the PEW Education Reform Program; and David Packard, retired chairman of the board and founder of the Hewlett-Packard Company.

Sixth Forum, April 1996. "Ethical Decision Making in Changing Healthcare Environment — An Interdisciplinary Approach." Presented speakers who represented healthcare providers, the managed healthcare industry (NYLCare of the Mid-Atlantic, Health Insurance Association of America, and Kaiser Permanente), and patients (AARP and Children's Defense Fund). Speakers and panels explored the many complicated issues involved in a balanced and constructive manner. Speakers included Reed Tuckson, M.D., President of Charles R. Drew University of Medicine and Science; Jeff D. Emerson, Chief Executive Officer of NYLCare of the Mid-Atlantic; John Banja, Ph.D., Coordinator of Clinical Ethical Education at Emory University; Elaine Larson, Ph.D., R.N., dean of the Georgetown University School of Nursing; and Stephen Sheingold, Director of Technology and Special Analysis Staff at the Health Care Financing Administration. As a result of this forum, a special NAP Task Force developed *Ethical Guidelines for Professional Care and Services in a Managed Care Environment*, which has been widely distributed and is available to the interested public.

Seventh Forum, April 1998. The topic was Interdisciplinary Creativity in Clinical Practice and Education. Over 30 papers and pos-
ters, all reporting on a current or planned approach to interdisciplinary healthcare in practice or education, were presented.

Membership Symposiums

To date, two Membership Symposiums concentrating primarily on
giving NAP members an opportunity to be involved in the policy-making
activities of the organization have been held. They are as follows:

First Symposium, March 1995. The NAP conducted a Membership Symposium at which members of all nine Academies separated into four workshops to discuss the Role of the NAP and Interdisciplinary Healthcare with Regards to Patients, the Marketplace, and New Technology and Economics. Task Forces were appointed to make recommendations to the NAP Council, many of
which have been implemented and others are currently under
consideration.

Second Symposium, March 1997. The NAP conducted a Membership
Symposium to consider how our then nine professions could work together to effect the USPHS *Put Prevention Into Practice Program*
(PPIP). This symposium, which was partially sponsored by the
Agency for Health Care Policy and Research of the USPHS, brought
together as speakers prevention experts from the USPHS, the U.S. Air
Force, the private sector, and the healthcare industry. Break-out
groups of the NAP members discussed the PPIP program and its
materials and how they could be used in an interdisciplinary program
of disease prevention and health promotion. A report of this
symposium has been prepared for distribution to the funding agency
and individuals involved in the USPHS PPIP program. It has been
distributed to all NAP members and is available to any interested
party.

Third Symposium, May 1999. The NAP will conduct a Membership
Symposium, re-named Forum on Interdisciplinary Management of
Chronic Health Conditions, featuring discussion of diabetes mellitus
and depression as case examples. Speakers will be drawn from within
the NAP membership, and from outside, with Dr. Frank Vinicor of

the CDC as keynote speaker. While some Academies will be represented by speakers, others will be represented by participants in the afternoon reactor panel. A "Best Practices" showcase poster session will highlight the end of the session.

Policy and Position Publications and Papers

In addition to the previously mentioned *Ethical Guidelines for Professional Care and Services in a Managed Care Environment* and the report of the Membership Symposium, "Put Prevention Into Practice: An Interdisciplinary Approach," the National Academies of Practice has developed position papers, which have been circulated to members of Congress, on the following subjects:

Neonatal and Early Care of Children
Whether There Should Be Mandatory AIDS Testing of Healthcare Professionals
The Use of Animals in Health Research
The Financing and Organization of National Healthcare
Healthcare Reform
The Ethics of Managed Care

Senator Daniel K. Inouye Award

Senator Daniel K. Inouye of Hawaii has been a longtime supporter and advocate of the National Academies of Practice in the U.S. Congress. An award in his name is given periodically to recognize individuals who have made significant and enduring contributions to health in the public interest. Past recipients of the Daniel K. Inouye Award were Representative Claude Pepper; C. Everett Koop, M.D.; and Senator Jay Rockefeller. In 1996, the Daniel K. Inouye Award was presented to Senator Nancy L. Kassebaum, who accepted the award at the Sixth Forum.

Other Awards

The following awards have been created but have not yet been presented.

Nicholas A. Cummings Group Recognition Award
Monetary award to recognize and support the continuation of an in-

terdisciplinary project/program that models and advances interdisciplinary practice and education involving at least four of the disciplines represented in the NAP. This award can be a self-nomination.

NAP Individual Recognition Award

Honorific award to an individual who, over a period of time, has been instrumental in recognizing and facilitating interdisciplinary practice and education involving four or more of the disciplines represented in the NAP. The award is to be nonmonetary. Candidates must be nominated by another individual or group and can be from any healthcare discipline.

The following are new awards, one has been presented and the other is to be presented.

The Interdisciplinary Creativity in Practice and Education

The award was presented at the April 1998 conference to Dr. Dewitt C. Baldwin. This nonfinancial award could have been presented to either a member or a nonmember of the NAP and was recommended after a selection process by the Member Relations Committee.

The Nicholas Andrew Cummings Annual Award

The award was to have been presented for the first time at the May 1999 meeting "to an individual NAP Distinguished Practitioner who is a member of one of the NAP Academies, and who had demonstrated outstanding or extraordinary contributions to the interprofessional health-care field." The first awardee was Dr. Cummings. After the first year, funding is to be supplied through a generous donation of stock from two contributors.

Structure and Management

The National Academies of Practice is governed by a Council that is made up of two representatives of each of the 10 Academies, and who are chosen by the members of those Academies, and five officers elected by the Council. The Council meets three times a year. The current Executive Director is Constance R. Row, FACHE, Row Associates, LLC. The NAP office address is P.O. Box 1037, Edgewood, MD 20140. A quarterly journal was to be launched in the winter of 1999. An Internet home page has also been established at http://home.att.net/ ~ n.a.p/. The NAP is funded primarily by membership dues and donations. Corporate sponsorship of events, activities, and publications and Foundation funding is actively solicited. The NAP has been designated a 501(c)(3) corporation by the Internal Revenue Service, effective April 1987, with EID number 52-1246763 and holds tax-exempt certificate number 8399-0129852-001, issued by the District of Columbia, May 5, 1988.

Dated December 1998

{ 7 }

FOUNDATION FOR
BEHAVIORAL HEALTH:
CREATING A HOME FOR THE HAWAII PROJECT

ACCORDING TO PARKINSON'S LAW, the best way to prevent research is to build a research building. Amusing as this might be, this is a story of how two separate research institutes, both the indigenous homes of the Hawaii Project, would have prevented the successful promulgation of that project were not a third research institute created specifically to provide a legitimate home for the endeavor. That home was the Foundation for Behavioral Health, Inc. (FBH), formerly a California nonprofit corporation also know as the Biodyne Institute, and now a part of The Nicholas & Dorothy Cummings Foundation, Inc. (as described in a subsequent section).

The Biodyne Institute was founded in San Francisco in 1976 as a non-incorporated, private education and research company. It conducted collateral research with the mental health services of Kaiser Permanente in San Francisco, and also performed research that could not be conducted at Kaiser Permanente because the particular behavioral intervention was not a covered benefit of the Kaiser Health Plan. An example of the former was research on a large number of panic, anxiety, phobia, and agoraphobia patients in group programs that augmented in the community sector the research being conducted at Kaiser Permanente. An example of the latter was the research on biofeedback that could not be conducted at Kaiser Permanente because that intervention was not yet a generally covered benefit in all health plans. During those years, I was very active in defining data-driven protocols on a wide range of behavioral interventions, a process that received wide-scale verification in the Hawaii Project. The predecessor to FBH during the years 1976 to 1983 was the Biodyne Institute, which was privately financed and did not receive any public funds.

THE PALO ALTO EXPERIENCE

Late in 1978, I became the executive director of the Mental Research Institute in Palo Alto, California, a nationally recognized group of mental health professionals that was also known as the Palo Alto Group. The original Palo Alto Group, which was actually in Menlo Park and never in Palo Alto, was founded by Gregory Bateson, the divorced husband of Margaret Mead, shortly after World War II. For reasons he did not make clear, he disbanded it in the mid-1950s, and a second Palo Alto Group was formed by a Bateson psychiatrist associate, Don Jackson, this time actually in Palo Alto. A number of those associated with the first Palo Alto Group joined Dr. Jackson, while others remained closely or distantly related. Bateson himself never joined the Palo Alto Group, which, along with Dr. Jackson, included Richard Fish, Jules Riskin, John Bell, Arthur Bodin, Paul Watzlawick, Arthur Hardy, and John Weakland. More distantly associated were Jay Haley, Virginia Satir, and Murry Bowen. Although Gregory Bateson never formally joined the group, his influence was ever present. Possibly because of Bateson's objections, the so-called second Palo Alto Group formally named itself the Mental Research Institute (MRI) and occupied a two-story, one-block-long building donated by a benefactor. Following Dr. Jackson's untimely death just a few years after the MRI was established, the office of executive director was occupied first by John Bell, a psychologist and a member of both Palo Alto Groups, and then Jules Riskin, a psychiatrist who also was an original insider. I became the fourth executive director in MRI's 20-year-plus history.

A prime reason for accepting the offer from the MRI was that I was moving toward the extensive demonstration project that was originally planned for San Francisco, but was finally conducted in Hawaii. I was exploring federal funding and needed a bona fide research home, something the MRI could provide. As executive director, I could guide the internal process within the MRI, an attractive prospect, indeed. In accepting the position, I informed the MRI board of directors and faculty that should I join them, it would be my intention to base the anticipated research project there. There not only was unanimous agreement, but also widespread enthusiasm, especially since they were federally approved for a 75% research overhead (i.e., indirect cost rate). I accepted the position, and began spending three 12-hour days per week in Palo Alto. My first surprise was that only a limited amount of empirical research was being conducted there, as the MRI was more like a think tank.

The institute had several advantages, not the least of which was an international reputation and an enviable track record in obtaining grants. However, in the words of Dr. Watzlawick, who is still MRI's star, "The prestige of the MRI is directly proportional to its distance from Palo Alto." It housed one of the earliest brief therapy clinics in the nation, which was still flourishing, and was the home for the two NIMH-funded Soteria Projects, community living as alternatives to the hospitalization of young schizophrenics. As one of two pioneers (with the Ackerman Institute in New York) of family therapy, as well as innovations of its own, such as the concepts of the "schizophrenogenic parent" (from Bateson) and the "double bind," the MRI had mounted a significant challenge to the psychoanalytic dominance of the period. On the negative side, I had heard vague rumors of the parochialism of the MRI, but I had so focused on its positives that I had left myself totally unprepared for its insularity.

It reflected a strict orthodoxy that was both enforced and contradicted. On the enforcement side, the staff was perceived as loyal and rewarded for openly ridiculing insight, individual (rather than family) therapy, both psychodynamics and behaviorism, and other conventional mental health wisdom of the time. This would have been less curious were it not for the contradictions. Most psychotherapy conducted at the MRI was individual, not family, therapy. Furthermore, I heard more armchair psychoanalyzing at the MRI than I had during my psychoanalytic training, where it was least expected, but nonetheless unfortunate.

One of the most distasteful aspects of the MRI was the stranglehold maintained by its founding faculty, all of which regarded themselves as stars. Young people came to the MRI with hope, and they soon left, realizing there were no opportunities beyond subordinate roles, or they stayed, and thus allowed themselves to be permanently stifled by the older primadonnas. I created a new governance structure, bringing new blood into the decision-making process, but the Old Guard psychologically retained its preeminence and the system reverted quickly to the status quo after my departure. My warnings, now coming true, were that MRI would fade in its own renown and eventually be forgotten and superseded. During its heyday it was the most successful convener of brief therapy conferences in the world, drawing thousands to its biennial offerings. As of this writing, a number of the stars have died or retired, and few young people in the field today even recognize its name.

Shortly after I arrived, it became painfully apparent to me that the two Soteria Projects were not appreciated, but only tolerated because they brought a surprising 75% federally funded overhead to the MRI. This high level of overhead reflected the fact that Soteria represented a favorite NIMH thrust, at least until Jerry Klerman became the director of the Alcohol, Drug Abuse and Mental Health Agency (ADAMHA) and phased out psychosocial grants. The concept of community living for schizophrenics, no matter how laudable, or how favored in Washington, did not strictly fit into the cult of Don Jackson and the orthodox tenets that were so characteristic of the MRI. I could not help but wonder why I, an outsider, was brought in to run the place. In time, it became obvious to me that I was not expected to really manage the MRI, but to fulfill certain circumscribed goals. One was to make the MRI financially solvent for the first time, as it consistently ran deficit budgets. This I readily accomplished, leaving it after three years with a surplus of cash, as well as helping the MRI to launch its highly profitable biennial European conferences. The second unspoken assignment was far more complex.

Without anyone ever stating it openly, it became apparent that, as an outsider who was uninfected with the cult of Don Jackson, I was to resolve it. Dr. Jackson's untimely death was very early in the founding of the MRI. Thus, his followers were abruptly abandoned by him at the height of their adulation, and were curtailed by their emotional conflicts from evolving beyond him. One is reminded of the plight of Plato, whose mentor, Socrates, drank the hemlock early in Plato's association with him. As a result, Plato had difficulty going beyond where Socrates had taken his philosophical thinking. On the other hand, Plato lived a long life, granting Aristotle many years of tutelage under him. As a result, Aristotle was able to carry his thinking far beyond the horizons that limited his mentor. I do not know whether Plato felt guilty because he was unable to prevent Socrates' death, but this was an all-consuming, but strongly denied, emotion among Dr. Jackson's followers. When I first met Dr. Jackson, he was into a life of partying, with heavy drinking, flagrant womanizing, and drug abuse. His devotees anger appreciably at any suggestion that he committed suicide, even though such is not uncommon in a hedonistic lifestyle that is out of control. They prefer to believe that he suffered an overdose of antidepressant medication. In either event, a series of individual interviews with the staff convinced me that there was a collective feeling of guilt because, as mental health professionals, they were not able to foresee and forestall it. My status as an outsider permitted them to discuss their thoughts and feelings with me, with all but one confiding, "Please don't tell my colleagues, but Don told me privately that I was his favorite. I promised him I would never tell the others." These reports came from the board members, who were equally devoted to Dr. Jackson, as well as from the faculty.

The disdain of the MRI for the two Soteria houses was not limited to those projects. Not long after I began reporting, in the weekly staff meetings, my progress toward obtaining a federal grant for the then-planned San Francisco (rather than Hawaii, where it eventually took place) Medicaid project, I began to incur hostility. As I convened each meeting, Dr. Riskin, the just-retired executive director, would interject, "I have an agenda item I would like to make the first one for today. How do we keep the MRI from becoming like General Motors?" This was a not-so-veiled reference to the concern among many of the leaders that my project would catapult the MRI far beyond the small, rinky-dink organization it had chosen to remain. My reply was always the same: "Jules, there is not really much danger of that, is there?" Then I would merely continue with the previously announced agenda. This dialog was repeated every week for well over a year, convincing me that the MRI would never be a hospitable home for my project.

At about this time, the leaders of the Soteria Project, Alma Menn, a social worker, and Luis Fernandez, a psychologist, became disenchanted with the short shrift they were getting from the MRI. They decided to form a separate research organization, taking their grants with them, and they needed my help. They proposed that I be chair of the new organization, and that I bring my own project, if and when it happened, with me. I agreed, after considerable discussion.

THE IPI EXPERIENCE: AN MRI REDUX

The new organization was incorporated in California in 1981 as the Institute for Psychosocial Interaction (IPI) with Ms. Menn choosing the name and bringing the Soteria grants with her by permission of the NIMH. The MRI was required to approve the transfer of funds to IPI, and the readiness with which it signed off underscored the relief the members must have experienced at having been separated from this less than Jacksonian concept. I resigned from my position at the MRI after agreeing to stay on until a new executive director was chosen. It took almost a year before Carlos Sluzki was hired to replace me, but I kept my promise and stuck it out. I assumed the chair of the board of IPI concurrently with my winding down my affairs at the MRI. David Rosenhan, professor of psychology and law at Stanford, joined our board of directors, along with a psychiatrist and a judge who were strong supporters of Soteria and had been friends of Alma Menn for a number of years. The name Soteria comes from the Greek word for deliverance, with the implication that young schizophrenics were being delivered from a lifetime of off-and-on hospitalization through assisted community living. It was also hoped that IPI not only would provide a more friendly home for the Soteria Project, but also would become a hospitable home for the proposed Biodyne Medicaid Project.

In the beginning, all seemed to go exceptionally well, but it was not long before it became apparent that IPI was going to treat the Biodyne Project with the same disinterest that the MRI had previously accorded the Soteria Project. Monthly board meetings were devoted solely to matters concerning Soteria, and just before the attendees would get ready to disperse, the Biodyne Project would be accorded a begrudging 15 or 20 minutes. Paramount was the inability of Alma Menn to compile the Soteria research findings after almost a decade, and the NIMH had grown increasingly impatient over the last two years. Eventually, Loren Moser, the staff officer sponsoring the Soteria grants at NIMH, wrote an unprecedented letter accusing Ms. Menn of incompetence, and indicating his conclusion that she would never file the report.

In the meantime, it had become apparent that Hawaii, not San Francisco, was going to be the site of the Biodyne Project. Dr. Herbert Dorken, who was to become my co-principal investigator, and I had dogged this matter for two years without much help from IPI, and, in desperation, I brought several new persons to the board to bring some semblance of competence to IPI. Among these were Albert and Anita Waxman, the founders of Diasonics, the first manufacturer of magnetic resonance imagery (also known as MRI), and Bill and Susan Berkan, the owners of Berkan Farms, which supplied over 95% of the game birds for the nation's restaurants. The Biodyne Project was now funded, and the four new business-oriented directors and I were convinced that we would have to get out of IPI if the Biodyne Project were to succeed where Soteria was floundering. Dr. Rosenhan was convinced that the incompetence lay with

Dr. Fernandez, and he was unwilling to see that it extended also to the principal investigator, herself. In fact, Dr. Waxman, a physicist and engineer, referred to Ms. Menn as incompetence personified. He was particularly concerned that the Biodyne Project would suffer the same fate toward which Soteria was heading: the cancellation of the project by the federal government. The name IPI had garnered a very poor reputation in Washington by this time. As much as we wanted to break away from IPI, we faced a formidable hurdle. The Health Care Financing Administration (HCFA) had contracted the Hawaii Medicaid Project with IPI, as I had arranged. If the funds were to be transferred to another research entity, IPI would have to agree in writing. We feared that this was highly unlikely, as IPI would want to retain the Biodyne overhead funds to help rescue the Soteria Houses after the inevitable cutoff of federal funding.

THE FOUNDATION FOR BEHAVIORAL HEALTH

In spite of our fears, the five of us were determined to create our own research home, after which we would deal with the problem of transferring the Hawaii Project funds, which totaled more than $8 million. I converted the structure of the Biodyne Institute into a new entity and incorporated it as the Foundation for Behavioral Health (FBH), doing business as (d.b.a.) the Biodyne Institute. With the help of my savvy business associates, we obtained IRS 501(c)(3) status in record time. We hired a staff and were ready to assume the now very active Hawaii Project. All that remained was getting our funds out of IPI.

I developed a strategy, which was to convince Dr. Fernandez that Soteria's days were numbered, and that his best opportunity to continue his employment as assistant project director was to come to FBH. It was not difficult to persuade him of the impending cutoff of Soteria funds, and he accepted my offer. He, in turn, neutralized the surviving members of the IPI board, convincing them they would be free to rescue the Soteria House if unencumbered with the Biodyne Project. From his long friendship with Ms. Menn, he realized that any involvement with a project as complex as that in Hawaii was frightening for one with her limited competence, and she would be eager to be free of it. Further, she had become annoyed by my complaints that IPI was neglecting the Hawaii Project, and signing off on the transfer of funds would relieve her of my presence. The IPI board unanimously approved the transfer, which then received the rapid concurrence of HCFA. We now had our own research institute, funded with $8 million of combined federal and Hawaii state funds, and a 28% overhead rate for the nearly $6 million of the $8 million that was federal money.

In the agreement to sign off on the grant, there was the issue of IPI's commingling of the Soteria and Biodyne overhead funds. It was agreed that Uhlenberg and Associates, the San Jose accounting firm that had served IPI, as well as the MRI before it, would conduct an audit and inform IPI and FBH of how much the latter owed the former. To be on the safe side, we commissioned our own audit, which informed us that because of the sloppy bookkeeping on the part of IPI, an exact figure could not be determined. The accountants stated that the best estimates were a low of $100,000 and a high of $125,000. We were willing to pay the higher figure, but Uhlenberg determined that FBH owed IPI $28,000. We protested that the figure seemed low, but in response to IPI's own accountants' insisting on its accuracy, we issued a check that IPI did not cash during the next 12 months, leaving us to wonder what was going on.

Later it became apparent that IPI had decided that it had made a mistake in approving the transfer of our grant. It had also heard rumors that we were planning to launch a proprietary company, using the findings of the Hawaii Project, since new federal legislation was encouraging the translation to the private sector of knowledge gained through federally funded research. Almost one year after breaking free of IPI, we launched American Biodyne. Within two months after our achieving a substantial contract and revenue stream, IPI filed a RICO (racketeer-influenced corrupt organization) lawsuit for $2 million plus triple punitive damages as allowed by RICO. That legislation was enacted by the Congress specifically to aid law enforcement in combating the mafia and other racketeers, and its attempted application against both FBH and American Biodyne was sour grapes and the result of bad legal advice. The suit alleged that we had launched a for-profit company with funds "stolen" from IPI, and that IPI was entitled to compensation, punitive damages, and ownership in American Biodyne. The rapidity with which the suit was filed suggested that the paperwork had been prepared in advance of the successful launching of American Biodyne.

It must be noted here that some of the bitterness stemmed from the fact that several months before the filing of the lawsuit, I had to fire Dr. Fernandez. Behind the scenes, he was fueling the anger of Ms. Menn, whose own federal funding of IPI and Soteria was now history. My concern with the poor performance of Dr. Fernandez was based on a series of errors that were of serious proportions. While still on the payroll of

IPI, once the final contract application to HCFA was completed and signed by all parties, he left Honolulu for the mainland before the application was sent to Washington. Consequently, it was never sent and we missed the deadline, necessitating a wait of several months before we could reapply. In the meantime, a high ranking official referred to us in Senator Inouye's office as "those turkeys," a well-deserved appellation. Dr. Fernandez blamed an official with the state of Hawaii, but it was his responsibility to shepherd the contract to its destination. There were a number of other mistakes about which IPI was lax in spite of Dr. Rosenhan's repeated complaints. Once on the FBH payroll, his lack of performance was not tolerated, as it had been by the IPI board of directors.

We denied the allegations of the IPI lawsuit, and we reiterated our original contention that FBH owed IPI more than the $28,000 as determined by IPI's own accountants. We repeated our offer of $125,000, but IPI refused, while it petitioned the California Attorney General to intervene in a case the IPI attorneys described in court as "thievery." From the beginning, we were subjected to bullying and intimidation by a firm of particularly obnoxious and aggressive plaintiffs' attorneys. In our meetings with them, we had to endure rudeness and clouds of heavy smoke billowing from their cigars. It was particularly distasteful when I was subjected to three days of depositions. When I was informed that this was only the beginning, with the plaintiff's attorney planning 14 to 15 days, I balked and refused to honor the subpoena for further deposition. Joanne Condos, the late Assistant Attorney General, had become convinced that the suit was without merit and refused to entertain any of the plaintiffs' requests. Things dragged on for over three years, with the consumption during that time of at least three boxes of cigars by the plaintiffs' attorneys in our presence, when it became apparent to the plaintiffs that their case was going nowhere. Alma Menn had mortgaged her house to finance the suit, ostensibly believing she would recover the money severalfold. Now broke, and reputedly owing their attorneys over $100,000 in addition, they were ready to settle. We agreed to arbitration before the county bar association and went into the hearing reiterating our offer of $125,000, and not one cent more. The plaintiffs accepted, and the county bar association concurred.

Both the Hawaii Project and American Biodyne succeeded, and these events are described in other sections and in the research literature. Under the inhospitable and inefficient original research homes, the Hawaii Project might well have floundered. On the other hand, the FBH management efficiencies enabled the original funding to extend the project two additional years of follow-up beyond the original contract span. Of primary importance is that without the Foundation for Behavioral Health, the Hawaii Project might never have been completed and American Biodyne might never have been launched. We had both proved and defied Parkinson's Law.

APPENDIX 7A

THE VICISSITUDES OF OUTCOMES RESEARCH ON MANAGED BEHAVIORAL HEALTHCARE WITH THE STATE AND FEDERAL GOVERNMENTS AS PARTNERS[1]

Nicholas A. Cummings, Ph.D., and Herbert Dorken, Ph.D.[2]

Contracting with a state government to deliver healthcare services can be very risky at best, since a state legislature or a new and incoming administration can alter the rules of the game at any time in spite of contractual obligations. True, one has legal recourse, a lengthy and expensive alternative against a state government, which tars the litigating contractor with the onerous reputation of having sued one's client. The contractor then must live with a kind of "marketing leprosy," which leads to a shunning by all potential contractees, both public and private.

The healthcare industry's history of contracting with state governments is replete with horror stories, but there are just as many, if not more, success stories. It is helpful to expect, and be prepared for, anything, and to this need to be wary, a brief history of the HCFA-Hawaii Biodyne Project is dedicated.

---

[1] Reprinted by permission from Cummings, N. A., & Dorken, H. (1990). The vicissitudes of outcomes research on managed behavioral healthcare with the state and federal governments as partners. In N. A. Cummings, H. Dorken, M. S. Pallak, & C. Henke, *Medicaid, managed behavioral health and implications for public policy.* Healthcare Utilization Cost Series, Vol. 2 (pp. 24–29). San Francisco: Foundation for Behavioral Health.

[2] Dr. Cummings and Dr. Dorken were principal investigator and co-principal investigator, respectively, of the HCFA-Hawaii Medicaid Project, a seven-year outcomes research study in which the Foundation for Behavioral Health was the subcontractor.

With enactment of Titles XVIII and XIX of the Social Security Act, known as Medicare and Medicaid, the federal government became the major player in the healthcare industry in America. Added to the Federal Employees Health Benefits Program (FEHBP) and CHAMPUS, this is still only a fraction of what is expected of federal involvement if and when universal healthcare is enacted. The Clinton Administration has signaled it favors "managed competition," with decisions based on outcomes research. The difficulties of creating a delivery system and then adequately measuring its efficacy and efficiency are many under the best environment, but in the essentially political as opposed to clinical and scientific climates, the obstacles can severely hamper, obscure, or even destroy the endeavor.

The authors, over a seven-year period, conducted a successful outcomes research project in medical offset with Medicaid. They concluded, however, that doing field research on healthcare under the dual auspices of both state and federal governments is a nightmare in which repeated but unpredictable political problems continually threaten the scientific validity and clinical efficacy of the delivery system. Three times, the project found itself on the very brink of extinction, while several other times, political considerations could have eliminated the scientific basis of the research. We offer these experiences not in a hypercritical sense, but as case studies of what researchers must expect. Although Murphy's Law would predict that anything that can go wrong will, our experience led us to subscribe to O'Reilly's Law, which states that Murphy was an optimist! It is hoped that the problems encountered, presented here in a series of problem-solving case studies, will alert future researchers to the importance of adding a political problem-solving awareness to their clinical and scientific dimensions, while negotiating maximum independence for the conduct of their research.

History of the Project

The HCFA-Hawaii Medicaid Project, known also as the "Biodyne Medicaid Project" from the clinical methodology that was used, was funded September 30, 1983. Even the approval of the contract had strong political overtones. Because the perception of some of the Congressional leaders that the Health Care Financing Administration was lagging in its mission of conducting innovative demonstration projects in Medicaid, the Congress mandated in 1981 that HCFA conduct a medical offset study. In eventually complying in 1983 after more pressure from Capitol Hill,

HCFA decided to take advantage of monies remaining from FYI 1982: hence the award was dated September 30, 1983, which constituted the last day of the federal government's previous fiscal year. But no one bothered to inform the investigators, who learned that the contract had been awarded when they received a letter from HCFA in December asking why the first quarterly progress report covering the activities of the project to September 30 (one day to be exact) had not been received.

The real history of this project began a number of years before 1983, as follows:

Dropping Dead in California

During the last two years of the second term of then Governor Ronald Reagan's administration, the authors tentatively worked out an arrangement in which HCFA would award a contract to the State of California, which would then subcontract with the Foundation for Behavioral Health. Three successive Directors of the Department of Health Services supported the conduct of the research. It would be a medical offset study conducted in San Francisco with the entire welfare population residing there. Half of the study population would be randomly assigned to the control group and receive mental health and chemical dependency services under the existing Medicaid system, known in California as MediCal. The other half, designated the experimental group, would receive these services under what is now known as a managed care delivery system. Before the contract could be concluded, California elected Governor Jerry Brown to succeed Governor Reagan. The new administration put the MediCal fiscal intermediary function out to bid and granted it to the lowest bidder, a fledgling company with little or no prior experience. MediCal was plunged into a shambles for more than two years while the then unknown head of this new company, Ross Perot, worked out the glitches in his computerized system and went on to unprecedented success. In the meantime, providers were not being paid for many months at a time and the State could no longer randomly assign the San Francisco welfare population to control and experimental groups while guaranteeing to keep families intact. After several years, with travel to Sacramento and Washington, the authors concluded their project in California before it could be born.

Dropping Dead in Hawaii

Several years later, the principal investigator was contacted by Senator Daniel Inouye's office suggesting that the project be revived and conducted in Hawaii. Preliminary investigation indicated that there were advantages to Hawaii over California — Hawaii was the only state to have state-sponsored universal healthcare. Further, the Medicaid psychotherapy benefit was very liberal. It provided for 52 sessions annually, easily renewable for up to another 52 each year with merely a letter of justification from the practitioner, and the regulations recognized both psychologists and psychiatrists for these services. Risen from the ashes! Thus, the study would address the medical offset created by psychotherapy versus no psychotherapy, but also traditional fee-for-service psychotherapy versus targeted, focused interventions in a managed-care environment. Unfortunately, by that time, there was a new administration in HCFA, and there was no longer the desire to pursue a project that was important to a previous HCFA administrator. This seeming impasse was broken when the Congress literally mandated the project.

Once the project was revived within HCFA, the authors and their colleagues spent several weeks in Honolulu jointly working out the detailed proposal with the State of Hawaii. This required not simply approval by the state Medicaid agency, but approval with appropriation by the Hawaii legislative and, in particular, the health committees of both houses. When this was completed, and only the formal signatures of the governor and the director of the Department of Health and Housing had to be obtained, the authors confidently returned to the mainland two weeks before the November 1, 1981, filing deadline. It must be remembered that the State was the actual contractor, and it was the entity that had to submit the proposal to the federal government. The research would be federally supported, but the cost of the clinical services involved would be carried by the usual federal/state Medicaid matching funds. The Foundation would be the subcontractor to the state. It was not until November 9, when the administrator of HCFA called the senior author, that it was ascertained that the State of Hawaii had failed to file the proposal. It was later learned that the state official responsible for doing so had, instead, been admitted to a detoxification unit at a hospital, suffering from acute alcoholic toxicity. He apparently began drinking heavily immediately after we had left for the mainland. Although this official was subsequently fired for a number of other reasons, the proposal had to be delayed until the new filing date one year later.

The next year, the researchers had learned their lesson. Once the State had reapproved the application, they personally hand delivered the proposal to HCFA prior to the November 1, 1982 deadline. The contract when awarded in 1983, called for six months start-up in which a managed behavioral healthcare delivery system would be officed at a central point to serve the island of Oahu. Two small satellite offices were added later. The services were delivered in a staff-model setting with psychologists providing the psychotherapy and psychiatrists performing medication management, hospitalization, and treatment of the organic conditions. At that time, social workers were not licensed in Hawaii and were ineligible to provide Medicaid services. Of the multicultural Hawaii licensed professional staff of 10, only four were Caucasians.

Dropping Dead in Washington, D.C.

The clinical delivery system, which commenced on a full scale on July 1, 1984, had been in its fourth month when David Stockman, Director of the Office of Management and Budget (OMB), froze funds on all HCFA "waivered projects." There were a number of demonstration projects throughout the country that required a waiver of one or another of the Medicaid regulations as part of the demonstration. In our case, there were three important waivers: statewideness (Oahu only), psychologists (not medical) direction of the clinic, and restriction of services to only the experimental group. With $110,000 per month in payroll, rent, and other expenses, the principal investigators were faced with having to shut down the project. There was a disagreement between the HCFA and the OMB as to jurisdiction, and although it was a political squabble in Washington, the effects on our research were potentially devastating.

It was apparent from the nature of our delivery system, that if shut down, it could not be revived. The senior author risked his life savings for a period of five months, meeting the expenses of the project with no assurance the money would be reimbursed. In the meantime, the researchers made persistent appeals in Washington and the freeze on this project was lifted retroactively, and several months before any of the other frozen waivered project findings were released. Even so, staff morale and volume of professional activity suffered.

The Mainland Hippy Law

Just prior to the beginning of the project, Hawaii passed legislation requiring every able-bodied person to work as a condition of qualifying for public assistance. The only exception was to be certified as mentally disabled. Although not directly stated in the legislation, the acknowledged target of the new work force law was to discourage young people from the mainland who were "hanging out" on the Islands and abusing the welfare system. This "mainland hippy law," as it was generally known, had the effect of substantially reducing the number of persons qualifying for Medicaid. By significantly reducing the population of the study, the law forced a change in our experimental design. The problem was met by randomly dividing the study population into one-third control and two-thirds experimental groups rather than the equal random assignment originally planned.

But this law had another effect that was more difficult to solve. Because the exception to having to work was a mental disability certification, some practitioners generated a caseload of private patients whom they had certified. Certification required treatment, however, and so some mental health practitioners would not certify the person as mentally disabled unless they agreed to regular sessions with presigned vouchers. The incentives were all in the wrong direction: the patients sought to perpetuate their cash benefit, while the practitioner profited by keeping the patient in protracted, although fruitless, "treatment." Thus a segment of the study population was discouraged from actively entering the study population, while at the same time their medical costs remained high.

This problem was solved in a manner that underscores the thesis of this narrative: researchers need to add a political awareness to their clinical and scientific dimensions. The coprincipal investigator is a registered lobbyist with considerable political experience. He authored, and had introduced and passed in the third legislative session, a bill that forbade the practitioner who was certifying the person as mentally disabled from treating that person, and vice versa. The bill was passed by the legislature three years in a row, but vetoed by the governor for the first two years. His administration alleged that since psychologists could also certify under the bill costs would be doubled. On the contrary, once enacted, the problem vanished overnight and with the conflict of interest removed, state welfare costs (public assistance and Medicaid) were significantly reduced, and progressively so over the three years of our follow-up.

The Welfare Rights Activists

When the Biodyne Center opened a satellite center in an area predominately populated by persons on welfare, the welfare rights groups misunderstood the intent of the project, picketed the satellite, and threatened to close it down. Medical offset, which seeks to address emotional distress and thereby reduce somaticizing of stress into bodily symptoms, will reduce medical costs.

Emotional well-being, which then leads to a physical well-being, often results in persons becoming employable once again. This feature was misinterpreted as a surreptitious way of denying welfare rights to recipients.

It took a considerable number of meetings with the protesters before the value and meaning of the project were understood and accepted. But because Hawaiians tend to be suspicious of mainlanders, especially those from California, all negotiations were conducted with the local resident clinical staff.

Freedom of Choice

The University of Hawaii has its own medical school, which results in a greater number of physicians practicing in the state than would normally be extant. The exception is the outer islands, but Oahu (Honolulu) has more physicians than needed. Consequently, practitioners rely heavily on government programs to augment their incomes. Because there would be considerable anger if the Biodyne program became an exclusive provider for the experimental group, the state made the decision, and HCFA concurred, that there would be no waiver authorizing an exclusive provider design. Ensuring patient freedom of choice was essentially a political decision that placated local providers. The practitioners were confident that given a choice between them and a staff model managed-care system, the patient would invariably choose the private practitioner since Medicaid paid the fee, anyway. That the opposite proved to be true became a point of conflict later in the demonstration project when the project was viewed as a Trojan horse. Nonetheless, the freedom-of-choice condition was converted to a positive situation by redesigning the study to compare not only the conditions of no therapy, fee-for-service therapy, and targeted therapy, but also the dual condition of receiving both fee-for-service and targeted therapies.

However, guaranteed freedom-of-choice resulted in more serious problems. Severe somatizers would resort to "doctor shopping," seeking out the mental health practitioner who would not address their somatization. One such somatizer had 347 physician visits in one year, certainly a record, but not unique in a population convinced that emotional stress was a physical disease. They would seek out psychiatrists and psychologists who would not challenge this notion or question their out-of-control medical visits.

The State on federal waiver initiated a "lock-up" program for these overutilizers of medical services, requiring that they see but one physician, who had the sole authority to deny any other medical visits, or refer as needed. These high users, who would have been ideal for the project, were locked out. Despite three years of negotiation, the State could never resolve this impasse and make these patients available to the study, even though its primary purpose was the reduction of healthcare costs and the State was the sponsor of the research. Two components of one bureaucracy, we learned, have no need to be consistent.

Drug Diversions

Another form of "doctor shopping" was by addicts who sought practitioners, including dentists, who would supply their addictions. Experience has taught us that this is not rare, and it usually involves an impaired physician whose own addiction results in overly sympathizing with the addict's need. What shocked and surprised the experimenters was the existence of a not-so-rare practice of securing so many prescriptions that these patients could engage profitably in fraudulent drug diversion.

At the time of this project, on most occasions, Valium had little value as a street drug. The exception was when the supply of heroin dried up on the street, heroin addicts would tide themselves over by consuming large quantities of Valium. At such times, the price of Valium on the street went up tenfold. Street-wise Medicaid recipients would receive regular prescriptions of Valium from the psychiatrists, hoard the drug, and sell it when heroin became scarce. Of course, there were brief psychotherapy visits associated with the prescription in a transaction that sometimes took less than 10 minutes.

There were other methods of drug diversion as well, involving a number of controlled substances, leading the experimenters to conclude that drug diversion is a problem of considerable proportion. The fraud uncovered put the project on the horns of a dilemma. On the one hand was the medical responsibility to report fraud; on the other was the ethical and legal commitment to patient confidentiality. The problem was resolved, but the sensitivity of the issue precludes our disclosure. We did, however, seek funding from both the National Institute of Drug Abuse and the National Institute of Alcoholism and Alcohol Abuse. Both institutes were only interested in one abuse, alcohol or drugs, hewing to a jurisdictional cleavage while on the street these patients abused both. They also wanted clean experimental designs, not real-life field research addressing problems instead of hypothetical propositions. After several applications, we were referred to the Department of Justice, but time had run out.

Methadone Is Forever

At the time of this project, the regulations for federally licensed methadone centers required that the addict be titrated off of methadone after one successful year without heroin. This was flagrantly not being enforced, as we saw patients who had been taking methadone under the program for several years, and some for more than 10 years. They had grown tired of the way of life and wanted to be chemically free. One man, a patient at the methadone center for over 10 years, wanted to return to the mainland to see his father before the latter, who was seriously ill, died, but he wanted to do so drug-free. We were not surprised that this regulation was being flaunted, but we were startled that patients were discouraged and even threatened when they indicated they wanted to be titrated off methadone. Our own efforts to work with the methadone center were of no avail, and it appeared that we had come up against a self-perpetuating bureaucracy.

We never were able to resolve this impasse. Appeals to the federal government in Washington were stalled in red tape. The few brave individuals who worked with our addiction program and were successful in achieving drug-free lives had to "cold turkey" off methadone, as the methadone center made good its threat to drop them from the program.

Me Too!

The state social case workers who saw alcoholic patients were also reluctant to relinquish their patients even though their case assignments were overloaded. Many patients regarded this overworked and self-perpetuating bureaucracy as ineffective, and came to the Biodyne addictive program once they were informed of their eligibility by virtue of their being in the experimental group. The state social workers not only discouraged such a migration, but held the power of welfare eligibility over the patients' heads. And the agency administration, which was the research grant recipient, never requested its casework staff to cooperate with its own project.

As a way of encouraging these social workers to refer their alcoholic patients to the Biodyne centers, we offered them a free stress-management program for themselves if they referred 10 or more patients. State social workers must be under a great deal of stress, for the results were positive and instantaneous. However, this offer had to be withdrawn when the Hawaii Attorney General's office ruled that this was tantamount to bribing a state employee. The referrals stopped immediately, and we never found another solution. As a result of the attitudes of this bureau, as well as the methadone center, addicts were underrepresented in our research.

Our Vietnam

By design, and for reason of the language barriers, the recently arrived Southeast Asian refugee community was excluded from the study. This is a legitimate decision in a research project, but one local physician whose practice had a large portion of the Vietnamese community began to attack the project in the press. We were accused of neglecting the largest Southeast Asian community on Oahu, namely, the recently arrived Vietnamese, and the fact that this was a research project was lost sight of as we were continuously battered in the press. We knew the only solution was to find a Vietnamese-speaking psychotherapist. But it would have to be either a Ph.D. or M.D. as were our other psychotherapists, a very unlikely event, indeed. To do otherwise would merely court from this outspoken physician the accusation that our Vietnamese patients were receiving substandard care.

Almost miraculously, we located a Ph.D.-level, clinical psychologist in Maryland fluent in the language and who knew the culture and we arranged for her to relocate to Honolulu almost immediately. We contacted the physician who had created so much bad publicity in the press and encouraged him to refer this vast unmet need he had described to reporters. Then we braced ourselves for the onslaught of Vietnamese-speaking patients. In two years, this physician did not refer a single patient. It became obvious that he was grandstanding, basking in his being characterized in the press as a champion of the Vietnamese minority. It was also apparent he had a hungry practice and he was not about to risk losing any patients. Over the next years of the project, we did see a number of Vietnamese-speaking patients, but we literally had to outreach them by house calls by our newly recruited psychologist.

The Witch Hunt

As it became increasingly apparent that the project was succeeding, the practitioner community became more and more vicious in its attacks. Allegations were made before a legislative committee that the researchers had falsified data. When proof was demanded, the allegations evaporated. Professionals who are committed to ethical standards of patient confidentiality were exploiting patients by coaching them to write letters to state legislators and Hawaii's Congressional delegation in Washington. This is the essence of doing business with government: public officials are responsible to their constituents, right or wrong. An inordinate amount of time was expended in refuting false allegations, educating public officials, and working with the Hawaii Medical Services Association (HMSA), the Blue-Shield Affiliate, which was the fiscal intermediary in the Medicaid program. Throughout the project, HMSA maintained an aura of professionalism, neutrality, and reason. Eventually, the loud and vicious attacks, some by local psychologists, subsided, but the innuendo, the passive resistance, and the subtle sabotage never stopped.

Probably the most dramatic moment came when precisely at 9:00 one morning, an investigative television reporter arrived with her camera crew. She had received strong comments from a number of practitioners that the project was harming patients, and she came to investigate. She demanded that she be allowed to interview our patients on camera, and when she was reminded that there was such a thing as patient confidentiality, she accused the principal investigator of attempting to hide the true facts. She would not listen to reason, and after considerable acrimony, the principal investigator approached a waiting room full of patients and asked who would like to be on TV. They were advised of their right to privacy, and told the Biodyne Center was not recommending their participation. Three patients who represented a wide range of very severe problems volunteered. The TV reporter, who witnessed our session in the waiting room, knew there had been no time to coach or carefully select these patients, but she still demanded that we agree not to intrude or interfere in any way with her on-camera spontaneous interviews. All three patients were interviewed, and the reporter left quite impressed with the fine work the program was doing. She said so on the evening news for the next three nights, showed the interviews on TV and thanks to her integrity, the media became more circumspect in handling the wild accusations they received from the practitioner community.

Conclusion

In reviewing these events, as well as many others for which space does not permit inclusion, it is evident that this project would never have been initiated, conducted, or successfully completed without addressing manifold political sensitivities. It is no longer practical for outcome researchers in the field to be well versed only in clinical and scientific considerations. The very essence of working with government, by definition a political animal, demands a kind of acumen not part of the usual scientific armamentarium. As the government increases its role in health delivery and outcomes research, the examples cited here will reflect commonplace types of problems confronting the field researcher of the future. Without the active resolution and management of political concerns, those committed to scientific and clinical integrity and what should be scientific decisions are in danger of being thwarted in their research by external decisions that are political and unscientific.

{ 8 }

THE FOUNDING OF AMERICAN BIODYNE, A COMPANY THAT CREATED A PSYCHOLOGICAL INDUSTRY

Managing a Managed-Care Organization[1]

THIS CHAPTER DEALS WITH the creation of industry, financing and implementing the first company as the prototype of that new industry, and then building it within seven years to become the largest company of its kind. More appropriately, it is a case study in entrepreneurship rather than just management, and this may be of considerable value inasmuch as many mental health practitioners are energetically involved in the formation of a broad range of new and unique enterprises. These include not only managed-care companies (MCOs), but also contract research organizations (CROs), which as outside companies can perform the credible outcomes studies all MCOs need, sophisticated informatics to service the communications needs of the current health industry, and provider-driven networks to contract with the MCOs or directly with the regional pur-

---

[1] Chapter 8 is based on a chapter reprinted with permission from Cummings, N. A. (1999). Managing a managed care organization. In W. T. O'Donohue & J. Fisher, *Management and administrative skills for the mental health professional* (pp. 133–151). New York: Academic Press.

chasing consortia of employers. Other practitioners who developed their knowledge and skills in employment with successful "start-ups" have formed consulting services to help practitioners form their own enterprises, and even to provide management, financing, and marketing, all skills that are not readily acquired in the conventional education and training of the mental health practitioner.

MANAGEMENT VERSUS ENTREPRENEURSHIP

I founded American Biodyne, Inc., proximal to the so-called Silicon Valley in California and had the opportunity to get to know many of the legendary figures who created the "Golden Age" of Silicon Valley. I also had the opportunity to get to know the venture capitalists who financed their unique start-ups, from whom I learned as much regarding entrepreneurship as I did from knowing the entrepreneurs themselves, and by being one of them. As a group, we had two things in common: (1) the founder of a start-up already *knows* how he or she will make it work, and sees this successful outcome when no one else can; and (2) founders of start-ups are essentially entrepreneurs and not managers. An entrepreneur must have the propensity to listen to no one other than his or her own vision. This is so because everyone is telling the innovator that the idea is unworkable, too risky, and even preposterous. Listening to this advice will cause one to question one's own belief that the risk is irrelevant inasmuch as the implementation and subsequent success are obvious. The manager, on the other hand, must listen to everyone, distill all that has been heard, and accordingly make an appropriate and correct management decision.

Successful entrepreneurs usually make terrible managers, and timing is important: the founder must swallow his or her pride, and at the point where the company no longer is a start-up, pass the reins of the mature company over to second-generation (professional) managers. Many, if not most, entrepreneurs are incapable of letting go of their creation, forcing their venture capitalists or stockholders to evict them. This befell Steve Jobs, the brilliant founder of Apple Computers, who resisted all advice to resign as CEO and was painfully thrown out of his own company by Arthur Rock, the country's foremost venture capitalist, who had financed him and had become his close friend. Job's successor, John Sculley, all but destroyed Apple Computers before he, in turn, was thrown out, but that is another story. The fact is that such corporate blood-letting is avoided when the founder intuitively recognizes when it is time to step down. There are enough exceptions (e.g., David Packard of Hewlett-Packard, Armand Hammer of Occidental Petroleum, and perhaps Bill Gates of Microsoft) to persuade the unwilling entrepreneur that he or she will be the one-in-a-hundred exception to the so-called rule.

The Creation of an Industry

BACKGROUND

During the 1970s and 1980s, the inflationary curve for healthcare began to spiral out of control, often exceeding the inflation rate of the general economy by two and three times. The federal government grew increasingly concerned, and through a series of unsuccessful initiatives, such as monetary incentives to increase the supply of physicians in the expectation that this would increase competition and lower fees, sought to reduce the rate of inflation in healthcare costs. It was not until the mid-1980s before any of these government interventions affected costs, and then medical and surgical costs only. The cost of mental health and chemical dependency (MH/CD) services even accelerated sharply, nullifying the savings in medicine and surgery and driving the continued spiral of inflation. There are reasons why these initiatives succeeded or failed, but all were influential in the creation of managed care, and particularly managed behavioral care, both new industries.

Supply and Demand

When the government discerned that the shortage of physicians that plagued healthcare in the United States during the decades of 1940 to 1970 was about to come to an end, public policy began to rely heavily on the economic "laws" of supply and demand to curtail healthcare costs. There were enough physicians in the pipeline that not only would the shortage be met, but the result would also be a glut of physicians. When the era of physician surplus arrived, to everyone's dismay, not only did healthcare costs continue to increase, but the rate of increase actually accelerated. Soon it became apparent that the reason for this was that physicians controlled both supply and demand: as each physician experienced a reduction in patient clientele, he or she merely increased the number of billable procedures for each patient and for every condition. Not only was the temporary loss of income short-lived, but physician incomes climbed to new heights. It was not until the late 1980s when physicians lost control of healthcare to those who pay the bills (employers, taxpayers, government, and third-party payers in general) that healthcare began to respond to the laws of supply and demand.

The Federal HMO Legislation

The prototype of the modern health maintenance organization (HMO) was founded shortly after World War II and grew rapidly. This Kaiser Permanente Health System from the very beginning incurred the wrath of the medical profession, which retaliated by refusing to allow the Kaiser physicians to belong to the county medical societies. On the other hand, it captured the favorable interest of health economists. During the Nixon Administration, legislation was enacted that allowed the federal government to encourage and fund the formation of HMOs, which, until 1975, had been largely a California and Minnesota phenomenon. The White House saw HMOs as the possible solution to the healthcare economic crisis. Senator Edward Kennedy, who chaired the U.S. Senate Subcommittee on Health, saw it as bringing the nation one step closer to nationalized healthcare. With this empowerment, HMOs proliferated and grew from less than 1% of the insured population to their current status as the dominant healthcare system in the nation. Unfortunately, HMOs did not deliver behavioral care very efficiently, and sought to control costs either by providing crisis care only, or by capping the benefit at 10 or 20 sessions. The exception was Kaiser Permanente in Northern California, which experimented extensively with efficient/effective psychotherapies that later came to be known as Brief, Intermittent Psychotherapy Throughout the Life Cycle, or just "HMO therapy" (Cummings & VandenBos, 1981; Cummings & Sayama, 1995).

The Enactment of DRGs

Frustrated by the continued high inflationary curve in healthcare, the Congress put into effect a table of diagnosis-related groups (DRGs) for Medicare and Medicaid reimbursement to hospitals in the mid-1980s. This mandated a set number of days of hospitalization for each of almost 400 conditions. If the hospital exceeded the allowance, it lost money. If it used less than the allowance, it made a profit. Soon the insurance industry emulated the new cost structure and hospitals found themselves with as much as a 50% empty-bed rate in medical and surgical services. Hospitals were used to a reimbursement rate of cost plus 15%, and under the new rules, they fell into financial difficulty. Many closed their doors, while many more were sold to proprietary chains. Nonetheless, for the first time in history, medical and surgical costs were tethered and the inflationary spiral was slowed.

In direct contrast, mental health and chemical dependency (MH/CD) costs spun to their highest level ever. Alert hospital administrators, seeing that there were no diagnosis-related groups (DRGs) in psychiatry, converted all of the empty beds to MH/CD services and huckstered new 30-, 60-, and even 120-day programs in television commercials. Within three years, MH/CD costs had doubled, with the greatest increases going to new and highly touted adolescent programs. There was suddenly a remarkable behavioral healthcare cost crisis in America.

Turning the Private Sector Loose

Unable to construct DRGs for MH/CD, the federal government tacitly decided to let the private sector solve the problem. It was at this point that what is now known as managed care was born. Decades of laws and regulations restricting the so-called corporate practice of medicine were at first ignored, then either repealed or struck down by the courts. Companies sprung up to help HMOs and the new managed-care companies (MCOs) managed their MH/CD costs, essentially using utilization review (UR) as the primary tool. This is the process by which a payor company reviews utilization practice patterns, and compares physicians who provide a relatively high intensity of services with those who are ostensibly more efficient, resulting in a chilling effect known as the "sentinel effect." The new industry that came to be known as managed behavioral care working as an efficient/effective delivery system was yet to be established.

CONCEPTUAL PREDECESSORS TO
MANAGED BEHAVIORAL-CARE DELIVERY

Several events preceded the MH/CD cost-crisis DRGs, and had an impact in the conceptualization and implementation of what was to become the nation's first behavioral health delivery system. These were the discovery of the medical cost offset effect, the Bethesda Consensus Conference, and the Hawaii Medicaid Project.

Medical Cost Offset

In the mid-1950s, Kaiser Permanente discovered that 60% of its visits to its physicians were by persons who had no physical disease, or whose medical condition was being exacerbated by stress and emotional conflict (Cummings et al., 1965; Follette & Cummings, 1967; Cummings & Follette, 1968; Cummings & VandenBos, 1981). This later was verified as a general finding within the U.S. medical system, and the collateral finding that behavioral interventions would significantly reduce the overutilization of medical/surgical services became the focus of research by the National Institute of Mental Health and the Health Economics Branch of the then Department of Health, Education and Welfare. This medical cost offset effect was important in persuading the health industry to include psychotherapy as a covered benefit for the first time, and set the stage for the continued development of HMO therapy, a focused and brief therapy model.

The Bethesda Consensus Conference

In 1979, the federal government published a compilation of all the medical cost offset research available (Jones & Vischi, 1979) and subsequently convened the Bethesda Consensus Conference (Jones & Vischi, 1980). In reviewing all of the research findings, this conference concluded that medical cost offset savings were greater in organized settings and increased proportionally to the degree that the behavioral interventions were innovative and focused. At the same time, the Health Care Financing Administration (HCFA) was becoming concerned with the escalating cost of Medicaid, which was significantly exceeding that of the runaway costs in the private sector. It was decided to conduct an extensive research and demonstration project for Medicaid.

The Hawaii Medicaid Project

Hawaii was chosen as the site. This seven-year, $5.5 million project was funded and supervised by HCFA, and the contract required annual renewal, enabling the government to end the project at any time if it were shown to be unsuccessful or problematic. In serving as the principal investigator, I created a nonprofit delivery system name the Biodyne Centers, after two Greek words meaning "life change." It was here that what came to be known as the Biodyne Model was refined, and, in response to the then recent Congressional legislation encouraging researchers to take federally funded results into the private (proprietary) sector, American Biodyne was launched in 1985.

Interestingly, after the Hawaii Project results were widely disseminated, HCFA drastically altered its regulations to permit the states to contract their Medicaid services to managed care (Cummings et al., 1993). For the second time, medical cost offset had a significant impact on national public policy.

The Vision

A description of the new industry, along with the business strategy, was presented in a major address to the American Psychological Association coincidental with the founding of American Biodyne, and published one year later (Cummings, 1986). My objective was to give away the technology, indicating that I would cap American Biodyne at 500,000 covered lives, leaving an opportunity for another 49 such companies. American Biodyne would serve as a model where psychologists could come to learn and train in the new industry, and then emulate it with their own companies. In this way, practitioners would own managed behavioral care delivery, thus guaranteeing that it would remain clinically driven.

The prediction that this model would attract 25 million enrollees was modest in hindsight, inasmuch as the industry surpassed 100 million enrollees in some form of managed behavioral care within the first decade. Nonetheless, practitioners considered the plan grandiose, and leaders in the profession predicted that it would be only a passing fad (Wright, 1992). I kept my promise to cap American Biodyne for three years, at which point I realized that no one was going to accept the offer. I then marketed the company aggressively for the first time, and within five years had achieved an enrollment of 14.5 million. This success did not go unrecognized by business interests. The model was widely emulated, with dozens of competitors emerging within a brief period. This was in keeping with original predictions (Cummings, 1986), but the industry had not taken cognizance of a companion prediction: that these "carve outs," as they came to be known, would serve a useful purpose for about 10 years. They were necessary because health plans were unable to curtail their own MH/CD costs. Once the technology was known to all, it would be unnecessary to have outside companies performing the task, and it would be time to "carve back in." Rightfully, behavioral health belongs with, and as a part of, primary care.

Founding the Company

Three tasks must be completed before it can be said a company is launched. Once the company has been conceptualized, it is necessary to prepare a business plan, assemble the team, and obtain capital. Although interdependent, each is critical to the successful start-up, and each must be performed equally well.

THE BUSINESS PLAN

The business plan with its financial projections is integral to the start-up (Cummings, 1996). Most mental health professionals have never even seen a business plan, and that is an excellent starting point. Assemble as many business plans from successful start-ups as you can borrow. These do not have to be in the same industry, but they should resemble one's own start-up in size and scope. Fortunately, there now is software that will help in the organization and preparation, but it will not write the business plan.

The business plan must tell a compelling story. It must showcase the founders, emphasize the competitive edge, and have numbers that will make sense when potential investors crunch them. It must clearly determine the mission, goals, and strategies of the company, and honestly present problems and how they will be surmounted. There have been great ideas with poorly constructed business plans, and poor ideas with excellent business plans, neither of which is viable. The business plan produced in the preparation for the launching of American Biodyne was the best presentation of an excellent idea that I could muster. It told the story well: why a new industry was timely and why the assembled team could accomplish the mission. It presented one-, two-, three-, and five-year financial projections that were conservatively optimistic and believable. It is better to exceed the original financial projections, especially in the early years. If a company should require a second tier of funding for expansion, or even reformulation, having fallen short of expectations will render the task of tapping additional capital, or even a loan, more difficult.

Once the business plan has been written to its best possible presentation, it is then given to the lawyers to insert the necessary legal disclaimers, such as, "This is a risky new business that has never before been attempted, and the investor may lose his or her investment in total." When I saw this and the large number of other blood-curdling insertions required by the legal aspects of the process, I was appalled. But I soon learned that seasoned investors ignore these legal disclaimers and make their own experienced judgment as to the potential of a company.

Most sophisticated potential investors, and especially venture capitalists (VCs), will not explore a deal beyond the business plan. If it is lacking in either presentation or conceptualization, they will distance themselves without telling the founders why. It is literally the *key* to the start-up.

THE TEAM

Although sophisticated investors and VCs look mostly to the principal founder, they firmly believe that it requires a team to make a company successful. They shy away from what they refer to as "Lone Rangers," and look to a team that has a number of critical characteristics.

Overcoming Risk Aversion

Most mental health professionals are highly risk aversive, and as such would never undertake a start-up. A surprisingly impressive number, however, are currently proving that this is far from being typical. No matter how entrepreneurial the principal founder may be, the team of founders must also have overcome the risk aversion.

Many VCs have confided to me that their decisions are based only 25% on the excellence of the idea, and 75% on the ability and confidence of the founders to pull it off (Cummings et al., 1996). The ideal investor is a David Packard, who worked 18 hours a day in a rented garage because he was too poor to rent an office/workshop, and went on with his partner, Hewlett, to form one of the Fortune 500 companies. Few practitioners can match the confidence and dedication of a Dave Packard, Steve Jobs, or Bill Gates, and investors do not expect this ideal. Yet they are put off when the would-be entrepreneur desperately retains his or her faculty position, VA appointment, or other full-time job. This behavior telegraphs to the potential investor that the practitioner has little confidence in his or her own ability or idea, and the concept has been relegated to the status of an exciting hobby that deserves capitalization. The investors in American Biodyne years later told me that they were most impressed by my determination to start the company at age 62, risking my retirement savings, with little opportunity to regain them if the venture should collapse. When questioned by them, I responded, "This idea is so good

that if I can't make it work, I deserve to live my old age in poverty."
This one response turned a liability (the relatively advanced age for
founding a start-up) into an asset.

The Fire in the Belly

The zeal known among VCs as the fire in the belly is mostly expected
of the principal founder, but they also look for a somewhat lesser mani-
festation of it in the members of the team. American Biodyne was fortunate in recruiting three co-principal founders, who not only left prestigious
and well-paying positions, but were eager to accept low salaries in exchange for an equity position comprising 1% or more of the company.
For incomes substantially below their previous levels, the operations officer left a vice-presidency in a national medical supply corporation, the finance officer left a lucrative position with a world-class accounting firm,
and the clinical officer resigned a senior post with the nation's largest
HMO. All three were in their 30s, and knew that since equity was the reward, if they did not make the company succeed, they would have nothing 10 years later.

Risk taking and the fire in the belly are never touted in the business
plan, but their existence is readily apparent in the manner in which the
compelling story is told.

Eschew the Few

Most successful business executives or clinicians will not leave a status
position to join a start-up, but occasionally there are a few who are willing to do so because they have accumulated enough wealth to mitigate
the risk. They may want the greater reward possible in a start-up, or they
may seek the excitement absent in their present dull, but lucrative job.
Not only is the fire in the belly absent, but they are not taking the
chance of losing all that may be characteristic of the young competent
executive who has not yet "arrived." These applicants should be carefully
screened.

As American Biodyne grew, it was believed that the company would
prosper by hiring these prestigious and established types. Of several so
hired, not a single one remained long with the company, usually leaving
by mutual consent.

It is never comfortable to make sweeping generalizations, but it is almost as important to know what not to look for as it is to be aware of

what it is that is needed. The following characteristics, admittedly unfair to the many exceptions, should be regarded as signs necessitating further inquiry. The longer and higher a business executive has climbed the corporate ladder, the less useful he or she is likely to be. Such a person is used to the prestige, the perks, the authority, and the high salary. Similarly, the longer one has been cloistered in academia, especially in a tenured position, the less likely it is that one will adapt to the ambiguities and insecurities of a start-up. And the least acceptable prospects are to be found in government, where competence must take a back seat to politics. It must be emphasized that once American Biodyne learned these lessons and interviewed such applicants with a wary eye, we found excellent personnel from all three venues.

POSITIONING THE COMPANY

There are essentially three ways to position a company, and this must be done at the outset as it is difficult to change once the company has succeeded (or failed): a start-up with exit strategy, a start-up in perpetuity, or an options-open strategy.

Exit Strategy

Most start-ups have as their goal an initial public offering (IPO) within five years. The VCs insist on this as their best means for cashing out. It also makes the founders' stock liquid, establishes a war chest to use for acquisitions, finances expansion, and wipes out debt. At this point, ownership shifts from a closely held private company to one that is publicly traded; in the health industry, usually on NASDAQ. If this is to be a strategy, it should be positioned in the business plan with factors that would signal the successful initiation of an IPO, as will be discussed later in this section.

In Perpetuity

Although the preceding strategy is sought in almost every start-up, there is an unusual kind of group, seemingly limited to healthcare, where the goal is one of perpetuation without an exit strategy. The outstanding examples are the several Permanente Medical Groups that contract with the nation's original and largest HMO, the Kaiser Health Plan. The purpose is to provide a stable, practitioner-owned environment in which to practice for one's entire career. This strategy, which is particularly attractive to the practitioner, is discussed more fully elsewhere (Cummings, 1996).

Options Open

In the third type of strategy, the original intent may be to have a group practice in perpetuity, but the company can be positioned from the beginning so that it can keep open the option of being acquired or going public. American Biodyne positioned itself in this way, anticipating that as long as the intention was to cap the company at half a million enrollees, it would be an exciting atmosphere in which a "family" of practitioners could have successful careers. When it became apparent that the mental health professional community was not going to take advantage of the technology and own it, the subsequent spectacular growth to 14.5 million enrollees supplanted the "family" congeniality and made an IPO all but mandatory.

CAPITAL FORMATION

The most formidable hurdle for practitioners to negotiate is the acquisition of enough capital to launch the company. Often the task is so daunting that founders are tempted to move ahead with minimum capitalization, jeopardizing the project, as underfunded companies seldom succeed. Yet if all the foregoing have been accomplished well, this may actually be the easiest part of the project. The amount of venture capital available is vast, far exceeding the number of start-ups worthy of investment. At the present time, start-ups are fueling the nation's economy and differentiating it from all other industrialized nations, which lack such resources and facilities.

Source and Level Capitalization

Whenever practitioners contemplate obtaining capital, they immediately conclude that they should not hesitate to seek out VCs. Actually, the source of funding depends on the amount needed; venture capital is seldom for small projects. The founder of a start-up should roughly consider the following schedule: (1) Up to about $250,000 in either capitalization or seed money, the best source of which can be wealthy, interested friends. This resource both is overlooked by worthwhile projects, and is abused by unworthy concepts that have been turned down by everyone else. (2) From $300,000 to $1 million, the best sources are the venture capital clubs composed of successful entrepreneurs who are interested in funding the next generation of start-ups. They rely on their own entrepreneurial talent and experience in assessing a business plan and usually are fascile in their discernment. (3) Finally, projects over $1 million are more suitable for consideration by VCs.

Characteristics of Venture Capitalists

Practitioners are not generally aware that VCs differ widely from one another. Most tend to specialize, such as in technology or healthcare, as two examples. Some VCs will shun certain industries, while these same industries will be favored by others. If the potential entrepreneur has not done his or her homework, even the most compelling story will fail if the VC is not interested in capitalizing in the business sector represented in the business plan.

Venture capitalists range from those who choose an investment, and then trust their judgment by staying out of management's way, to those who are very involved, perhaps even intrusive. A seat, or even seats, on the board of directors is a frequent demand, and the history of start-ups reveals that it is usually the VCs who are instrumental in dislodging and replacing the founder. Some VCs even have the reputation of replacing up to 95% of the founding management, whereas others rarely intrude. Finally, in the rush to cash in, some VCs pressure a company toward a premature IPO, when waiting one or two years would have resulted in greater market valuation for the company. Clearly, there are great differences in the degree of intrusiveness among VCs, and entrepreneurs need to assess the investors with whom they might have to live for a number of years. American Biodyne was fortunate in attracting a surplus of capital, and I interviewed potential investors for compatibility and decided to avoid VCs altogether. I relented somewhat in the latter decision when I was advised that it would benefit the company if the legendary Arthur Rock were allowed to take a minor investment position.

A frequent, and reasonable, requirement is that there be two forms of stock at the outset: common stock for the founders and *preferred stock* for the investors. This arrangement requires that, if a distressed company is liquidated, the preferred stock (the investors) will be paid first.

Big Problems with Big Solutions

Venture capitalists like big problems, because this signals the potential for big solutions. Behavioral healthcare is a $60 to $80 billion industry, with several times that amount in such annual costs as suicide, absenteeism, disability, and human suffering. There is room for big companies providing big solutions for big problems. If an industry has less than a $5 billion portion of the economy, VCs are generally not interested.

Avoid Going Back to the Well

Overcapitalizing a company can be almost as bad as undercapitalizing it. In the latter case, the company will run short of operating capital and find itself having to go back to VCs and suffering dilution. In an overcapitalized company, the temptation is to make expenditures prematurely or unnecessarily. This, too, can result in having to seek additional capital, along with the fact that initially too much of the company was given to the investors in obtaining the excess capital.

The American Biodyne Experience

American Biodyne was capitalized at a modest sum: $500,000 in preferred stock to the investors, and $1 million in common stock to the founders. With a total initial valuation of $1.5 million, the "sweat equity" of those who founded the company was two thirds, a very enviable position. The company never returned to the well. Rather, each contract financed future contracts, and the initial capital formation was never spent. It remained to be used as part of a future acquisitions war chest.

Managing the Company

Managing the initial phases of start-up often requires defying conventional wisdom, and for this reason, the entrepreneur is often the person upon whom ultimate decisions should rest. These entrepreneurs are seldom trained managers, and need the advice of a good M.B.A., to whom they must listen, and from whom they will learn. Then, on critical, but rare, occasions, they must have the courage to reject the advice. If the founder is the CEO, his or her lack of skill will result in a number of management mistakes, none of which will be fatal. On the other hand, the conventional wisdom that would have certainly damaged the company will have been avoided. The energy of a start-up team is its enthusiasm. There is a firm belief that it is not disgraceful to make a mistake, but it is unforgivable not to recognize it and correct it. The founder/CEO treats the team as family, and the team will follow him or her anywhere. All have risked their careers; the formula is, "Succeed or die."

THE FIRST YEAR

Only 20% of all start-ups make it to the fifth year, the traditional benchmark of success. Of those that fail, 40% will do so in the first year, and another 40% will seemingly be succeeding, only to meet their demise in the third year. Venture capitalists know this and calculate it in their formula: the one in five that succeeds will have a ratio of investment to reward of 25:1 or more, making it all very worthwhile to the VC (Cummings, 1996).

The Struggle to Guarantee Clinical Preeminence

American Biodyne almost died the first year because I gave unwarranted credence to conventional wisdom. Wanting to assure that the company would always be clinically driven, yet recognizing the lack of management acumen among clinicians, I, as the founder/CEO, accepted the advice of the M.B.A.-degreed operations officer. A parallel, dual management system was implemented in which those managing the clinical part of the enterprise reported up the ladder to the CEO, whereas those directing the operations side (i.e., day-to-day management, finance, human resources) reported ultimately to the chief of operations. This worst of all possible systems almost destroyed the company. Authority and responsibility fell between the cracks, and each side blamed the other. Very quickly, the faulty system was dismantled.

Faced with the dilemma of assuring sound business practices while maintaining the clinical preeminence of the company, there were only two choices: either train business managers to be clinicians, a plan deemed by all as impossible, or train clinicians to be business managers, deemed highly improbable, but not impossible. The latter plan was adopted. In each state and in each region, doctoral-level practitioners were placed in charge of both clinical services and operations. They were accorded release time to pursue seminars and courses in management and finance, and they were encouraged to enroll in part-time or evening M.B.A. programs. All received the requisite training, and several obtained the M.B.A. degree.

No matter how high on the ladder the clinician/manager was, he or she would be required to spend two full days per week in hands-on treatment with patients. This included the CEO, as all were admonished to promote and implement sound business practices, which would always be subordinate to clinical imperatives. This worked well and not only did the company flourish but it never had to resort to the artificialities of session limits, utilization review, and preauthorization. Simply, the effective clinician is an efficient clinician.

The Clinical Retraining

It became evident during the Hawaii Medicaid Project that even when the best clinicians are chosen, they have to be retrained in focused psychotherapy. A 130-hour training module was developed that was conducted in a two-week period and limited to 35 clinicians. The training was carried out on an as-needed basis following each new contract, but it averaged 10 training modules per year. Literally, over 1,000 clinicians were retrained during the first seven years of the company's history.

It was also ascertained during the Hawaii Medicaid Project that in spite of the retraining, if clinicians were left to practice without follow-up, they would soon revert to their original learning. Consequently, intensive on-the-job supervision and continued training included two hours per week of supervision (one hour of individual and one dyadic) and three hours per week of clinical case conferencing during which psychotherapists were expected, and encouraged, to present their most baffling cases. Of a clinician's time, 15% was spent perpetually in quality assurance.

Finally, each Biodyne Center, composed of six to eight clinicians, would be subject to an intensive three-day annual clinical audit. The audit team would sit in on individual and group sessions, supervisory sessions, and business meetings. The patient charts and all aspects of the center would receive intense scrutiny, at the conclusion of which an audit report would discuss the strengths and weaknesses of the center, and list its deficiencies, which required a six-month plan for correction. Center directors spent six months preparing for, and then six months recovering from, each audit.

During the first two years, I as CEO conducted all of the retraining and all of the clinical audits, involving a team each time so that at the end of this period, others could, and did, conduct both.

On the surface, the system may seem rigorous and, to some, even harsh. It cannot be overly emphasized that the exact opposite was true: the atmosphere was so accepting and rewarding that clinicians clamored for the opportunity to present their therapeutic failures. I was constantly bombarded by requests for help. Many consultations were conducted by telephone, but in the majority of cases, the individual clinicians received attention on my frequent visits to the centers. In later years, there were master clinicians available to continue this tradition, even though the company had hundreds of full-time psychotherapists.

Marketing Strategy

The marketing of a totally new healthcare delivery system is difficult, as the health industry moves slowly and conservatively. Several unconventional strategies were adopted with stellar success. For the first four years, I as CEO did the marketing. As the founder, I was best able to describe the system and its advantages, and had the credibility of having created the mental health system at Kaiser Permanente at a time when no insurer covered psychotherapy. I also had an impressive track record in research and in the creation and management of several previous enterprises. My being a former president of the American Psychological Association was important in identifying me as having credibility among my peers.

The product being marketed not only was capitated, but the provider was at risk to provide the agreed-upon coverage for all the MH/CD treatment of a particular third-party payer, be it a health insurance, Blue Cross/Blue Shield, HMO, or government plan. The coverage would include hospitalization, outpatient treatment, and a continuum of MH/CD services. It was a staff model with centers spaced geographically so that no patient would require more than a 30-minute drive in normal traffic. The MH/CD services were what came to be known as a "carve-out," and patients would have freedom of choice, but only among Biodyne providers.

Because of the newness of the concept, marketing was conducted not by brochures, but face-to-face and only with the CEO of the company being marketed. Subordinates in the health industry seldom possess the knowledge to assess innovation, and never have the authority to implement it. The CEO-to-CEO marketing was inordinately successful when it took place. If a particular CEO being marketed assigned the meeting to a subordinate, Biodyne would decline.

As part of the overall strategy, only contracts for coverage of over 100,000 lives were sought, and preferably those approaching a potential

500,000. It is as much work to implement a program for 10,000 lives as it is for 500,000.

Financial Strategy

American Biodyne's "black box" was its ability to reduce the then-bloated psychiatric and chemical-dependency hospitalization by 95%, leaving much of the capitation for expansion of the innovative outpatient programs that made this possible. Nonpsychiatric clinicians were trained in 24-hour coverage, and in the importance of seeing a presenting patient even in the middle of the night before sanctioning admission. Psychiatrists of the era typically would respond to an emergency room by saying, "Hospitalize the patient and I'll be there in the morning." The following morning, by virtue of having spent the night in a "crazy place," every patient would need hospitalization. The assessment, by its very nature, is only possible at the time of presentation. If at that hour the patient responds to outpatient techniques, then these are continued on a daily, and even twice-daily, basis, with hospitalization having been averted (Pallak & Cummings, 1992).

Using doctoral psychologists with additional training to perform this emergency service was highly successful. In seven years, there was not one mortality or one liability suit, which enraged beleaguered hospital administrators and the psychiatrists who were thus preempted. American Biodyne was the first, and therefore the most controversial, managed behavioral care company to address successfully the national crisis of psychiatric overhospitalization.

The second financial strategy contributing to the company's success was the decision to create centers and services only *after* a contract was in hand. This prevented a drain on capital as the revenue stream and the service expenditures were concurrent. However, it always necessitated a scramble to create new centers, recruit and train the clinicians, and prepare all of the required logistics, regularly within 60 days, and twice within 30 days. The company never failed to meet the time constraints of its many turnkey operations, and saved millions of dollars in setup costs.

MANAGING BEYOND THE FIRST YEAR

The crises of the succeeding years included having to manage a consistent 200% annual growth, and having to shift beyond the staff model. The successes were reflected in the company's several acquisitions, its going public, and its eventual sale.

The Staff–Network Model: Another Innovation

The staff model in which the practitioners are salaried and work out of a center is far more efficient than the network, but it does present some formidable difficulties. The first is the need for critical mass, making it impossible to implement centers in rural areas. Another is the resistance of many patients who feel managed in coming to a staff center, but do not feel managed sitting in a network provider's private office. The third is that most providers do not wish to be salaried staff, preferring to work as part of a network. As the company continued to expand, it became apparent that growth would be stymied under a staff model. Rather than convert to a solely network model, a new model was created: the staff-network arrangement. In this model, the staff conducts the clinical case conferences, covers the emergencies, manages the network, and treats the most problematic cases. This arrangement served the company well as the clinical culture continued to be reflected in the staff, while engaging what eventually was to be 14,000 contracted providers.

The staff of each center was always able to identify the best providers in the network, which the company then encouraged to form group practices and serve as "prime" or "core" providers treating American Biodyne referrals exclusively. In some cases, the company also supplied the capital, as well as the encouragement, for the formation of such provider groups.

Managing 200% Annual Growth

The company found itself in the enviable position of having runaway growth. This was met with the decision that although difficult, the company could manage 200% annual growth without jeopardizing quality. Growth was capped at that figure, and potential client organizations were given a time estimate of when they could be serviced. Rather than hampering the growth, the decision rendered the company more attractive and perpetuated the inordinate growth beyond the point at which it might have abated.

Acquisitions

There are four reasons why a successful company makes acquisitions:

(1) to acquire market share, (2) to penetrate new geographical areas where it had been shut out, (3) to acquire new technology, and (4) to obtain a distressed company at a bargain price, and then turn it around. American Biodyne used all of these strategies. For example, obtaining the California HMO license involves two to three years of red tape and as much as $2 million. By acquiring a small California company that had such a license, American Biodyne then filed a revision and thereby substantially reduced the complexity of the task. It acquired new technology by purchasing a national employee assistance program (EAP), and in buying several other companies, it entered arenas that would have been difficult to penetrate with traditional marketing.

The acquiring company always assures the acquired company that senior management will not be altered and downsizing will not occur. This promise can never be kept, as duplication must be eliminated and a new company culture must be infused. Founders of a company that is considering being acquired should take this inevitability into consideration.

The Initial Public Offering

Criteria for an IPO are formidable, and usually require five years of successful operation. Among these are three consecutive quarters of profitability, with the fourth quarter demonstrating a projected annualized income of at least $1 million. The growth and revenues should resemble a staircase: there should be an overall upward trend even though at points it is flat. The initial market capitalization should be at least $40 million for an industry that is on the scale of $1 billion. The company should be experiencing at least 35% annual growth, with increasing margins. These criteria will bring the required institutional support for the IPO (Cummings, 1996).

American Biodyne far exceeded the criteria. In fact, the company was profitable from its first quarter and in every quarter thereafter, a rare track record. Its determination to go public was postponed for one year by the Gulf War, and the expensive and exhaustive legal, underwriting, and other preparations had to be performed twice at a price exceeding $1 million. The IPO was successful at a split of three times for each share. Opening at $10 per share, it never faltered, and continued to increase steadily to $34 before the company was sold, less than two years later.

Once a company is publicly traded, its quarterly reports are public and become a management obsession. Falling short of expectations in such a report depresses the stock, and the company must constantly educate stock analysts about the company so as to assure proper analysis of the stock. A stock that loses 25% to 30% of its opening value will very likely be subjected to a stockholder's suit alleging that the company misrepresented the stock on the prospectus. Once such a suit is filed, it becomes a self-fulfilling prophecy, as the stock plunges even further because stock analysts downgrade a company facing such litigation.

The Sale of the Company

American Biodyne received a number of overtures from large corporations that wished to buy it, but it was only after I, the principal founder, reached the age of 70 that such offers were seriously considered. The company was now covering 14.5 million lives in all 50 states. Furthermore, the time was nearing in which my initial prediction as to the lifetime of the "carve-outs" was maturing. It would soon be time to carve in, heralding the end of an industry (Cummings, 1997).

Along with its spectacular growth and the maintenance of high quality, and its having defined an industry, American Biodyne had two national acknowledgments: (1) the December 1990 issue of *Inc. Magazine* named it number 42 among "America's 500 Fastest Growing Private Companies," and (2) the May 25, 1992, issue of *Business Week* listed it as number 14 of "America's 100 Hot Growth Companies." American Biodyne's successes brought a good price on a stock swap with MedCo Containment Services, which a year later, was acquired by Merck. Those who invested $1 in 1985 and held on to all three of the successive stocks (American Biodyne, MedCo, and Merck) in 1996 would be realizing over $150 in value.

Conclusion

The decade of 1985 to 1995 has demonstrated that doctoral-level mental health practitioners can apply their education and training, augment it with additional training and experience, and become leaders in healthcare. Several hundred psychologists who were with American Biodyne in its first seven years have gone on to become captains of the industry, ranging from CEOs and vice-presidents of successful companies to founders of their own innovative firms. Many have created new concepts within the reconceptualized health industry, whereas others have applied their ability to predict and control costs to the formation of new clinically driven companies and regional group practices. They attribute this to their early training and experience as pioneers with American Biodyne, and at a recent informal gathering in Dallas, these practitioners named those years the "Biodyne boot camp."

In addition to the research and clinical education and training of a sound doctoral program, these practitioners have several characteristics in common: a shared vision, enthusiasm for change, skepticism toward conventional wisdom, risk-taking ability, an optimistic view of the future, innovation, and self-confidence. They are entrepreneurs who have lifted the previous barriers for those future mental health practitioners who possess, or can acquire, these qualities.

APPENDIX 8A

PSYCHOLOGY AND THE NEW ENTREPRENEURSHIP: POSSIBILITIES AND OPPORTUNITIES[1]

Nicholas A. Cummings

Foundation for Behavioral Health

The University of Nevada–Reno

Psychologists do not ordinarily think of healthcare as a technology, yet clinical technology abounds and is readily available for use in developing an organized, evidence-based system of behavioral care. One successful national company, created by the author and described in this article, melded clinical technology, business acumen, and entrepreneurial vision, yielding a model that can be emulated. The article demonstrates that concepts and systems developed in the Silicon Valley are readily transportable to the healthcare industry, but only by those who understand the clinical technology. The flaws of the current system of managed behavioral care are described especially by the fact that those who know the clinical technology are not in control. The author contends that behavioral healthcare is in the hands of business interests who know only how to manage costs, not how to manage care. He further contends that this is about to change, creating opportunities for the future psychologist-entrepreneur who will rescue our currently failing system.

[1] Reprinted with permission from *The Psychologist-Manager Journal*, 2000, 4(1), 27–43.

To most psychologists, an entrepreneur is one who organizes, manages, and assumes the risk of a business or enterprise. This is essentially an accurate description, but it does not capture the vitality, innovation, and enormity of a new kind of entrepreneurial activity that is peculiar to, and characterizes, the current American economy. Rather than just organizing a business, it creates an industry where there was none. It melds knowledge and technology in response to a business need, even before the market has identified that need. This new entrepreneurship finds its epitome in its birthplace, the Silicon Valley of California, but it also stretches across the United States through a number of new locations, such as Seattle, WA, Austin, TX, and Manhattan, where it is called "Silicon Alley." This new entrepreneurial wave is in keeping with the information age, and has created far more jobs than were lost due to the deceleration of manufacturing. It has fueled an economy that is the envy of the world. It is decidedly American.

The new entrepreneur is intimately acquainted with the technology that is to be the basis of the company he or she is forming. At the same time, this entrepreneur is skilled in business principles, and often has an M.B.A. degree. That alone is not enough, as will be seen when the specific attributes of the new entrepreneur are described below. But the person or team forming the enterprise must be steeped in the technology that will drive it. Keeping in mind that a new industry is being created, leadership in another business is usually irrelevant, and may even be counterproductive, as illustrated in the case of Apple Computers. After the enormous success of Apple's personal computer (Butcher, 1988) had crested, a misguided and overly zealous board of directors replaced the company's founder, Steve Jobs, with John Sculley, the business genius from Pepsi-Cola (Scully & Byrne, 1987). They reasoned that extraordinary business acumen would rescue the somewhat sagging PC pioneer. They overlooked the fact that PepsiCola thrived in an established and hardly unique industry, and that its protégé, Sculley, knew nothing about the new high-tech industry of which Apple was a leader.

Interestingly, the Apple board of directors used Lee Iacocca's rescue of the almost-bankrupt Chrysler Motor Company (Iacocca & Novack, 1984) as a model. But Iacocca was leaving one automobile company for another, whereas Sculley knew nothing about the computer industry. He had been bottling soda pop — hardly a comparable endeavor — and in his short tenure with Apple, he all but destroyed the company. Apple was saved when a chastened board desperately asked Jobs to return.

The more technologically oriented the new industry, the greater the need for the founders to be grounded in that technology. This is obvious with regard to the high-tech companies of the Silicon Valley, but is less immediately apparent in healthcare. However, the technology of healthcare is vested in the healthcare professional and is not generally understood by the nonpractitioner. Managed behavioral healthcare, for example, began as a clinically driven system in the early 1980s, and was quite successful in melding business with clinical knowledge and technology so that quality and clinical integrity not only were protected, but enhanced through outcomes research and increased effectiveness. From my perspective, by ignoring the industrialization of behavioral healthcare, mental health professionals let it fall into the hands of "soda pop bottlers," a euphemism for Wall Street investors who knew nothing about the nature of psychological practice. Consequently, these investors had no idea of how to control costs by first effectively managing care, and they resorted to the usual cost-cutting techniques known by all bean counters. Impressed by the so-called inefficiency of long-term therapy, the investors saw an obvious solution: curtail costly services by limiting access. The technology was there to increase therapeutic efficiency and effectiveness, but they had no way of ascertaining that fact through the literature, as might an enlightened practitioner.

It is the further premise of this article that the current flawed system is on the cusp of change, with the resurgence of the practitioner at the helm. Competition will continue, as neither the employers nor the U.S. government (which is the largest purchaser of healthcare in the world) will again fuel a noncompetitive health economy. The practitioner-owned, clinically driven provider groups that will emerge as behavioral caretakers in the next evolutionary cycle will be led by psychologist-entrepreneurs who know the technology and are skilled in business. My perspective comes from having created the first managed behavioral care delivery system in the nation, marketing it and managing its growth to a half-billion dollar company, with 14.5 million enrollees in 49 states and over 10,000 practitioners, in seven years.

That company, American Biodyne (later MedCo/Merck, then Merit, and now Magellan), was founded and managed on the edge of the Silicon Valley. I was intimately involved with many of the now-legendary figures there, and I was able to extrapolate much of the vitality and verve of the Silicon Valley into a tech-oriented, practitioner-dominated healthcare company. The need within the foreseeable future for the new psychologist–entrepreneur is great, and the purpose of this article is to alert and inspire those colleagues in the next generation of behavioral healthcare. I shall not repeat the history of how American Biodyne was founded, organized, successfully marketed and managed, and then sold, all within the space of only seven years. These events have been extensively documented elsewhere (Cummings, 1999; Cummings, Pallak, & Cummings, 1996). Rather, I will focus on the attributes and abilities that will be required of this new psychologist–entrepreneur, who must run the risk of creating, managing, and rescuing the behavioral-care system of the future. Throughout, I shall use the creation of a new industry by American Biodyne as an illustration of how, despite conventional wisdom to the contrary, behavioral health-care is basically a high-tech endeavor.

The Fire in the Belly

Our chosen company name, American Biodyne, as well as our location in the Silicon Valley, led to the mistaken notion that we were a high-tech company. Accordingly, I was invited to attend one of the regularly scheduled industry luncheons. I attended out of curiosity, fully intending to rectify the "error" and disappear thereafter. Within the first ten minutes of arriving at the meeting, I met Steve Jobs, Michael Dell (Dell, 1999), and scores of other young entrepreneurs who are now legendary, and I was captivated by their enthusiasm and unbridled optimism for what they were doing. I decided to join the club, and rarely missed one of the luncheons. Even more fascinating, I was included in many of the social activities, and it was during this time that I learned I had the same fire in the belly that characterized each of them, even though at 63 I was considerably more than twice their mean age of 26. It was not age that mattered; it was the absence of risk aversion that bonded us.

As a psychologist, I was used to being surrounded by individuals displaying risk-aversive behavior: the tenured professor, the Veteran's Administration civil service psychologist, the practitioner who saw solo practice as the height of individualism, and the researcher shielded from most of the real world. Not that there is anything remiss in those worthwhile activities but I had founded a number of risky, controversial endeavors prior to American Biodyne, always avoided "safe" jobs, and I had felt a bit odd among my own colleagues for having been the way I was. Here in the Silicon Valley, I understood the entrepreneurial mentality and was, in turn, understood. David Packard, who became a good friend before he died, and who was even older than I, was very much at home in the Silicon Valley, having defined it in the mid-1930s when it was still known by its rightful name of Santa Clara Valley. He and his partner, William

Hewlett, had been two young engineers who had an irrepressible vision but no money with which to launch it. So they rented a cheap garage from a widow who did not drive and worked day and night, moving their equipment whenever it rained to avoid the big holes in the roof. Without ever intending to do so, they created a *Fortune* 500 company.

As in the 1980s and 1990s, bright, enthusiastic young entrepreneurs were still working 16 hours a day in their bedrooms, their parents' garages, and drafty sheds. One group of eight I visited rented a small apartment that housed all of them. During the day, every nook and cranny was an office/workspace. At 10:00 p.m., the makeshift desks were folded and cots emerged, for they worked and slept in the same cramped quarters. Two years later, their vision had been implemented and they were managing a multimillion dollar company.

Before investing money, venture capitalists look for two ingredients in the founders: a great idea and fire in the belly. The latter is their term for the enthusiasm and persistence in making an idea a reality, and these investors know that many a good idea dies from lack of a visionary with drive. On an almost weekly basis, I have very good ideas brought to me by innovative colleagues who are having difficulty obtaining the necessary capital to start a company. They have been shunned because of their risk aversion; they do not believe firmly enough in their idea to plunge. Instead, they hang on to their academic and clinical appointments, fear losing a comfortable home and a prestigious car, and relegate what could be a life's dream to the status of a hobby. Venture capitalists want nothing to do with them.

The dean of all venture capitalists, Arthur Rock, told me several years after he had invested in American Biodyne why he had done so. He had capitalized Apple, Intel, and scores of other inordinately successful companies, but he knew nothing about healthcare. So he decided to base his decision mostly on what he saw in me. He bluntly asked how a man in his 60s could risk his retirement nest egg on an idea, knowing that if it failed, he would be too old to rebuild his savings. He recalled that without hesitation I replied, "This is such a good idea, if I can't make it work, I deserve to spend my old age in poverty." That was the moment he decided to invest.

What Rock did not know was that three years earlier, as principal investigator (PI) in the Hawaii Medicaid Project, I had literally put all my savings on the line. David Stockman, who was director of the Office of Management and Budget (OMB) under President Reagan, without warning froze funding to all "waivered" Medicaid research studies, of which our project was one. Realizing that if I shut down the behavioral health-care system we had created as a demonstration project it would never again get started, I cashed in my retirement trust and met the $50,000+ monthly overhead for several months. There was no way to know whether I would ever recoup my savings, but this allowed the project to continue without interruption toward its successful conclusion. Fortunately, our pleas in Washington were heard and the freeze was lifted retroactively. It was what was learned from the Hawaii Medicaid Project that became, with governmental approval, the blueprint for American Biodyne. The risk had been worthwhile.

It Is Not About Money

It is possible to identify five types of aggressive entrepreneurs, all of whom may be extraordinary, but each in a different way. The first of these I have called the *rescue genius*, a manager who turns failing companies around. Classic examples include Lee Iacocca, who saved Chrysler from bankruptcy a number of years ago. A more recent example is Gordon Bethune (Bethune & Huler, 1998), who took command of Continental when it was the worst airline in the business and already in bankruptcy, and within a short time transformed it into one of the best carriers in the air. A second type has often been termed the *deal maker*, portrayed in the 1987 motion picture *Wall Street* starring Michael Douglas. Examples include Henry Kravis (Baker & Smith, 1998) of KKR, as well as Richard Rainwater (Morthland, 1996) and his spouse, Darla Moore. To them, the merger, the acquisition, and the money are all-important and exciting ingredients. A third, which can be called the *plunderer*, makes an enormous amount of money by acquiring a successful company, partitioning it, and selling off its components. Carl Icahn (Stevens, 1993) has often been associated with this approach to entrepreneurial activity. The *venture capitalist* is a fourth class. These are persons who participate indirectly in entrepreneurial endeavors by using their skills to pick just the right prospective companies. Arthur Rock told me that he expects four out of five start-up companies to fail, but he anticipates making as mush as 50 times his investment in the remaining one. The fifth type, the *visionary entrepreneur*, differs from all of these as one who is driven by a need to implement a vision that will result in a very significant change. The money is secondary, or even unimportant. It is this driven technology "nerd" who inhabits the Silicon Valley and is the subject of this article. Most in this category who sell their companies hang around the Silicon Valley as venture capitalists, recycling their money into the technology of the future. Their parties are characterized by intense shop talk, and although I personally am more gregarious and crave actual socialization, I have enjoyed these soirees where incredible ideas swirl about the room while being freely discussed.

In my own experience in forming American Biodyne, money was never a consideration. My vision was to give away the technology to the practice of psychology, which would then own it as clinically driven systems well out of the clutches of Wall Street. My article in the *American Psychologist* (Cummings, 1986) and subsequent writings (Cummings 1988, 1991, 1994) constitute a series of "do-it-yourself" kits. I indicated from the outset that I would limit Biodyne to 500,000 enrollees, using it as a model for colleagues to visit in order to learn about the technology and process, after which they would go out and form the other 49 Biodynes of 500,000 enrollees each. The response from the two APAs (the American Psychological Association [APA] and the American Psychiatric Association) was one of derision, calling my initial half-million enrollees grandiose. For two years, I kept my foot on the brake, limiting American Biodyne to the announced number, during which time business interests were copying my formula. In disgust, I removed the restriction, and within five years, the company had shot up to 14.5 million enrollees nationally — after which, with the disappointment only of one who had reached age 70, I sold the company to MedCo/Merck. If I made money, I owe it to the myopia of organized psychology and psychiatry, which rejected the notion that our healthcare system was industrializing, and chose instead to believe the trends were a passing fad (Wright, 1991, 1992). Today, managed behavioral care is far different than it would have been if clinicians were in charge, but its 175 million covered lives far exceeds the modest estimate of the 25-million enrollee industry I predicted in 1986.

Nonprofit Entrepreneurship: An Oxymoron?

It is the contention of this article that a nonprofit endeavor can fulfill most, if not all, of the characteristics of the new entrepreneurship. Society abounds with examples of successful nonprofit organizations that created an industry where heretofore there was none, in spite of seemingly insurmountable odds, and often at great risk to the founder. Often these examples demonstrate unprecedented vision, dedication, and energy. These range in diversity from the founding of Alcoholics Anonymous by Bill Wilson (Raphael, 2000) in the 1930s to the creation by Dr. Sidney Garfield in 1946 of the Kaiser Foundation Health Plan, the world's first and largest HMO (see, e.g., DeLeon, VandenBos, & Bulatao, 1991), which remains a nonprofit to this day.

Over the course of my own career, I founded a series of successful and enduring nonprofit entrepreneurial endeavors, of which American Biodyne would have been one if the profession had not rejected the gift and inadvertently pushed me into a highly profitable enterprise. Of the several such organizations, the founding of the California School of Professional Psychology (CSPP) is an example. It launched the professional school movement, creating an industry where none existed before. It was opposed not only by the APA, but by academia in general. Most considered it an impossible dream, and one that would go nowhere. In spite of overwhelming odds, I was able to ignite the imagination of psychology's practitioners, and tap into the almost universal dissatisfaction with their own graduate training at the hands of teachers who had never seen a patient. They rallied behind the concept, and over 250 Ph.D.s and M.D.s volunteered to teach between one and four courses without pay during the first 18 months of the school's existence. This was the school's "endowment," permitting the doors to open and classes to begin with an initial capitalization of less than $35,000. Not only was CSPP inordinately successful in attracting students, it grew from two to four campuses within two years (San Francisco, Los Angeles, San Diego, and Fresno).

Why did I personally work 90-hour weeks for seven years for no pay during the first four years and little pay during the other three? I did this because I saw this enterprise as the only way to break the monopoly of the APA's Education and Training Board concerning rules that prevented "doers" from becoming faculty. It is only recently that I have thought back to my own training in psychoanalysis with Erik Erikson, now more than half a century ago. After I had been seeing him four times a week for nine months, he announced that we were concluding my analysis in three months. I was shocked and did what was unpardonable at the time: I jumped off the couch and faced him. I objected strenuously, stating that I expected my analysis would take place over several years, and demanded to know why he had come to this arbitrary decision. He replied in his thick European accent, "If we continue, you will undoubtedly become a highly successful and stodgy psychoanalyst. If we conclude now, you will spend your career creating exciting new things." I argued against termination throughout the remaining three months, vowing to replace him with a new training analyst. He, of course, won and we concluded in the 12th month. I probably would have spent my career as he predicted had we continued. Did he plant a life script into my life, or did he discern a propensity that further analysis would inhibit? I believe it was the latter, because I can now recall how even in high school I created innovative organizations, along with the more conventional successes of being an "A" student and president of the student body. The innovations I implemented in high school were highly controversial among the school authorities, who attempted to block each one of them. Perhaps the most innovative creation at the time was the student "credit union," which invested in real estate and enabled many of the participants to finance part of their college tuition within two years. Upon my graduation, the principal shook my hand, congratulated me on having been his greatest challenge, and said he hoped he would never see me again. When I look back, I am amused that many of my colleagues feel the same way about my later innovations.

Sweat Equity

The new entrepreneur thrives on sweat equity. He or she works for a very modest salary in return for an ownership in the company. This is the grease that lubricates the start-up, as those involved know that if they make the concept work, they are set for life, whereas if they fail, they have spent the last several years working for very little return. This constitutes a supreme incentive, along with the satisfaction that important change will have been wrought on the technology landscape.

In hiring the founding staff of American Biodyne, sweat equity was an absolute criterion. Those who asked arduous questions about salary levels, frequency of raises, fringe benefits, and job security were quickly rejected. I used a formula according to which, in return for a single percentage of ownership, the new employee would relinquish one third of the salary paid in the previous employment. I assembled an eager, experienced, motivated staff. My chief operating, financial, and clinical officers were all under 35 years of age. Staff members never watched the clock, and they did anything that needed to be done without regard to nonexistent job descriptions. Their drive resulted in two national acknowledgments: the December 1990 issue of *Inc.* magazine had American Biodyne at number 42 on its annual list of "America's 500 Fastest Growing Private Companies," and, after we had gone public, the May 25, 1992, issue of *Business Week* magazine put the company at number 14 on its list of "America's 100 Hot Growth Companies." This success helped bring a good price one year later in a stock swap with MedCo Containment Services, which another year later, was bought by Merck. Those who invested $1 in 1985 in 1985 and kept all three successive stocks realized over $150 in value in 1996. For the staff members, their own sweat equity was a resounding success.

Scouting

Before a group of visionaries can even begin to structure a start-up, they must gather all of the available technology pertaining to their concept. This process is called "scouting"; when completed, it informs the founders of the gap between what already exists and what they will eventually have developed as the product line. That gap constitutes the task that must be financed and completed through research and development before the company will have something marketable.

In founding American Biodyne, our scouting brought in a surprising body of information on effective and efficient psychotherapies, as well as methods to reduce unwanted or unnecessary psychiatric hospitalization. We were amazed how psychology had ignored its own technology, preferring to continue in traditional modes of practice. It was abundantly clear to us that effectiveness and efficiency were based on both available and yet-to-be-developed technologies, and we never lost sight of this. Therefore, in the beginning, we created a data-gathering system that was built into the clinical delivery, and one that would make possible continuous outcomes research. The model called for ongoing, perpetual enhancement of our effectiveness and efficiency.

"Technology Driven" Means Clinically Driven Healthcare

The development of a technology-driven healthcare delivery system required that all of the practitioners be retrained. There is probably no form of practice other than psychotherapy in which the formal training and subsequent activity are more out of touch with the existing body of knowledge. We created a two-week, 10-hour-per-day, total immersion program that was intended to undo traditional practice in a manner somewhat akin to the way in which cowboys break a wild horse, and we conducted it several times a year over the seven-year period. It is affectionately remembered in the industry as the "Biodyne boot camp," and it is worn as a badge of honor among the hundreds who participated.

The clinical delivery system made use of all verified mental-health treatment protocols, pertaining to both to individuals and to groups, that were then in existence. This was the era that preceded the current interest in standardization, however, so most of our guidelines and protocols had to be developed through our own ongoing outcomes research. Our methodology employed medical cost offset as the dependent variable, and it continues to be one of the most useful outcomes research approaches (Cummings, 1994). Our treatment system was based on 68 empirically developed protocols, which were subjected to continuous improvement.

Even all this was not enough, for traditionally trained clinicians, if left alone, will inevitably drift back to the narrow approaches in which they were originally trained. To counter this, 15% of all clinicians' time was spent in quality assurance. This program included a three-hour clinical case conference every Friday morning, as well as supervision, both individual and dyadic. A climate of trust and comfort was created in which clinicians clamored to bring in not only their most difficult cases for help, but also their failures. Patients entering the system agreed to the quality assurance program, which meant that any session might be monitored at any time through the one-way screen with which every office was equipped. This was an ongoing and expensive investment, which was rejected almost immediately by the nonclinical business mentality of those who succeeded my management. However, during those seven years, there was not a single malpractice suit, while after the quality control was dismantled the company was bombarded with such suits. In the long run, our meticulous address of quality had paid off handsomely.

In the Silicon Valley, the integrity of the technology is ensured by the fact that the technological experts are trained in business, so that they manage their own enterprise. We adopted this concept, and trained promising clinicians in business. At first, it was not easy to find clinicians interested in business training, but that soon changed. As a result, all of our line managers, whether at the corporate office or in the field, were practitioners who had been so trained. This ensured that when there was a conflict between the clinical side and the business side, the decision would be such that clinical integrity was maintained. And to further ensure clinical integrity, every manger — including me as CEO — spent at least two days a week in the hands-on treatment of patients.

All of these procedures are commonplace in the Silicon Valley. They are startling, and for the most part still absent, in the field of healthcare, even though its expenditures constitute one-seventh of America's gross national product (GNP). By applying the technology model to behavioral healthcare, we were able to create an effective and efficient system with high patient satisfaction and excellent staff morale, all the while enjoying economic viability.

Decentralization

Bureaucracies see decentralization as a threat, and their perpetuation of tight central control stymies innovation. In the Silicon Valley, where daily, and even hourly, problem solving is the name of the game, the answer has been small, decentralized teams. Bill Gates favors an interesting approach. He hires eager young people with inordinately high levels of intelligence, places them in a retreat-like setting, and waits for them voluntarily to cluster into groups of five to eight persons. He then declares each of these self-defined groups to be a working team, provides a long list of problems to be solved and products to be developed, and lets each team pick its own work assignment from the list. He then turns these teams loose to solve the problem. If they do, they have a significant equity stake in the emerging product. If they fail, they have nothing. Failure is a rarity.

American Biodyne adapted this approach to its staff model. Each Biodyne Center consisted of six professionals, one of whom was the center director, and was responsible for the behavioral care, on both outpatient and inpatient (hospitalization) bases, of 30,000 covered lives. If in that locale a contract was obtained for an additional 10,000 covered lives, these were never added to the existing center. Rather, two centers of 20,000 covered lives each were established, thus preserving the importance of small, manageable units.

Although protocols and guidelines existed, there was awareness that one size does not fit all. Centers were encouraged to modify and enhance these protocols in accordance with local needs, but only after strict verification. Healthcare does not have the same detailed demands from region to region. For example, the 100-mile-long and 20-mile-wide "stringbean" region of Florida's east coast has at least three distinct patient climates. The large Cuban population of Miami generally does not want "psicoterapia," but prefers to be given medicine. Moving north, alcoholism is a large problem, with families eschewing psychotherapy in favor of long-term hospitalization. The demand in such regions is to get the person "out of sight." Then things change dramatically in Palm County, where the mostly Jewish retirees from New York, New Jersey, and Massachusetts expect *perpetual* psychotherapy. Only localized problem solving can meet these very different challenges.

American Biodyne was consistently experiencing 200% annual growth, which could have been even greater had we not decided to refuse contracts that would have caused us to exceed that figure. Such growth is not easy to manage, but throughout we maintained both smallness and decentralization. When we moved according to market demand to a staff-network model, the Biodyne Centers remained the nerve centers, being responsible for the 24-hour on-call schedule and for the treatment of difficult patients, while also supervising the network providers. The latter were required to attend the clinical case conferences, and each was assigned a supervisor from the center staff. The professionals in the centers had their workload adjusted to accommodate their management of the local network.

There comes a time in the early years of a rapidly growing company when mergers and acquisitions are necessary in order to achieve a significant national presence (in the Silicon Valley, a global presence). This puts additional strain on decentralization and smallness; nonetheless, this model was maintained throughout, even as American Biodyne continued to dominate the market as the largest behavioral-care delivery system, achieving an enrollment of 14.5 million in its seventh year. In the process, we bought a number of companies and had to assimilate several very different cultures. Shortly after its sale, however, the company was rapidly centralized, as eventually was the entire healthcare industry. It is my belief that much of the difficulty of managed healthcare today comes from the fact that it is overly centralized and its leadership is far removed from healthcare technology. Not being able to tell good practice from bad, "beancounters" must rely on doing what they do best: count beans. I could not conceive of one set of benefits, procedures, and regulations that would suffice for the east coast of Florida alone, much less the entire United States.

Technology Increases Healthcare Benefits

Technology enabled American Biodyne to manage costs by first managing care. The efficient and effective protocols brought the patient's condition to remission rapidly, thus saving money while still effectively treating the patient. Consequently, the Biodyne Model never employed "benefit design," which is an insurance euphemism for restrictions and disclaimers of care. The benefits were entirely open, with no limits on the number of therapy sessions or lengths of stay in the hospital. In addition, we provided services usually excluded by health plans. These ranged from assertiveness training to marital counseling and parenting training to occupational counseling, all with the knowledge that these generally excluded procedures could prevent much costlier psychotherapy and hospitalization. Weight management, smoking cessation, and stress management were standard offerings for our firm long before wellness had become a buzz word. Accrediting teams were sometimes startled to see patient charts indicating that the patient was seen for 300 or more psychotherapy sessions. It was difficult to explain that when such cases occurred, our technology and therapist training provided assurance that this extensive treatment was the result of patient need, not therapist bias or ineptitude.

A genuinely open benefits package, coupled with an expensive quality-assurance system, and accompanied by higher-than-standard remuneration so as to attract above-average psychotherapists, all in a competitive climate, would suggest an inordinately high overhead. It may surprise the reader well versed in business to learn that we consistently maintained 40% margins, all largely attributable to the technology we called the Biodyne Model.

Business Plans

All of these principles and assumptions were embodied in our business plan, the document that is every start-up's rite of passage through the complicated world of venture capital. But a good business plan does more than just convince investors. It is the blueprint that embodies all of the company's technology. This includes the manner in which data will be gathered and utilized to revise the technology continuously, giving the operation ever-increasing effectiveness and efficiency, and guaranteeing its competitive edge.

To satisfy the venture capitalist (VC), the business plan must tell the story of the proposed enterprise in an understandable and convincing way, and the projections must be proved accurate when the numbers are reviewed. This is not an easy task, but it is infinitely less difficult than detailing the technology that the company will use on its road to success. The VCs are looking for innovative companies and are not put off by new ideas. On the other hand, one can expect considerable resistance from the practitioners. Yet a company cannot exist without its labor force, so our business plan had to include a strategy that would attract, and hopefully inspire, behavioral-health specialists to join the new company. This we succeeded in doing in spite of ongoing negative attitudes on the part of the practitioner guilds (Wright, 1991, 1992). Individual practitioners, especially psychologists, who wanted to be on the cutting edge were attracted to Biodyne, and lamented the subsequent changes as the technology was steadily eroded and eventually abandoned. Without a clinical technology, the successor to our company relied on such accounting-driven techniques as utilization review, case management, precertification, and the deadliest of all such procedures, provider profiling. Having no technology to give the practitioner, a centralized company has no choice but to limit, frighten, punish, and eliminate the practitioner who, without protocols and guidelines, is expected to treat the patient in other than a traditional manner.

Marketing

The advantage offered by technology is meaningless unless it somehow translates into economic attractiveness for the buyer. The purchasers of healthcare are generally conservative, resistant to change, and seemingly unmoved by "mere" arguments about what is best for the patient. The core of our company's marketing strategy was to meet a disquieting economic crisis in the health insurance industry. The first two years I did most of the marketing myself, and was intimately acquainted with the purchasers' needs.

In the mid-1980s, diagnosis related groups (DRGs) (e.g., Senior, 1989), as enacted by the Congress and implemented by the Health Care Financing Administration, succeeded in significantly reducing the annual inflationary rate of medicine and surgery. No one had succeeded in writing DRGs for psychiatry and substance-abuse treatment, so the hospitals began to fill their empty beds with lengthy, heavily advertised inpatient programs in adult psychiatry, substance abuse, and particularly adolescent psychiatry. Around this sudden surge in hospitalization there developed an extensive psychotherapy follow-up, and the combination sent mental-health and substance-abuse treatment (MH/CD) from its previous 2% annual inflation rate to 16%. Defensively, the health insurance industry began dropping the MH/CD benefits, a practice that was rapidly gaining momentum when American Biodyne came on the scene.

My organization was able to cut an insurer's MH/CD costs to 80% of the previous amount, while assuming the risk and impressively expanding the benefit. In addition, we were able to guarantee the reduced cost and the increased services for the following three years. The response was immediate, as we were making it possible for the insuror to continue the MH/CD benefit, thus avoiding the loud criticism that followed its elimination. We were soon deluged with far more business than we could accept, and we worked out a schedule as to when we could phase in prospective client organizations, not infrequently as much as a year away. This was an enviable marketing position; it reminded me of when, as a boy, I went into a bakery with my mother and she had to take a number and wait her turn to be served.

We never created a Biodyne Center until we had the contract in hand that that particular center would service. I had too often seen a health plan build its facilities in advance, and then hemorrhage cash while scrambling unsuccessfully to enroll subscribers. The Silicon Valley industries create infrastructure on an "as-needed" basis, a strategy that requires less initial capitalization, thus making it possible to commit less of the company's stock to the VCs. I also adopted the strategy of accepting only large contracts, since it required as much work to create a system to service 10,000 covered lives as would be required to create one for 100,000 to 200,000 covered lives. These strategies not only fueled American Biodyne's rapid growth, but also created a system in which each new contract provided the capital to service the next contract. The company was profitable from its very first quarter, and in every quarter thereafter, and it never spent its initial capitalization. That money remained available for the "war chest" used to buy competitors in the company's fifth and sixth years. This track record was unheard of in the Silicon Valley, on Wall Street, or elsewhere, and it earned American Biodyne kudos from *Inc.* magazine and *Business Week*.

Capitations

Capitation is a technology that came directly from the healthcare sector and is not applicable to the high-tech industry. It was developed and perfected by the Kaiser Permanente Health System, the prototype of the modern HMO, on the West Coast following World War II (see DeLeon, VandenBos, & Bulatao, 1991). Under such a system, the health plan is given a set rate each month for each covered life, called the rate per member per month, or pm/pm. American Biodyne was founded on a system of capitation, a rarity for behavioral healthcare at that time. The advantages of capitation include the fact that each service does not have to be billed and justified, a procedure also know as claims processing. This frees the behavioral healthcare system to use all of its technology when and where it sees fit, in order ultimately to provide the services guaranteed in the capitated contract.

Under capitation, we were able to do the unusual, such as make house calls to treat a house-bound agoraphobic. As another example, we consulted with a school that was inadvertently churning out depressed students. By helping them change a simple but depression-producing procedure, we diminished a clog in our treatment system caused by the large number of such boys. In fact, preventative and wellness programs are encouraged by a capitation system. American Biodyne initiated scores of preventative programs that were found to reduce the demand for more costly psychotherapy and hospitalization.

The IPO

The initial public offering (IPO), through which a privately held company becomes a public company, is what eventually legitimizes the success (or lack thereof) of the start-up. It makes the founders' stock fluid, for at that point it is easily traded on the stock exchange, whereas prior to the IPO, it had only "paper" worth. It allows the investors to cash in, and, quite important, it provides the company with the capital to expand into new markets and to make acquisitions. Often the latter process increases the company's market position by resulting in the purchase of its competitor(s).

American Biodyne went public in 1991 with the stock symbol ABDN assigned by NASDAQ. This is the stock exchange that accommodates the IPOs of most start-ups, and currently suffers the volatility prompted by the new Internet stocks. These seem to defy the law of gravity when it comes to trading at inordinate multiples of their earnings. At the time we went public, the Internet had not been fully developed and financial fundamentals still determined the worth of stocks on the NASDAQ, as they continue to do on the New York Stock Exchange. When the Internet sector settles down, as it eventually will, the need to pay attention to financial fundamentals will be more important than ever. In addition, healthcare stocks will never have the glamour of high-tech issues, and so for behavioral health start-ups, the financial basics will always remain paramount. At the time American Biodyne went public, a cost of $1 million was fairly standard for concluding an IPO.

There are a number of determinants to keep in mind before going public. Timing is the first. A company should have had several quarters of profitability and at least a 20% growth prior to its IPO. This usually occurs about five years from a successful company's inception. The VCs who are in a hurry to cash in their investment often try to push the "going public" date forward, often resulting in a lower figure being obtained for the initial stock offering. To wait until after a company has crested may also be a mistake. Second, the underwriters for the initial offering must be picked carefully, as should the law firm, generally based in New York, that will do the legal work. American Biodyne prepared to go public in 1990, but the plan was interrupted when the equity markets dried up during the Gulf War. So we went public a year later, our sixth rather than our fifth year, and we had to pay the $1 million tab twice, since the Securities and Exchange Commission (SEC) would not accept the previous year's preparations. Our underwriters were first-rate, with Dean Witter primary and Piper Jaffrey secondary.

Our underwriters valued our privately held stock at $36 per share and suggested that we split it four ways, setting the initial offering at $10. I insisted that we split it three ways and go to market at $10. I was criticized for leaving money on the table, but the strategy proved correct. I was wary of the law firms in New York that regularly buy a few shares of every new stock, wait for it to drift downward, and then file a class-action suit, ostensibly on behalf of the stockholders, based upon the claim that an inaccurate prospectus was issued. Once the lawsuit is filed, the stock plummets, seemingly verifying the accusation that the founders overvalued the company. These suits never help the stockholders; rather, the law firm bringing the suit receives millions of dollars in fees upon settlement. Intending to avoid such a consequence, we undervalued the initial offering. The stock analysts immediately spotted the underevaluation of ABDN and sent "buy" recommendations to their clients. Instead of drifting down, the stock steadily appreciated, such that each share, even after the three-way split, had reached $38 when we sold to MedCo/Merck 18 months later. The investor's $1 per share purchased in 1985 cashed in at $114 after seven years. For those who held on for another year while Merck stock soared, it rose to $150.

Psychologists might criticize such a profit as coming at the expense of the patient or the provider. This is not the case, since Biodyne always provided value to the patient and excellent remuneration to the provider. Most psychologists are economic illiterates, and see wealth as a zero-sum game: if someone profits, someone else must lose. This is not the case, as our economy is constantly *creating* wealth, as did American Biodyne in this instance. Unfortunately, once the managed-care industry slid into overcompetitiveness, "bottom-feeding" and "low-balling" became prevalent, and, indeed, both the patient and the provider were negatively affected (Cummings, 2000).

The Entrepreneur as Manager

There is a distinct difference between the attributes required of the entrepreneur and those needed by the ongoing manager. The skilled manager must listen to everyone, assimilate and evaluate the information, and then make a decision. The entrepreneur, on the other hand, must be a determined optimist who listens only to that voice from within, when the outside world is saying the idea is unworkable and will never succeed. The greater the innovation, the stronger must be the defiance of conventional wisdom. The entrepreneur must have a peculiar and especially virulent form of self-efficacy, allowing him or her to shut out the din of the "nay-sayers." These are qualities that will be a hindrance once the company has matured.

Some few entrepreneurs can make the transition to manager; among them have been Dave Packard (Packard, Kirby, & Lewis, 1996) and Michael Dell (Dell, 1999). Steve Jobs (Butcher, 1998) was fired after Apple Computer was no longer a start-up, but he was brought back and he has learned to be an ongoing manager. Bill Gates (Gates, 2000), probably the greatest genius of them all, has been a clumsy manager since Microsoft became a successful giant. The part of him that is an entrepreneur continues to succeed, as he is constantly spawning start-ups within Microsoft. On the other hand, a skilled manager would not have stumbled blindly into a monopoly lawsuit as he did, and would have made a far more credible showing on the witness stand in his own defense. In my own life, I learned years ago that I am an entrepreneur at heart; I admire ongoing managers, but I find the work tedious and boring. Therefore, I have formed a string of successful enterprises and organizations, moving on as each has matured and entered the mainstream. The danger in leaving is that the company one started may take a decidedly different turn. It has been my great disappointment that the behavioral healthcare industry that I founded has lost its clinical/technological roots and not only has become overly business-driven, but remains in an ever-escalating war with its own labor force (Cummings, 2000).

Summary and Conclusions

Although this article has concentrated on the for-profit sector of healthcare, the same principles are applicable to nonprofit entrepreneurship, an area in which psychologists will find that opportunities and challenges abound. The decision to largely address the for-profit behavioral healthcare industry was based on the indications that we are about to embark on the second wave in the industrialization of healthcare, and that the need for psychologist-entrepreneurs will be intense.

Current clinical technology is sufficient to warrant the creation of successful, practitioner-driven behavioral healthcare companies that will replace the outmoded managed-care systems of today. American Biodyne, using a high-tech approach, melded verified clinical techniques with business acumen and entrepreneurial vision, and created a model dedicated to clinical integrity. Growing rapidly to 14.5 million covered lives and 10,000 providers, it had not one malpractice suit or serious complaint in the seven years it operated by the principles and the procedures known as the Biodyne Model. The technology is out there and can be easily emulated. We are on the threshold of the next evolutionary step in the industrialization of behavioral care. The new companies will be clinical/technological and will be established by savvy practitioners who are knowledgeable, and comfortable with the evidence-based psychotherapeutic procedures that already abound. And the next evolutionary step will find behavioral care integrated with, and indistinguishable from, primary care (Cummings, Cummings, & Johnson, 1997).

As these endeavors grow, there will be a need for psychologists trained to engage in the new entrepreneurship. This will require a new curriculum and a training program that will produce psychologists who are grounded in research, who will know how to use technology, who will be knowledgeable in business, who will be competent clinically, and who will be inspired and energized as entrepreneurs. This is a tall order, challenging the template for the current APA-approved doctoral training programs. Accordingly, the University of Nevada, Reno, has established the world's first endowed chair in organized behavioral-health delivery. This initiative not only will seek to train this psychologist of the future, but will be active in stimulating the organized practice settings in which these students will train and then go on to create the healthcare systems of the future. As noted by Delbecq (1999), the renowned expert in innovative organizational design, our flawed healthcare system cannot be saved by the overly centralized bureaucracies that currently dominate it. Rather, the innovation will have to come from a small, unlikely source that is not stifled by emotional and economic investment in the present inadequate system. Herein lie the possibilities and opportunities for the entrepreneurial psychologists of the future.

MEDICAL COST OFFSET AS A ROAD MAP
TO BEHAVIORAL ENTREPRENEURSHIP:
LESSONS FROM THE HAWAII PROJECT

*The things that need to be learned before
we do them are often the things that we
must first do in order to learn them.*
— Aristotle

If the knowledge of organizational behavior were a true guide to entrepreneurship, Silicon Valley would be populated by college professors. That this is not so neither is surprising, nor does it diminish the importance of behavioral analysis. But it does indicate that other crucial and overriding factors are present. It is the purpose here to identify some of those factors, using the case history of the first, and only successful, clinically driven, national psychology-run behavioral-care system. It was created and administered by psychologists at its headquarters on the edge of the Silicon Valley during the early 1980s, the heyday of e-commerce and the new economy. Intensive research went hand in hand with extensive field demonstrations, interrelated and timed so that each led to the identification of the next step in the other.

Although there are no immutable reasons why academia and entrepreneurship should not mutually proceed, certain intrinsic characteristics of each result in an unfortunate chasm between the two. The first, and perhaps the most defining, of these characteristics is *risk aversion*. Academia prefers the security of tenure to the uncertainties of the sweat equity model of a start-up, whereas the entrepreneur thrives on the concept of risk, and ultimate reward for this risk. Further, academia leans heavily toward order and planning, and hence favors a planned economy, the very antithesis of entrepreneurial endeavor, whereas the entrepreneur insists that there has never been a planned economy that was able to outproduce free-market capitalism. It is not surprising, therefore, that the universities are populated by one of these, and the Silicon Valleys of the nation by the other.

There are a number of striking exceptions in which renowned academics have founded and run successful start-ups, and although these are few, I am not aware of a single example of the reverse, where a highly successful entrepreneur later became a scientist of stature. An obvious example of the former is Ed Fredkin of the Massachusetts Institute of Technology (MIT) faculty, who achieved such wealth from the company he founded that he bought his own Caribbean island, where for many years he hosted top-level scientific conferences by special invitation.

An even more unlikely example is that of Stephen Wolfram, whose academic credentials are dazzling and entrepreneurial success most impressive. He attended Oxford on a scholarship, and by the age of 14, had written his own book on particle physics. At the age of 17, he published a scientific paper in the journal *Nuclear Physics*, and shortly thereafter went to work in the High Energy Physics Group at the Argonne National Laboratory. While there, and at the age of 18, he wrote a scientific paper on heavy quark production that soon became a classic in the field. At 19, he received an invitation from the legendary scientist Murray Gell-Mann to attend the California Institute of Technology (CalTech) where he earned his Ph.D. degree in his first year. The following year, he joined the CalTech faculty, and at the age of 21, he was awarded a MacArthur "Genius" Fellowship. When in his late 20s, he founded a highly successful software firm whose *Mathematica* is the most used computer program in mathematics, physics, chemistry, and biology. Now in his early 40s, he spends the hours from 10:00 o'clock every night until 5:00 every morning in his home laboratory, working on his new conceptualizations of cellular automata. He awakens at noon and devotes his afternoons to his post as CEO of his company. His highly remarkable conceptualizations challenge much of the fundamentals of mathematics, as well as the basic notion of natural selection in biology. His latest book, *A New Kind of Science*, published in 2002, enjoyed the largest advance sales of any scientific book in history. Dr. Wolfram is a celebrated and dedicated scientist, as well as a consummate entrepreneur, and demonstrates that these seemingly disparate qualities are not necessarily so.

Characteristics of the New Economy

The Beginnings

Forty years before the information technology (IT) revolution, two young Stanford engineering graduates, David Packard and William Hewlett defined the sequence under which struggling "techies" would one day be creating their start-ups in the Santa Clara Valley, later to be dubbed the Silicon Valley. Unable to afford either an office or a laboratory, they rented a garage with a leaky roof in the home of a widow who did not drive. They never dreamed that if their pioneering work could survive the frequent rain damage, Hewlett Packard would one day be one of the *Fortune* 500 companies. They started their endeavor in the midst of the Great Depression of the 1930s, and although the economy was strong during the growth of the Silicon Valley in the 1980s, the garage, attic, bedroom, and basement were the beginning locations of what is now one of the giants of the new economy. Capital was difficult to come by, necessitating the use of meager savings and asking relatives and friends to invest. This was the ambience in which I founded my own company, sharing hard times with such legendary figures as Steve Jobs and Michael Dell, and learning much from Dave Packard, himself. Most Americans are not aware that Oracle, second in size only to Microsoft in the IT world, was capitalized with only half a million dollars, the exact sum that had launched American Biodyne in the early 1980s.

The Irrational Exuberance

All of this changed in the mid-1990s. The success of the IT revolution found investors, a predictable type of herd animal, almost throwing money at start-ups as long as their corporate names were followed by a dot-com. The average start-up capitalization jumped from a few hundred dollars to $30 million. Every young M.B.A. with any modicum of an idea rushed to take advantage of the opportunities, and investors rewarded them with money. The garage was replaced by a posh office, and fast-talking marginal business types, several of whom had been convicted of fraud in the past, moved in to take command of the fledgling companies and their naive founders. They spent much of the millions in capitalization on slick advertising, a lot of it incomprehensible, but which nevertheless gave the illusion that the dot-coms were doing well. Investors took the bait and kept bidding the tech stocks up in the absence of any earnings, until the bubble burst in 2000. Again, in predictable herd animal fashion, investors abandoned the dot-coms as rapidly as they had espoused them. The new economy had its first shake-out.

During the period described by Alan Greenspan of the Federal Reserve Board as irrational exuberance (1997–1999), I had occasion to advise a venture capital firm on a number of the start-ups seeking funding. The ideas were at best questionable, with little indication that they could ever be profitable. There was a preponderance of young, patently opportunistic M.B.A.s and an absence of technologists. One company, which would create a data bank of customers who would list the significant dates of friends, family, and associates, to whom the company would dispatch gifts, sought a $5 million initial capitalization. For this, the founders were willing to give up only 10% of the company in spite of their being at the stage where they had not even begun to develop the software. The principals were four M.B.A.s just out of school, and anyone with IT ability was glaringly absent. On my advice, the venture capital firm refused them, but they easily got their money from others. The company was launched, and it went bankrupt two years later. My favorite, however, was DogDoo.com, which sent canine excrement neatly packaged to whomever the customer selected, obviously as a prank. The company actually was liberally capitalized, but it never established much of a customer base and it quickly vanished when the start-up money was spent.

Characteristics of the Start-up Winners, 1997–2000

Over 130 dot-coms launched during this period met their financial demise in the year 2000. *Inc. Magazine* (Mangelsdorf, 2000) gathered data on these companies and found that they resembled those described above: high initial capitalization, mediocre business ideas, little likelihood of profitability, founders who were oriented toward a quick cash-in, and an absence of founders with the requisite IT. In contrast, the 500 companies that were founded in 1997 and that achieved a revenue stream of $100 million or more within three years reflected characteristics of the companies that started up in the mid-1980s rather than those of the mid-1990s.

As Tables 1 and 2 reveal, 42% of these successful start-ups had initial capitalization of under $10,000, an amazing 79% had an initial capitalization of under $100,000, and only 21% had a capitalization of over $100,000. These funds were derived from personal assets (92%), cofounders' personal assets (36%), and assets of family and friends (33%). Obvious-

Table 1.

Amount of initial start-up capital available to the 2000 Inc. 500 companies. The criterion for inclusion was $100 million or more in annual revenue within three years. All were 1997 start-ups. (Source: Mangelsdorf, 2000)

Less than $1,000	16%
$1,000 to $10,000	26%
$10,001 to $20,000	16%
$20,001 to $50,000	10%
$50,001 to $100,000	11%
More than $100,000	21%

Table 2.

Method of raising initial start-up capital for the 2000 Inc. 500 companies. The criterion for inclusion was $100 million or more in annual revenue within three years. All were 1997 start-ups. (Source: Mangelsdorf, 2000)

Used personal assets	92%
Used cofounders personal assets	36%
Tapped assets of family or friends	33%
Received venture capital	4%

ly, many of these companies had a combination of all three. The startling statistic is that only 4% of these 500 successful start-ups received initial funding from venture capitalists (VCs), a fact that rendered them free of the pressures that VCs, who usually are business oriented and lack technological knowledge, frequently impose on the company, often to its detriment. And the final figure is the most crucial of all: fully 100% of these founding CEOs of successful start-ups were intimately acquainted with the technology involved in their companies. In other words, they were techies who had the vision for a company and knew how to tap the necessary business/financial expertise.

With these facts and background in mind, it is time to consider how a successful entrepreneurial behavioral-care company was established. The similarities with successful IT companies will be apparent. The difference, however, was the way in which the requisite technology was derived:

field testing of various models in a cohesive at-risk delivery system, using medical cost offset as the criterion for the adoption of the protocols.

Elicitation and Application of Behavioral-Care Technology

In the late 1970s, I had become convinced that the industrialization of healthcare was inevitable. Not only was it the last major sector of our economy that was not industrialized, but it was predicted that it would eventually account for 12% of the gross national product (GNP). All other major sectors of the economy had been industrialized: manufacturing in the 1900s, mining in the 1930s, transportation in the 1950s, and retailing in the 1970s. In addition, I was convinced that the government would seek private-sector solutions inasmuch as the thrust toward government-sponsored universal care had gone nowhere. This was loudly signaled by the Congress when, in 1974, it passed the HMO Enabling Act, rendering moot many of the state laws that prevented what had been defined as "the corporate practice of medicine." However, my attempts, as well as those of others, in the late 1970s to interest the private sector in an organized system of psychological healthcare failed. At that time, psychological services were such a small part of the overall health expenditures that it hardly seemed worth the effort. The only large healthcare provider that foresaw how behavioral interventions could save medical/surgical costs was Kaiser Permanente.

This all changed in the early 1980s, when the Congress created a system of diagnosis-related groups (DRGs), as these inadvertently ushered in the era of managed care. However, the impossibility of writing DRGs for psychiatry threatened the existence of mental health and chemical dependency (MH/CD) as a covered healthcare benefit. The cost of MH/CD skyrocketed at a time when medicine and surgery costs were beginning to be tethered, and insurers were dropping the benefit. As an alternative to psychiatric DRGs, the government opened the way for the private sector to contain MH/CD costs, and I responded quickly with a plan to create a national behavioral healthcare company.

The Mission

As there were no effective precedents in existence, a mission statement for the new company was enunciated with the following requirements.

1. Since health plans wanted to be rid of the responsibility for the MH/CD benefit because they neither understood nor knew how to deliver

it without unacceptable costs, the new company would have to be independent and free-standing (later to be termed a carve-out).

2. It would have to be able to go at risk, relieving the contracting (client)
   health plan of any down side or liability, while guaranteeing to provide the promised services.

3. In assuming such responsibility, it would have to be able to accept
   capitation (or other prospective reimbursement) rather than fee-for-
   service. The latter would leave the client health plan still at risk.

4. The cost to the client health plan would have to be competitive,
   reducing and capping its runaway MH/CD costs while expanding the
   benefit.

5. Cost efficiencies would be achieved by therapeutic effectiveness, not
   by limiting services or access. Procedures that at the time were rapidly
   becoming popular in an attempt to reduce untoward MH/CD costs
   would not be used. These included therapy session limits, utilization
   review, precertification, case management, and therapist profiling.

6. The use of the best in behavioral-care technology (protocols, guidelines, quality assurances) would be the basis of an MH/CD system
   that made use of these in a cohesive, reliable delivery system that was
   consistent on a nationwide basis, but flexible enough to accommodate
   regional demands.

Scouting

The entrepreneurial activity of scouting involves the determination of
market needs and the technology available to meet these demands. The
difference between the technology available and that required to produce
the product and accomplish its application and delivery constitutes the research and development that must be immediately tackled by the start-up.
The striking features of behavioral health was, first, the surprising amount
of behavioral-care technology that existed in 1981, and, second, the remarkable degree to which it was being ignored by the mental health
professions.

There existed at the time brief, behaviorally oriented therapies that
were being developed by a number of practitioner researchers, but these
were essentially open ended. Whereas they demonstrated therapeutic effectiveness to a greater or lesser degree, none had been subjected to the criterion of cost effectiveness in an at-risk delivery system. The researchers
were largely in university and other nonprofit environments where the
concern was therapeutic effectiveness, not cost. Therefore, nothing decidedly useful to an at-risk, capitated delivery system existed beyond the

extensive, but incomplete, work on group and individual protocols under development by me and my colleagues during the 25 years I was with Kaiser Permanente in San Francisco. As important as these were, they were tested in the world's largest HMO and its attendant limiting bureaucracy, leaving the question of how well these would or would not operate in a carve-out.

It was apparent from the beginning, therefore, the most of the technology would have to be redeveloped and retested, a daunting task, indeed. In the words of Dave Biegelson, longtime scientist at Xerox Parc in Silicon Valley, "The best way to change the future is to invent it" (personal communications, 1983). This is what, in effect, the Biodyne Institute, a nonprofit research organization and predecessor to American Biodyne, a for-profit outgrowth and start-up, set out to do.

The Funding, the Setting, and the Population

Whereas the private sector generally showed little interest in a study of this kind, the exception was Albert Yuen, the president of the Hawaii Medical Services Association (HMSA, the Blue Cross/Blue Shield affiliate in Hawaii), who was keenly concerned about runaway healthcare costs. In addition, several U.S. senators, and particularly Daniel K. Inouye (D-Hawaii), saw the importance of an empirically derived delivery system that had the potential of saving significant dollars in Medicaid and Medicare. It was not long before the Health Care Financing Administration (HCFA) put together a four-way contract for a several-year demonstration project among Hawaii, HMSA, the Biodyne Institute, and HCFA. The combined state/federal funding exceeded $8 million, and the Hawaii Project, as it came to be called, originally scheduled for five years, actually went for seven (1981–1988) with such efficiency that no additional funding was necessary. In fact, the Biodyne Institute returned several hundred thousand dollars to the federal government at the conclusion of the project.

The Hawaii Project has been extensively reported (Cummings et al., 1991, 1993; Pallak et al., 1994, 1995), and only a few salient features will be discussed here. The setting was the Island of Oahu (Honolulu) and the population included both the 36,000 Medicaid recipients and 90,000 federal employees participating in a prospective study. These 126,000 subjects were randomly assigned, two-thirds to the experimental group and one-third to the control, accomplished in a manner that kept nuclear families intact. The control group received the extant Medical benefit of 52 sessions of psychotherapy a year, renewable each January 1, with any licensed psychiatrist or psychologist of the patient's choice. This was perhaps the most liberal psychotherapy Medicaid MH/CD benefit in the United States, and one that was extensively utilized, since by Hawaii state law, a patient on "emotional or mental disability" had to be in continuous therapy. The study, therefore, did not compare MH/CD services with no services. Rather, it compared fee-for-service psychotherapy in the private community with capitated MH/CD services offered in a highly organized setting.

The experimental group would receive its MH/CD benefit through a new delivery system that was created from the ground up. Well-placed Biodyne Centers were established, a staff of psychologists was hired and intensely trained, and communication with potential patients through newsletters, bulletins, and phone calls became routine. In addition, an outreach program directed toward the 15% highest utilizers of medicine was instrumental in bringing the somatizers in for therapy, and, in addition, six medical conditions were targeted: asthma, emphysema and other chronic airway diseases, diabetes, hypertension syndrome, ischemic heart disease, and rheumatoid arthritis. These conditions account for 40% of medical expenditures in those aged 20 to 55.

For ease in acquiring a large number of practitioners in a short time, all psychotherapists were hired half-time and were encouraged to maintain their private practices the other half-time. Since all of them did, a number of comparisons that otherwise would not have been possible were made. HMSA was the state's fiscal intermediary, so data on what practitioners did in their independent offices versus their performance at the Biodyne Centers were readily available. Table 3 portrays the number of comparisons possible among patients in this study: control-group patients seen privately by Biodyne and non-Biodyne therapists; experimental-group patients seen by Biodyne; all patients seen in these settings according to experimental versus control, and as to diagnosis of the six chronic medical diseases; and, finally, all patients seen in all of these settings with a diagnosis of substance abuse.

Data Analysis

The psychotherapists received extensive training during the initial period of six months in which the infrastructure of the Biodyne Centers was being created. I, as the principal investigator for the Hawaii Project, flew to Honolulu every other week to conduct the hands-on training, which included the direct delivery of services by the trainees. In the intervening weeks, the trainees conducted their own practices in their private offices. Thus, the trainees received 480 hours of hands-on training (12

Table 3.

Five levels of comparison and three diagnostic delineations within these levels in the research design of the Hawaii Medicaid Project. Biodyne refers to the treatment model of focused, targeted interventions (from Cummings, Dorken, Pallak, & Henke, 1993).

Levels of Comparison

1. Experimental group with behavioral treatment from Biodyne.
2. Experimental group with no behavioral treatment.
3. Control group with private fee-for-service behavioral treatment.
4. Control group with private fee-for-service behavioral treatment from half-time Biodyne therapists.
5. Control group receiving no behavioral treatment.

Further Delineation Within Five Conditions

1. Psychological problems with no chronic medical condition.
2. Psychological problems plus one of mroe of six chronic medical conditions.
3. Psychological problems plus addiction or chemical dependency.

---

weeks times 40 hours per week), during which they were on salary. At the conclusion of training, they became salaried half-time staff members, and 15% of their time was devoted to quality assurance in the forms of supervision and clinical case conferencing.

The trainees (all doctoral-level psychologists or board-certified psychiatrists) were specifically trained in Focused, Intermittent Psychotherapy Throughout the Life Cycle, which is designed to raise the motivational level of the patient by making her or him a partner in the therapeutic process. This therapeutic approach was developed over 25 years at Kaiser Permanente (1957–1982) and has been extensively described (Cummings & Sayama, 1995). The trainees were also trained in 68 individual and group protocols that were developed over the same quarter of a century at Kaiser Permanente.

A psychotherapist's performance by protocol was measured in terms of both its therapeutic effectiveness and its cost efficiency. Thus, the results with each patient were measured on a cost-therapeutic efficiency-effectiveness ratio. The criterion for therapeutic effectiveness was medical cost offset; that is, a reduction in the patient's medical and surgical utilization following the beginning of therapy as compared with the full year's utilization in the year prior to the beginning of therapy. The criterion for efficiency was a combination of number of sessions and the weight of each session. For example, an individual session would count as one hour of a therapist's time, whereas a group session lasting two hours with one therapist and eight patients was weighted as one fourth of an hour per patient. This weighting would depend on whether there were more or fewer patients per group, as well as whether the group session lasted one, one and a half, or two hours. Finally, the individual session would also be weighted as to whether it was one hour, half an hour, one-quarter of an hour, or a seldom-used two hours. (For a full description of this method, see Cummings, 1994.)

The cost effectiveness ratio is the average number of medical services tabulated for a group of patients for the year before psychotherapy began (1B), divided by the average tabulation of medical utilization the year after (1A) plus the average number of weighted psychotherapy sessions for that group of patients. Additionally, this can be tabulated for two (2A), three (3A), or more years after. It is written as follows:

$$r = \frac{\text{Medical utilization 1B}}{\text{Medical utilization 1A} + \text{number of therapy sessions}}$$

For example, if a group of patients averaged 1B utilization of 128, while their average 1A utilization was 62, but it required an average of 46 sessions to accomplish this, the ration would be:

$$r = \frac{128}{62 + 46} = 1.02$$

This ratio is low, indicating that the intervention was therapeutically effective (average medical utilization was cut to less than half), but the gain was obviated by the large average number of therapy sessions needed to accomplish it. In such an event, the protocol would be accepted as therapeutically effective and it would be continued, but additional research would be conducted toward refinement of the protocol to make it more efficient. No protocol was accepted as efficient but not therapeutically effective, as this would constitute an oxymoron. For a protocol or an intervention to be accepted as part of the clinical delivery system, it must consistently result in a ration of 9.0 or above. In time, the median score for all Biodyne Model interventions was 15.2. A troublesome exception was the protocol for borderline personality disorder. No matter what was done, this never exceeded a ration of 7.8, mostly because of the large number of individual and group therapy sessions required for a medical cost offset sufficient to relieve the physicians of constant barrages of non-medical issues from this kind of patient.

It would be useful to trace this procedure through the development of this difficult protocol (Cummings, 1994). A group of 83 borderline-disordered patients was placed in individual focused psychotherapy as described by Cummings and Sayama (1995). The result was that medical utilization declined slightly, but with an enormous expenditure of both individual sessions and emergency room visits:

$$r = \frac{163}{141 + 68} = 0.8$$

The ratio is low, indicating that the interventions were neither therapeutically effective (reduction in medical utilization) nor cost efficient (number of mental health units). The staff over time created a focused set of interventions more appropriate to this kind of patient, but again in individual psychotherapy. In a group of 73 patients, there was some improvement in cost efficiency but little impact on therapeutic effectiveness:

$$r = \frac{167}{148 + 51} = 0.7$$

The overall effectiveness/efficiency ratio actually declined. With another population of 76 patients suffering from borderline personality disorder, a great deal of care and effort was expended in designing a 20-session group therapy, augmented by 10 sessions of individual therapy, and then by monthly follow-up sessions. Emergency-room visits were virtually eliminated, and the ratio rose dramatically:

$$r = \frac{166}{27 + 31} = 2.8$$

Learning a great deal from this group of patients, the therapy was sharpened to 15 group sessions, followed by 10 psychoeducational sessions, and with subsequent monthly follow-up sessions. A critical feature paired off patients with the requirement that they call each other, not the therapist, for help between sessions. This resulted in a dramatic diminution of acting-out behavior, yielding a markedly improved ratio:

$$\underline{r} = \frac{171}{11 + 12} = 7.8$$

The research team continued to experiment with honing the program even further. However, the work with borderline personality disorder, a category of resistant and highly acting-out patients, never achieved the ideal of 9.0 or higher, which became the standard, and remained less than half the median ratio of 15.2 found in most of the 68 protocols. This protocol was adopted, nonetheless, because of consistent reports of satisfaction from both physicians and patients. As this illustrates, medical cost offset does not always yield the degree of therapeutic cost efficiency sought, but helps define the primary component: the most effective, not the cheapest, treatment.

A Caveat

In order to conduct medical cost offset research, the system must have been in place a sophisticated electronic system in which computerized medical records can be compared with the computerized psychological records. Often these requirements are not met because the sophisticated behavioral records are carved out. And in still others, the management information systems (MIS) of either/or both of the medical and behavioral delivery systems are inadequate. In the case of the Hawaii Project, the MIS of HMSA was state of the art. Furthermore, HMSA was the physical intermediary for both Medicaid and the Federal Employees Benefits Program (FEBP). In addition, it was the payer for the independently practicing psychiatrists and psychologists in Hawaii, making possible the extension of medical cost offset research into the fee-for-service sector.

Results and Conclusions

Levels of Comparison

The design and implementation of the Hawaii Project made possible the comparison of several groups on the medical cost offset dimension.

1. Experimental-group patients receiving treatment from Biodyne.
2. Experimental-group patients receiving no behavioral health treatment.

3. Control-group patients receiving fee-for-service psychotherapy from private practitioners in the community.
4. Control-group patients receiving fee-for-service psychotherapy from private practitioners in the community who practiced half-time at Biodyne.
5. Control-group patients who received no behavioral healthcare.

Within these five conditions, the patients were further delineated as having one of the following characteristics.

1. Psychological problems with no diagnosed chronic medical condition.
2. Psychological problems plus one of six diagnosed chronic medical conditions.
3. Psychological problems plus diagnosed addiction or chemical abuse.

Results

It is important to point out that the data were collected, tabulated, and stored by both HMSA in Honolulu and HCFA in Washington. The final report of the Hawaii Project (HCFA No. 11-C-98344/9) was distributed by the Health Care Financing Administration. It included a number of results that will be only summarized here, and are displayed graphically in Figures 1, 2, and 3.

The State of Hawaii funded the creation of the Biodyne carve-out on the Island of Oahu (Honolulu and environs), as well as the training of the practitioners in the Biodyne Model. It recovered its investment through medical cost offset within 18 months, and the savings continued to accrue throughout the years of the clinical demonstration. This was the result of outreach and subsequent interventions with the experimental-group patients seen, with several hundred dollars of medical cost offset in the group with nonchronic medical conditions and twice that in the chronic-medical-condition group. The medical cost offset demonstrated by the substance-abuse group was halfway between the savings from the two foregoing groups.

A substantial group of patients responded to none of the various outreach methods that were successful in bringing in most other patients. Attempts to send psychologists to the home failed, but substituting nurses dressed in full regalia resulted in 100% admittance into the home. It was found that these patients not only were resistant to seeking medical care, but also manifested a wide range of serious and neglected medical

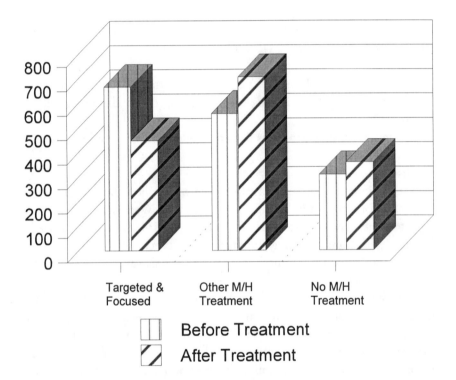

Figure 1.

Nonchronic group. Average medical utilization in constant dollars for the Hawaii Project nonchronic group for the year before (vertically striped columns) for those receiving targeted and focused treatment, other mental health treatment in the private-practice community, and no mental health treatment, and for the year after (diagonally striped columns) for each condition treatment (from Cummings, Dorken, Pallak, & Henke, 1993).

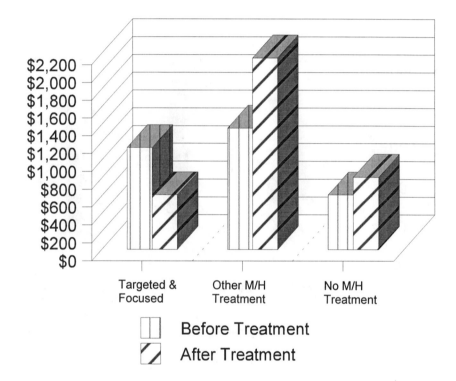

Figure 2.
Chronically ill group. Average medical utilization in constant dollars for the Hawaii Project chronically ill group for the year before (vertically striped columns) for those receiving targeted and focused treatment, other mental health treatment in the private-practice community, and no mental health treatment, and for the year after (diagonally striped columns) for each condition of treatment (from Cummings, Dirken, Pallak, & Henke, 1993).

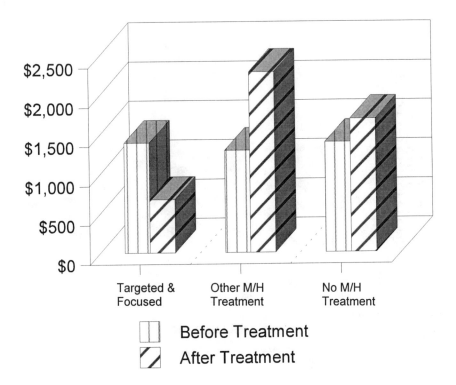

Figure 3.
Substance-abuse group. Average medical utilization in constant dollars for the Hawaii Project substance-abuse group for the year before (vertically striped columns) for those receiving targeted and focused treatment, other mental health treatment in the private-practice community, and no mental health treatment, and for the year after (diagonally striped columns) for each treatment condition (from Cummings, Dorken, Pallak & Henke, 1993).

conditions. The task was to get them into the medical system as quickly as possible, thus raising their medical utilization substantially. Getting the patients to a physician was often critical, and was both the appropriate medical and ethical response. Even with the increase of medical utilization among these needy patients, the impressive overall medical cost offset prevailed. The Hawaii Project was committed to the appropriateness of care, whether medical, behavioral, or both.

The private fee-for-service sector significantly raised medical costs among all patients seen, but particularly among those suffering chronic medical conditions. Subsequent interviews with the independently practicing psychiatrists and psychologists revealed that these psychotherapists, rather than addressing somatization issues or the lack of compliance with a medical regimen, concentrated on assertiveness issues. Patients were admonished and encouraged to go back to their physicians and demand more laboratory tests and/or a different treatment. This had the effect of increasing medical costs without resolving the patient's somatizing or noncompliance.

The private fee-for-service sector increased the already high medical utilization of the chemical abusers. Patient abstinence was the goal with the experimental patients, whereas "social" drinking or drug use was the theme of the independent practitioners. Consequently, there was a significant drop in medical utilization among the addiction/chemical-dependency patients.

The Biodyne therapists, who were instrumental in bringing about medical cost savings while practicing at the Biodyne Centers, actually raised medical utilization in the patients they treated in their private offices. Although the increases in medical costs were not as dramatic as those resulting from non-Biodyne private practitioners, it demonstrated that once out of the Biodyne environment, psychotherapists reverted to the treatment approaches they had used before their intensive retraining.

Implications for Entrepreneurship

After only three years of research and experience with the Hawaii Project, there followed, in 1985, the launching of American Biodyne, a clinically driven organized behavioral-healthcare carve-out. This was permitted by newly enacted federal legislation that encouraged the translation into the private sector of findings resulting from government-funded research. The new delivery system was launched into uncharted waters and would have been at considerable risk were it not for the knowledge gained through the use of medical cost offset research in the preceding

Hawaii Project. Overcoming risk aversion, therefore, does not involve behavior that resembles closing one's eyes in the face of fear and diving into what turns out to be the shallow end of the swimming pool. It is the deliberate movement forward from data and experience that enables the formation of a start-up based on knowledge, albeit the type of comprehensive knowledge that cannot emerge from the laboratory alone. Consequently, risk is still extant, but it is mitigated by research, as well as its applications beyond the laboratory.

One is reminded in this regard of the development of new drugs and their certification by the federal Food and Drug Administration (FDA). The laboratory can only provide a standard of safety, substantial as it is. Eventually, the FDA must take the risk and certify the drug for use. It is now that heretofore undiscovered side effects, some of which may prove disfiguring or fatal, are discovered. Drugs, such as the benzodiazapines and others that revealed no addictive properties in clinical trials, are found by experience to be highly addictive or subject to abuse. Others have been found to cause such severe physical harm over time that they have been withdrawn by the medical community after a period of use by patients. These untoward effects were not foreseen during the clinical trials. Similarly, when one moves from the laboratory to entrepreneurship, the risk can never be zero. Consequences must be weighed against the degree of assurance, but many excellent researchers are not able to bridge the gap successfully because they are reluctant to take the next step and move out of the laboratory. For those who do, the risk must be tempered by data and experience.

Well-conducted medical cost offset research, embodying both laboratory research and field demonstrations in an optimal timing and mix, is one key to behavioral healthcare entrepreneurship. In my experience, it gives the practitioner the basis and courage to use newly discovered, effective interventions; it satisfies the investor who must finance the endeavor; and it emboldens the health payer system that must ultimately share the risk.

In addition to these general considerations, there are lessons to be learned from the new economy. The organized delivery of behavioral healthcare involves technology, and the ultimate decisions are best vested in those who fully understand the technology, not in those trained only in business. All decision makers at American Biodyne were clinicians who were further trained in business procedures and management. No matter how high up the ladder these clinicians were promoted, each had to spend at least two full days a week in hands-on clinical work with patients. Their involvement in the ongoing research, both medical cost offset and other empirical studies that were characteristically built into the delivery system, was also required.

Critical Considerations in Organizing a Behavioral-Care Delivery System

Expanding and Redefining the Technology

Treatment protocols empirically derived in the laboratory are invaluable, but not sufficient. The academic researcher is interested in normative data, along with effectiveness. In the field, the therapist is concerned with the individual case, and how much protocol noncompliance is necessary to respond to exigencies. Furthermore, in the search for effectiveness, laboratory-derived treatments are open-ended. A delivery system is a closed system, having to be efficient (cost effective) as well as therapeutically effective. Scouting reveals the extant technology; entrepreneurs must expand and redefine this technology to make it applicable and appropriate in the real world. The success of this extrapolation will depend on the reliability and validity of the field demonstrations where the pristine controls of the laboratory are absent, but the loose variables in a delivery system are paramount. My colleagues and I found medical cost offset measures reliable and rewarding. Thus, we were able to create from scratch a system with 14.5 million eligible lives nationally, and one that in the seven years during which I was founding CEO was not subjected to a single malpractice suit or complaint that had to be adjudicated. The business-driven systems of behavioral care are plagued with malpractice suits, and the lack of technology is forcing most to abandon delivery, while essentially becoming third-party intermediaries.

Infusing the Technology

It is critical, but not sufficient, that the leadership be steeped in the technology that will drive the delivery system. It is also important that this technology be infused throughout the delivery system, and especially to those who will be doing the hands-on treatment. If the technology is not present at the point of treatment application, no amount of administrative business monitoring, such as precertification, utilization review, case management, and therapist profiling, will render effective/efficient results. This is another reason why the present industry is failing as a care-delivery system.

Training in the Technology

Since the organized behavioral system has defined the technology, it does not yet exist in its potential practitioners. Training of the practitioners hired, therefore, is essential. But Biodyne found that merely exposing hires to the technology is far from enough. Practitioners tend not to heed the retraining, to keep doing what they were taught in graduate school, and to remain loyal to the particular system, or psycho-religion, in which they were trained. In order to assure the inculcation of the technology, an intensive training system was developed that came to be known as the "Biodyne boot camp." It involved intensive, hands-on participatory training for 12 hours a day for 14 straight days, with no time off. This was necessary to break through the resistance, and it was akin to a cowboy's breaking a horse. But it worked. The practitioners moved through the 14 days from resistance, to hostility, to rejection, to taking a second look, and finally to appreciation. After boot camp, they embarked with trepidation on applying the technology in their treatment rooms, and they were accorded the support and supervision to enable them to make the transition from the old to the new. Within six months, the therapists not only became facile in the new technology, but they also became enthusiastic because it accorded them new, effective skills.

Continuous Quality Assurance

Even with the retraining, most therapists who are left to their own devices will drift back to their original approaches. Therefore, to maintain quality and prevent drift, fully 15% of every therapist's time was spent in quality assurance. This included three hours of clinical case conferencing every Friday morning, as well as weekly individual and group supervision. As costly as spending 15% of the therapist's time in this way was, the system more than recovered these expenditures in effective outcomes, patient satisfaction, and the total absence of malpractice suits.

A unique feature of the ideal Biodyne Center as it eventually evolved was the placing of all the therapists' offices in a circle or a hollow square, with the director's office in the center. That office would have one-way mirrored screens into every therapist's office (the usual Biodyne Center had five psychotherapists and the supervisor), along with a sound system. At any moment, the center director could observe and hear whatever was going on in any therapy session. This direct observation greatly energized the supervisory sessions, and in extreme cases in which the therapist was off on a tangent with the patient, the center director could ask that the therapist step out for a two-minute consultation with the supervisor.

This degree of scrutiny worked because a nonpunitive atmosphere deliberately was created and meticulously maintained. The psychotherapist was never chastised or demeaned. This atmosphere of acceptance and help was so pervasive that the therapists would save their worst failures to present to me as the CEO on my frequent visits to the centers throughout the country.

Patient Participation

Every patient who presented at Biodyne for treatment was asked to sign a form acknowledging that in the interest of assuring that the patient received the best possible care, his or her case would be monitored at any time, either directly or indirectly. With the exception of a handful of paranoids who refused, and whose refusals were honored, the patients agreed to, and expected, monitoring. In scores of difficult and baffling cases, the therapist, patient, and I conducted a session, which the entire center staff observed through a one-way screen. These procedures were implemented with fanatic dedication to quality patient care, an attitude that did not escape the patient's notice, and who responded with appreciation. Interestingly, there was never an instance where the therapist lost favor or stature in the patient's eye because I or a supervisor had come in to recoup a stalled therapy.

Self-selection

One of the things that often ensures success in entrepreneurial ventures is an incentive system known as "sweat equity." The participants accept low salaries in exchange for an ownership of the new company. If the company succeeds, the rewards are extensive. If the company fails, then the participants has worked for several years at "minimum wages." I often refer to this as a Bunsen burner at the behinds of the participants, causing them to put in as much sweat as may be necessary to succeed. This is one of the secret weapons of the Silicon Valley, for the participants have self-selected, with those who may be risk aversive, or unwilling to work back-breaking hours, opting out. Biodyne also learned that practitioners as well will self-select. There are those who are appalled when they first hear what is expected of them, whereas others (about 10%) will quit in the middle of the training.

The opportunity to advance was a significant feature of Biodyne employment. The company was growing 200% a year, and met this by promoting and relocating successful, but willing, therapists to staff the new centers. It was not unusual for a skillful therapist to advance in one year from staff psychotherapist to center director to state director. But in all cases of advancement, which often involved relocation, the clinician had to agree. Those who did not desire such advancement could work toward achieving the status of master clinician, which had a different set of rewards: supervisor, researcher, and higher pay with no administrative duties. This was an extension of the original system of self-selection.

Outcomes Research

Research was an ever-present feature, with the research built into the delivery system so as to cause the least amount of interference or disruption. Outcomes research was ongoing, as was the refinement of the protocols and the delivery system. Of importance were the kinds of studies that elicited regional differences, necessitating adaptations of the procedures and protocols. These studies underscored what has come to be a given in the industry: healthcare is a local and regional matter.

Organized Systems of Care

Medical cost offset can only be demonstrated in large, appropriately organized systems of care. Solo practitioners or small group practices can never have the critical mass necessary to provide the wide range of services necessary to address each of the many conditions that must be appropriately treated. Purchasers of behavioral healthcare prefer one-stop shopping where all the services are offered in one place. Even if a solo practitioner or small group practice were to succeed in carving out a niche market, such as anorexia, for example, the impact on the total medical system would be too small to measure. But even more important, the ability to track the patient's psychotherapy vis-à-vis the same patient's medical care through a sophisticated electronic system would be absent. Medical cost offset would be difficult to assess or prove.

Addendum

The managed behavioral-care organizations (MBCOs) have not been successful in delivering quality care that is both within their financial constraints and satisfactory to the consumer. Consequently, they are rapidly getting out of the delivery of care, leaving it open to providers to form at-risk delivery systems while the MBCOs fall back to being intermediaries in the healthcare industry. This is underway as of this writing, and will be largely completed by 2002, leaving tremendous opportunities for providers to create at-risk delivery systems.

The psychologists who will be able to seize the opportunity are those who not only have the clinical technology, but also can expand this technology to meet the exigencies of a healthcare system in flux and in jeopardy. The difficulties and failures of managed behavioral care today are the kinds of problems that foster risk aversion. In addition, when it comes to entrepreneurship, most psychologists seem to have a hefty amount of their own free-floating risk aversion. Medical cost offset research, properly conducted, can reduce risk by serving as a road map to the creation of an effective, efficient delivery system, and to the continued success and growth of such a system by keeping it grounded in data.

Finally, I would be remiss if this article did not mention the potential savings in medicine, and the lack of potential savings in behavioral care. All of the fat has been removed from behavioral care, leaving it underfunded, yet there are enormous potential savings in a medical system that is overburdened by patients manifesting stress, depression, noncompliance with medical regimens while suffering chronic diseases, and faulty lifestyles. A 10% to 15% reduction in medical utilization as a result of organized behavioral interventions is conservative in most medical cost offset research. Yet it would mean a savings to the health system of $120 billion to $180 billion a year.

{ 9 }

Every Industry Needs a Trade Association: Founding the American Behavioral Healthcare Association

ALTHOUGH EVERY INDUSTRY needs a trade association, as a newly industrialized endeavor, behavioral healthcare did not acknowledge this for almost a decade. My efforts to convince my fellow CEOs of the then over 200 managed behavioral healthcare organizations (MBHOs) that an industry-sponsored, collective voice representing our industry was imperative fell on deaf ears. The MBHOs were riding high, growing at almost warp speed and heading toward the surprising crest of 175 million covered lives. The acrimony that would soon beset the industry had not yet shown itself, and my argument that no industrialization could go from ground zero to encompassing most of the population without incurring unwanted regulation, litigation, and purgation was ignored. Furthermore, the climate had already become very competitive, a harbinger of the cutthroat aggression toward each other that was to come. It was believed that there was advantage to remaining guarded, and the sharing of information and the collective protection of the industry were resoundingly rejected. Finally, as the CEO of the largest MBHO at the time, my attempts were viewed with suspicion. My efforts would have to await my retirement as CEO of American Biodyne in 1992 before they would be taken seriously.

THE ADVENT OF BEHAVIORAL HEALTHCARE TOMORROW

Michael Freeman was a bright, young psychiatrist who had completed the unique and ill-fated doctor of mental health (DMH) program in San Francisco. Founded by a consortium among the University of California Medical School in San Francisco; the School of Public Health and the Department of Psychology, both in Berkeley; and Mount Zion Hospital, also in San Francisco; the program lasted six years beyond graduation from college. Two years each were spent in the graduate school of psychology, the master's program in public health, and in the first half of medical school. About two dozen students graduated from this program, only to discover that neither the medical profession nor the psychology profession would allow them to qualify under their respective licenses. Unable to practice, most finished the last two years of medical school, one completed a doctorate in psychology, and several seem to have disappeared. Michael was one of those who went back to medical school. He worked his way through school as a freelance journalist, and I met him when the APA commissioned him to do a profile of me the year I was elected its president.

Early in 1988, Michael came to me with the idea of founding the Institute for Behavioral Healthcare (IBH), whose purpose would be to convene an annual meeting for the personnel of MBHOs, as well as to conduct several smaller topical meetings throughout the year. Further, it would publish a much-needed industry journal. Both the annual meeting and the journal were to be named *Behavioral Healthcare Tomorrow*. I encouraged him to go forward, and was privileged in the fall of that year to give the keynote address at the first annual meeting, in San Francisco, which drew a total registration of 139 persons. It was the beginning of what was to become, within a short time, an indispensable forum for the industry. It also provided a place where those working in MBHOs could network, and it was the one place where the CEOs of all the MBHOs gathered. It is no wonder that within two years, Behavioral Healthcare Tomorrow was attracting more then 2,000 attendees annually. The IBH also founded CentraLink, a subsidiary that published books relevant to managed care.

The IBH was built on a model that encouraged industry participation. Financial support ranged from benefactor ($25,000 annually) through several categories, and down to a few hundred dollars. In its heyday, IBH could boast over a dozen benefactors. One was The Nicholas & Dorothy Cummings Foundation, which chose Behavioral Healthcare Tomorrow as the venue in which to present the Cummings *Psyche* Award (see next chapter). The IBH staff attracted a number of talented and highly respected psychologists, among whom were Gerald and Joan Piaget, Tom Trabin, and Daun Martin. No wonder Michael began to think of IBH as the industry's voice in spite of the advice to the contrary he had received from those of us close to him.

During this time, a number of trade papers were founded for those in the industry, one of the very first being Herb Klein's *Psychotherapy Finances*. Soon Gayle Tuttle created *Practice Management Strategies*, and Monica Oss founded *Open Minds*. If anyone had earned the reputation of being a remarkable strategist for the MBHO industry, it was Monica Oss rather than Dr. Freeman. Soon there were to be a dozen or more monthly trade newsletters. Then came a number of journals as further competition to *Behavioral Healthcare Tomorrow*, an early and important one being *Managed Care Quarterly*, edited by Peter Boland. There were many voices addressing the industry, not the one voice Michael had hoped IBH would become. However, he did succeed in making the Behavioral Healthcare Tomorrow annual meeting the outstanding gathering place for MBHOs. But managed behavioral care still did not have a trade association to speak for it.

The first four or five years for IBH were inordinately successful, but then difficulties developed. The American Managed Behavioral Healthcare Association (AMBHA) was formed in the IBH's sixth year, and established itself as the only voice for the industry. A surprising succession of rapid mergers took place, shrinking the number of major players from as many as 200 to about 10. This had a profound effect on attendance at IBH's annual meeting. In spite of strong financial support, registration for Behavioral Healthcare Tomorrow remained $1,000 to $1,500 per person. When 200 organizations paid for several of their management teams to attend, the annual meeting made money. But as the number of MBHOs shrank, each sent only its usual few, and attendance dropped dramatically. An attempt was made to make up the difference by attracting practitioners, but the tuition had to be lowered to 10–15% of what the industry had been charged per attendee. Financial distress beset IBH, necessitating a number of layoffs. Soon the publishing arm had to be sold to pay off accumulated debts, and in 2000, IBH itself was bought by a group headed by Comprehensive Neurosciences, Inc. Michael left, and with him went the elusive ambition that IBH was to become the voice of the industry.

Before that time, the Behavioral Healthcare Tomorrow gatherings were joyous events. Everyone enjoyed the industry's annual forum, and it was fun just exchanging information and seeing how many new companies had been formed since the previous year's meeting. There was enough market share for all, and those of us who were pioneers were delighted to see the MBHOs flourish and grow. At one point, Eugene Hill, the chief operations officer of U.S. Behavioral Health (USBH), enthusiastically declared in an open meeting, "We have an industry"! This was before merger mania set in, and the largest MBHOs, in order from the largest, were American Biodyne, American PsychManagement, Preferred Health, and USBH. We were friendly competitors and the CEOs (in the order of MBHO size as above), myself, Ken Kessler, Alex Rodriguez, and Saul Feldman, enjoyed getting together over drinks and dinner to exchange information and share each other's successes. There was a mutual respect and recognition that we were pioneers, creating something unique that was not there before.

ONLY IF I AM IN CHARGE

In 1992, American Biodyne became a part of MedCo Containment Services, which in turn became a part of Merck the following year. Subsequently and rapidly, Merck spun off what had been American Biodyne into Merit Behavioral Care, a combination of management and Kohlberg, Kravitz and Roberts (known as KKR). The CEO of Merit was my former partner, Albert Waxman, who actually put the deal together with Merck and KKR. At this point, I owned shares in Merck, and found myself pleasantly independent of any financial interest in the industry I helped found. This gave me an aura of neutrality, and it was time for me to seriously address the task of being the midwife for the American Managed Behavioral Healthcare Association (AMBHA).

By this time, merger mania was rampant and competition was keen. My independence from any of the potential member companies of AMBHA was imperative but not sufficient. Dr. Waxman had made it obvious that he wanted to be the first chair of AMBHA, and there was a widely held misperception that I was secretly creating a post into which he could step. The first organizational meeting was held early in 1994 in San Francisco. It began with enthusiasm, but had disintegrated into distrust by the end of the day. Nonetheless, the leaders of the industry were willing to try again, and I convened a second organizational meeting in Chicago that summer. Again, it began with enthusiasm, but distrust set in as Al lobbied throughout the meeting to be AMBHA's first chair. Al even came to me and unabashedly said, "You do know I want this, don't you?" I replied that I did not have the power to give him the office, and I would not even if I did. I pointed out that I had brought Dr. Michael Pallak along as a possible executive director as a way of signaling to those assembled that the position of the chair was wide open. Al was visibly upset with me, but I further indicated I would have to make it very clear to the representatives of the potential member companies that nothing was predetermined, and that the choice of chair would be up to the members.

I spent the next three months getting that word out, and when the Behavioral Healthcare Tomorrow conference assembled that September, it was apparent my message had been believed. Everyone agreed to a hastily scheduled breakfast meeting that I convened and chaired, and after announcing the parameters, I bowed out, to everyone's surprise. Al Waxman was overwhelmingly voted chair pro tem to continue the organizational process. That evening, Alan Shusterman, founding CEO of CMG, was elected first chair. All of the players from the largest MBHOs were eyeing the leadership role, and were, at the same time, suspicious of the candidacy of anyone from the major companies. Dr. Shusterman was a respected colleague from a small company, and obviously a compromise candidate. The first hurdle that had delayed the formation of AMBHA for over a year had been vaulted.

Mark Covell was hired as the first executive director, but he left in less than a year. The executive director most remembered, and the one who shaped the office, was E. Clark Ross, who resigned in 1999 to go to the National Association for the Mentally Ill (NAMI). In addition to being a capable administrator, Ross was an excellent writer whose articles appeared frequently in important publications. Pamela Greenberg replaced him, and she continues in the office as of this writing.

The unwritten rule that the chair not be from among the giant companies continued and although some of these elected were later, by virtue of mergers, a part of the giants, they were with smaller companies when elected to the office. Following Dr. Shusterman, Henry Harbin was elected. He was to become the CEO of the largest MBHO, Magellan, but at the time of election, he was with Greenspring. Similarly, Ian Shaffer, who was the third chair, later became medical director of Value/Options, the second largest MBHO. In the same vein, the fourth chair, Keith Dixon, later CEO of United Behavioral Care, was with Vista at the time of election. To round out the roster, David Nace, Jerry Viccaro, and Alan Daniels followed Dr. Dixon. Dr. Waxman left the industry when Merit merged with Magellan without ever realizing his ambition to be chair of AMBHA.

THE TENSION CONTINUES

All along, the tension within AMBHA was related to the overly competitive climate. A series of mergers created two giant MBHOs (Magellan and Value/Options) that controlled 60% of the market, while the ten largest companies controlled 95% of the market. Stated another way, five companies (Cigna, Magellan, MHN, United Behavioral Care, and Value/Options) managed the mental-health coverage of 135 million of the 175 million Americans with some kind of managed behavioral healthcare coverage. With the "open range" of market share already gobbled up, the giants could only try to underbid and undercut each other at contract-renewal times. Feelings were fierce, and suspicions abounded. It became popular for the MBHOs to sue each other, making it difficult to conduct business when two litigants sat across from each other at the AMBHA board of directors table.

Without belaboring the intensity of the competition, one prime example will suffice. The State of Montana combined all of its mental-health services under one umbrella and put the contract out for bids. Three finalists — Merit, Value, and CMG — were determined to win the contract. It was a battle of two giants (Merit and Value) and one dwarf (CMG), with Merit so determined to obtain the contract that it appointed a full-time staff to remain in Montana during the bidding period. To everyone's surprise, CMG was awarded the contract, Value came in second, and Merit trailed as third. Value sued CMG for misrepresenting its capabilities, pointing out that the winner lacked the resources to deliver the promised services. During the months in which Value and CMG were locked in litigation, Merit quietly bought CMG, took over the contract, and rendered the lawsuit moot. Picture, now, the representatives of these three companies sitting in the same room, purportedly conducting the business of AMBHA. Value was furious, but eventually got the last laugh. CMG so mismanaged the contract with Montana that Merit was unable to salvage it. Shortly after Merit, along with its Montana contract, was acquired by Magellan, the Montana state legislature took the matter out of Governor Marc Racicot's hands by canceling the funding for the contract, thus killing it. The Montana-CMG-Value-Merit-Magellan caper is one of the greater, but little known, fiascoes that occurred under the watchful eye of AMBHA, which could only stand by helplessly.

AMBHA's ACCOMPLISHMENTS

1. Perhaps AMBHA's most important accomplishment was that it focused the federal government's attention on managed behavioral healthcare. Whenever legislation and regulation were being proposed, or policy was being considered, AMBHA was always brought to the table. Thus, its influence, although quiet, was always present, and in this regard, for the first time, the industry not only had a voice, but a respected one.

2. Few entities outside the MBHO industry and the federal government have availed themselves of it, but AMBHA has amassed a large amount of data on behavioral healthcare. The practitioners, who are oblivious to its existence, would be startled to learn how much about their practices is known and documented. The provision of behavioral care is no longer a mysterious endeavor cloaked in psychobabble, and those who pay for healthcare (i.e., the employers) can easily differentiate effective from ineffective services. At one point, AMBHA documented a frightening amount of data on its network psychotherapists' (and especially psychologists') questionable, and even unethical, practices, ranging from outright misrepresentation of the treatment plan to fraudulently reporting the length, or even the existence, of alleged sessions. At first, it was thought that the industry could use it defensively against the professional societies that were demonizing managed behavioral care, but it was decided that the facts would be so damaging to the confidence the American people have in psychotherapy that the data should never be released. To this day, the data remain entombed.

3. AMBHA over time created working alliances with various provider groups throughout the country. This fact has not come to the attention of most psychologists because they, of all providers, have been the most recalcitrant. Bryant Welch, the founding head of the APA's Practice Directorate, had succeeded in making militancy appear like progress to rank-and-file psychologists. His denunciation of managed care was so fierce and so widely accepted by psychologists that organized psychology was deemed incorrigible and was bypassed by AMBHA. The many successful provider alliances were with psychiatrists, social workers, counselors, addictionologists, and physicians, as well as with a surprising number of hospitals, partial hospitals, rehabilitation centers, and day treatment centers. Dr. Russ Newman, who succeeded Dr. Welch, is more approachable, but psychology continues to be regarded as essentially intransigent.

4. The provider community would be loath to admit it, but AMBHA was a major driving force in the coalition for parity. This movement has scored a number of recent impressive gains, but real parity has yet to be realized in the actual delivery world. It can also be said that in spite of good intentions, the concept of parity perpetuates the division of physical and behavioral health into two systems, underscoring with potential financing the mind–body dualism.

AMBHA's Shortcomings

Considering its brief history, in responding to the industrialization of behavioral healthcare that was itself in its infancy, AMBHA has been remarkably effective. Some of its problems were not of its own making, whereas others might have been surmounted by paying more astute attention. A third category of shortcomings stems from the industry's own resistance to the next phase in the evolution of behavioral healthcare.

1. Although considerable consolidation is necessary and expected in a new industry, AMBHA was crippled by the mergers that reduced the number of MBHO members. As time went on, a number of smaller players were brought in to compensate, but this was only a partial solution. A great deal of time and effort were expended in preventing the giant MBHOs from dominating AMBHA, and even the giants themselves joined in to prevent other giants from exerting undue influence.
2. A major problem continues to be that AMBHA has not mainstreamed into healthcare. It remained aloof and isolated from those organizations, such as the Health Insurance Association of America (HIAA), that are integral to public policy in America. This isolation cost AMBHA a friendly helping hand, and left it to fight its battles, many of which overlapped with those of mainstream healthcare, by itself.
3. This failure to mainstream reflects AMBHA's commitment to keeping the carve-out alive even though it has outlived its usefulness, and the next evolution of healthcare will be to integrate behavioral health into primary care. All along, AMBHA has paid lip service to such integration, but the fact remains that the carve-out industry is both unwilling and unable to integrate into primary care.
4. The greatest problem was the refusal of Cigna and United Behavioral Care to join AMBHA. Their absence is tantamount to having an automotive trade association without General Motors or Ford.

LOSING THE PUBLIC RELATIONS BATTLE

As unfortunate as are the foregoing, there are also problems of magnitude that can be attributed to AMBHA's own shortsightedness, and the result has been the loss of the battle for public opinion.

1. Providers are well aware that their patients appreciate and are loyal to them, not to the third-party payor. AMBHA failed to realize that practitioners easily convey their own anger at managed behavioral care to their patients, who then pressure the MBHO, its employers, and its legislators.
2. Accordingly, AMBHA was unable to separate practitioner concerns from patient concerns in the public's mind. The providers wanted patient access to themselves and their long-term psychotherapy. The MBHOs denied such access to them and their long-term psychotherapy and reaped the public accusation that they had denied vital treatment to save costs. They joined with providers in lobbying state legislators to pass "any willing provider laws," forcing MBHOs to expand their networks far beyond anything needed, and preventing them from raising quality standards for providers.
3. The issue is not long-term versus brief therapy, but effective therapy versus ineffective therapy. Had the MBHOs stepped aside from the cost-containment mode and espoused the stance that patients are entitled to being relieved of pain, anxiety, and depression in the shortest time possible and with the least intrusive intervention (the Biodyne Patient Bill of Rights), the focus would shift dramatically. The issue then becomes patient care, not cost containment. The case can be made that therapy is most often long-term because it is inefficient and ineffective, and this cheats the patient of the achievement of rapid relief. It then follows that long-term therapists are arguing for their survival in an era of provider glut rather than their being concerned with patient welfare, as they purport to be.

It would have required funding for a public relations campaign to change the public's perception of the case manager from one who prevents care to one who is a patient advocate devoted to finding the most effective treatment for each patient. Part of the mission would be to fulfill the Biodyne Patient Bill of Rights, sparing patients months of unnecessary suffering while they are undergoing inefficient long-term psychotherapy.

{ 10 }

THE DAWNING OF A NEW MILLENNIUM:
INITIATIVES FOR THE 21ST CENTURY

As A CHILD, I realized that if I lived long enough, I not only would welcome the 21st century, but would experience the rare event of a new millennium. When I began grammar school, recorded history reflected only six millennia, so reaching the year 2000 would be a remarkable event for someone born in 1924. This would make me 76, an age few reached during the era of my boyhood. Men especially in those days looked elderly, and even grizzly, in their late 50s and early 60s. They began to carry canes, either out of necessity or affectation, and were patronizingly (and sometimes affectionately) addressed as "Dad" by total strangers. It was widely accepted when the Roosevelt administration signed Social Security into law in the early 1930s that few men would live long enough to collect it for more than a few years, if at all.

By the age of 6, I was determined to see the year 2000 arrive, a goal that was unlikely since I was born with partial hemophilia. The slightest bruise or cut was a potential disaster, until, late in my childhood, medicine discovered a treatment. My hopes for reaching that goal were severely shaken by crippling poliomyelitis at age 9 and near-fatal combat wounds in World War II. It was only by my attitude of sheer defiance engendered by my grandmother that I learned to walk again by age 12, and a fluke that I am alive at all because an overwhelmed battlefield medical officer was taken by my determination to keep on living after he had triaged me to die. I was also cognizant of the fact that my grandfather had lived past 100, whereas my father died at 35 when I was only 4 years old. A resort physician had prescribed castor oil for my father over the telephone in the face of an undiagnosed appendicitis. His appendix burst and within hours he died of peritonitis in that era before antibiotics.

My childhood imagination concluded that I would either die young, like my father, or that I would enjoy longevity, like his father. As I approached age 35, the zest seemed to go out of my life. I could not understand why, until I suddenly realized I was experiencing an anniversary depression. I was now at the age at which my father had died. Was I dying? At age 4, I was too young, either to mourn my father or to resolve my disappointment that he had abandoned me, emotions that were postponed until now. Once these issues were addressed, my energy resumed and the years seemed to fly by. Suddenly, I was in my 70s and in excellent health. It was obvious that I would greet the new millennium, and it was even more obvious that I wanted to attend to unfinished business spilling over into the 21st century. This section will chronicle the founding of The Nicholas & Dorothy Cummings Foundation; the establishment of The Nicholas Cummings Chair in Organized Behavioral Healthcare Delivery at the University of Nevada, Reno; and the founding of the University Alliance for Behavioral Care (U/ABC).

PERSISTENT NEEDS FOR THE 21ST CENTURY

Managed Competition

The term "managed care" is a double misnomer. First, it is costs that are managed, not care, and second, the basis for it has not even approached the concept of managed competition it erroneously has been purported to have. *Managed competition* was conceptualized by the Jackson Hole Group, composed of a number of health economists, such as Alain Enthoven (Stanford), Paul Ellwood (Minnesota), Eli Ginsberg (Columbia), Uwe Reinhardt (Princeton), and Stuart Altman (Brandeis), to name only a few. These experts met regularly at Jackson Hole, Wyoming, and were ostensibly provided the platform that had attracted the ill-fated Hillary Rodham Clinton Healthcare Task Force. Very quickly it became apparent that this was far from the case, and the members of the Jackson Hole group disassociated themselves from Rodham Clinton and her policy wonk, Ira Magaziner. To date, managed competition has never been implemented in spite of managed care's claim to have done so. It is important to took at what was actually formulated in Wyoming during the 1970s and 1980s, and how managed care fell far short.

Managed competition has three cardinal features:

1. The employer contributes a fixed amount of money to an employee's family healthcare. This contribution is sufficient to purchase a basic health plan (single or family, depending on the employee's status) of the employee's choice, and if the employee wishes a greater array of benefits, he or she pays the difference in premium to obtain the more comprehensive coverage.
2. The employer makes available to each employee an assortment of approved health plans, ranging from indemnity insurance to health maintenance organizations (MHOs). There are at least a dozen plans within the price range of the employer's subsidy, and an equal or greater number offering wider coverage than that found in the basic plans. It is totally the employee's choice as to which health plan he or she wants, as well as whether to choose a more expensive one. It is expected that the plethora of offerings will include bronze (basic employer-subsidized) coverage, through silver, gold, and platinum plans that reflect increasing cost (with commensurate increases in benefits) to the employee above the basic coverage paid for by the employer.
3. It is required that the employer not only offer a large number of approved plans, encompassing indemnity through HMO care, but also provide comprehensive information and independently derived quality ratings for each. This information is updated and provided every year before the annual period during which the employee either renews the previous choice, or chooses a new health plan. A rating system easily understandable to the employee/consumer is consistent and available. The employer abstains from otherwise influencing or limiting the employee's choice. The Jackson Hole group believed that 25 available health plans should be a minimum, and that as many as 50 available plans would not be too many.

A remarkable feature of this formulation is that value, defined as price plus quality, is built into the system. Within each price range, the employee has information regarding the extent of the coverage, as well as the quality rating. This makes possible informed consumer choice, and also controls costs because the purchaser must pay for extended benefits. This gives the employee the incentive to help keep costs down, as increased benefits are the financial responsibility of the employee, not the employer.

Strong competition among the approved plans would ensue, but that competition would reflect striving for value rather than the cutthroat low-balling and bottom-feeding that are prevalent in managed care today. As previously stated, managed competition, as conceptualized, has never been approached, much less implemented. A few employers offer their employees a choice of two plans, both fully employer paid, and a handful offer three. The kind of extensive information leading to informed consumer freedom of choice, as well as employee responsibility for increased coverage, all envisaged at Jackson Hole, would constitute a high level of competition never before realized. Access, for example, would not be a problem: a company that unduly limits access would not be a likely consumer choice. In comparison, the paltry features of current managed care pale into insignificance, and simply do not reflect the quality competition needed to restore our health system.

Curriculum and Training

Curriculum developed in doctoral clinical psychology programs has lagged behind, and the training of clinical psychologists today reflects the needs of the 1980s for solo practice, rather than the market-driven demands of the present. The initial iconoclastic enthusiasm of the professional schools disappeared long ago, resulting in a lost promise for innovation and consumer concern. The scientifically based, more traditional university programs have failed to address economic issues whose absence most often results in otherwise excellent evidence-based protocols falling short of usefulness and applicability in the real world. Unfortunately, doctoral training in clinical psychology is approaching irrelevancy.

Everyone seems to be paying lip service to curriculum reform, without any substantive movement. Any actual reform has addressed social concerns (e.g., ethnic and gender sensitivity in psychotherapy) rather than delivery/economic concerns. Without diminishing the importance of social concerns, even those that might be overblown, economic issues need to be addressed as the past decade has seen psychologists' incomes decline, the unprecedented censure of the APA by the U.S. House of Representatives, health decision makers who refrain from inviting psychologists to the table, and fewer and fewer students applying to doctoral programs. If there were ever a time when a profession needed drastic curriculum changes, that time is now and the profession is clinical psychology. We find ourselves in the 21st century with clinical curricula and training lagging by at least two, if not three, decades in including business, finance, economic, delivery system, and administrative courses. Of utmost importance is training in program planning, which would enable the graduate to bring scientific data from the laboratory to delivery in the real world.

A Most Unfortunate Omission

When I wrote the first prepaid psychotherapy contract over four decades ago at Kaiser Permanente in San Francisco, it systematically addressed both primary and acute care. It was never conceived as a chronic-care system. Neither did I anticipate that first psychiatry, and then psychology in its "me too" mode, would set out to squeeze long-term psychotherapy, which is a form of chronic care, into the acute-system. Medical cost offset is derived in an organized primary/acute-care setting, not in the fee-for-service solo practice of long-term therapy. This admonition, repeated in my writings, was consistently ignored while psychiatry and psychology misquoted medical cost offset research in a self-serving drive to justify inefficient, and even ineffective, psychotherapy. The result has been that third-party payer actuaries and financial officers, not having an appreciation of the research versus the professional societies' spin, now dismiss the finding that appropriate behavioral interventions in appropriate delivery systems save medical dollars.

When one looks at the original Cummings and Follette research, published in the 1960s, the focused nature of behavioral interventions addressing somatization and stress-related exacerbations of chronic illness are so apparent that it never occurred to me that my colleagues would use the findings to justify psychoanalysis. The interventions were brief, focused, empirically based, incisive, and delivered in an organized healthcare setting. One would think that these characteristics would speak for themselves, and their use to promote long-term solo-practice psychotherapy at the expense of the employer and the taxpayer would constitute a quantum leap that only a less than honest profession would make. I never dreamed that my colleagues, who obsess endlessly on the interpretation of their ethics code of how long after therapy a psychologist must wait to engage in sexual intimacy with a former patient, would crassly misinterpret the seminal research that identified behavioral interventions in primary healthcare to be an acute-care model. In hindsight, I should have made this explicit in billboard-size language. Its omission still causes me emotional pain as I see healthcare decision-makers dismissing the medical cost offset phenomenon as a cynical invention of mental-health professionals bent on getting more money for themselves.

THE 21ST CENTURY INITIATIVES

There was no question but that I was straining to begin addressing unfinished business, but this once again necessitated my coming out of retirement. This could not be a unilateral decision, and I entered into what I thought would be a protracted discussion with Dorothy, my partner for well over half a century. The circumstances were more complicated than before. Not only were we much older, but we also had the means to live any kind of life of leisure imaginable. I should not have been surprised that our discussion was quite brief. She strongly encouraged me to move ahead, and expressed her eagerness to join me in whatever endeavor I thought would be fruitful. For the third time, we both bade farewell to retirement. In her words, I was "flunking retirement again."

Our first thrust was a failure. I thought that if I bought a well-administered, clinically driven carve-out, it could be converted to a carve-in and used as a showcase for the industry, much like both the Hawaii Project and American Biodyne. Managed behavioral care was now a mature industry, a most difficult environment for a start-up coming at the end of the wave rather than at its beginning, as had Biodyne. We inadvertently found a likely candidate to purchase, the Holman Group in Encino, California.

One day I received an unsolicited call from Ron Holman, whom I had never met, asking for my advice. He was in the midst of negotiations to sell his company to Greenspring, which, unbeknown to us, one day would become an integral part of Magellan. In the course of our discussions, Ron indicated that the Greenspring deal was about to unravel, and he asked what I thought about the future of the MBHO. We entered into a long discussion regarding the probable evolution of behavioral healthcare into primary care, and he expressed an enthusiastic interest. Soon after, Dorothy and I met with Ron and Linda Holman, and there followed several months of negotiations to buy his company. The Holmans would retain a significant interest, and they would be able to cash in with several million dollars. The company, which had half a million covered lives, would continue as an MBHO as it was gradually converted as contracted client's interest moved toward an integrated model. We both liked the Holmans in spite of their shaky reputations in the managed-care community. As a small player, he often had to be rough, and he had rubbed many people the wrong way. To counter this, Ron and Linda agreed to take a back seat in management, and even agreed that their stock in the new company would have nonvoting status for five years. We began due diligence in earnest, and it went well until we hit a snag.

Both our lawyers and our accountants were praiseworthy of the Holman Group, citing its excellent administration, loyal and satisfied customers, surprisingly enthusiastic and dedicated employees, and lack of debt or other encumbrances. It owned its own large building, with spacious outdoor areas and considerable room for expansion. In fact, the company could well double its staff before it would need to look for other space. Further, it was in the center of Encino, a headquarters community for a number of large healthcare and insurance companies. The information system (IS) was somewhat obsolete and would have to be updated, but it was adequate for the moment and claims and other data were flowing well. Plans would be formulated to update the IS, which was not an insurmountable problem. With all these positives, what could go wrong in the due diligence?

Almost at the conclusion of the process, the lawyers began to look at the contracts with top management, all of whom I had found highly competent and intended to retain. This is usually the final step in due diligence, long after all customer contracts have been verified and clients' intentions to renew have been assessed. We were shocked to find that during the negotiations with Greenspring, and out of loyalty to and affection for his management team, Ron had signed with each of them, not a so-called golden parachute, or even a platinum one. They all had diamond parachutes they could use once the company changed ownership. I met with the managers and asked if they would be willing to relinquish this package for at least three or four years. None would, and it was apparent to me that even if they liked the new company, the temptation to invoke their exit contracts and receive several years of full salary for doing nothing would be more than most people could resist. This added several million dollars to the purchase price and was, unfortunately, a deal buster. I ended the negotiations. Ron and Linda were very disappointed; my family was relieved.

During this period, I was working more than full time, and it was anticipated that I would be the chair of the board and CEO of the new company. My family became uncomfortable with my resuming 90-hour work weeks at my age, and expressed the desire to have more of my time than such a schedule would permit. It was understandable that my spouse would want this, but my grown children wanting to be with me was a blessing that surpassed all others. So I promised I would never again be a CEO.

The Nicholas & Dorothy Cummings Foundation, Inc.

Dorothy and I decided to look in other directions, and we formulated a plan, the first step of which was for me to form a nonprofit foundation through which to address the behavioral-care issues upon which we wished to have an impact. After our deaths, this foundation would receive a sizable amount of money that would fund projects that our children, Janet and Andy, would administer in accordance with our intent. They were eager to participate, but felt strongly that some of these projects dear to our hearts should be undertaken during our lifetime so we could have the joy of seeing them come to fruition. They also insisted that the foundation should be named after us; thus, the Nicholas & Dorothy Cummings Foundation was incorporated and sought IRS 501(c)(3) tax status. This turned out to be more problematic than we anticipated. All was fine until it was decided that Dorothy and I would be active in the foundation, at which point, the IRS had to be satisfied that this was not some kind of tax dodge. This took longer than expected to resolve, but eventually all was accomplished as planned. Dorothy and I provisionally funded the foundation, with the bulk of the funding to come after our lifetime.

The Nicholas & Dorothy Cummings Foundation was incorporated in the State of Nevada in 1994 as a nonprofit educational and research institute solely dedicated to the excellence, innovation, and importance of behavioral-health services, especially as these pertain to organized systems of care in which behavioral health is integrated into primary care. To fulfill this mission, it funds a number of internally generated research, educational, and demonstration projects. It has sponsored the publication of several books, and has funded the following projects: (1) The Nicholas Cummings Chair in Organized Behavioral Health Care Delivery, (2) The University Alliance for Behavioral Care (U/ABC), (3) the Cummings *Psyche* Award, and (4) the Cummings Collaborative Healthcare Medal. Each of these will be discussed below in the order in which they were established. The Cummings Foundation maintains an informational Web site at www.thecummingsfoundation.com.

The Cummings *Psyche* Award

In order to create a centrifugal force to stress the importance of behavioral health within primary care in organized settings that are innovative and integrated, The Nicholas & Dorothy Cummings Foundation has established the Cummings *Psyche* Award. This is given annually in recognition of the pioneers who have furthered integrated, collaborative practice in some significant way. The first four awards were presented at the Behavioral Healthcare Tomorrow (BHT) conference in 1996–1999. In the year 2000, the venue was changed to the National Managed Health Care Congress (NMHCC) in Boston, Massachusetts. The Cummings *Psyche* Award carries with it a $50,000 tax-free prize and a bronze statuette of the Grecian Goddess Psyche, sculpted by San Francisco artist Maxi Harper. Awardees are recognized for their significant and enduring contributions to behavioral-health practice, especially for pioneering efforts that have made possible the new organized systems of behavioral/primary healthcare. The recipient must be a licensed (or certified) healthcare professional who has made a major career commitment to practice.

As an aside, it was originally conceived by me that the Cummings *Psyche* Award would be presented at the annual meeting of the APA. Janet was opposed to this, believing that APA cosponsorship would be limiting, and also not interdisciplinary. I approached the APA president, Robert Resnick, who liked the idea, as did the APA's chief executive officer, Raymond Fowler. Both indicated support at the outset, but, not surprisingly, the APA board of directors ultimately rejected the idea of cosponsorship. The ostensible and official reason was that the Cummings *Psyche* Award would "dwarf all other APA awards." The excuse for this rejection of significant resources was so lame that it made sense only in the context of the report conveyed by Rogers Wright and Bryant Welch, then heads of the Association for the Advancement of Psychology (AAP) and the APA Practice Directorate respectively. According to them, the APA board, being staunch opponents of organized behavioral healthcare, set out to persuade Ray Fowler that the MBHOs were planning to gain influence over the APA by infusing it with "managed-care dollars." This was said to be only the first step, and eventually managed care would have enough influence to deprive CEO Fowler of his job. This claim was so outlandish that its believability could exist only in a highly charged anti-managed-care environment. The rejection was a relief to Janet, and she established the relationship with Behavioral Healthcare Tomorrow and its parent, the Institute for Behavioral Healthcare (IBH). It was immediately apparent to me that Janet was right all along, and that my well-meaning loyalty to the APA was misplaced.

The caliber of the awardees has established the Cummings *Psyche*

Award as the premier recognition in behavioral healthcare. These award-ees are:

1996   Arnold A. Lazarus, Ph.D., of Rutgers University, for being "the Father of Behavior Therapy."

1997   Aaron T. Beck, M.D., of the Beck Institute of Philadelphia, for being "the Father of Cognitive Therapy."

1998   Leonard I. Stein, M.D., of the University of Wisconsin, for the model of community-based treatment of the chronically mentally ill.

1999   Don Lipsitt, M.D., of Harvard University, for establishing the pioneering integrated program at Boston's Beth Israel Hospital.

2000   Simon H. Budman, Ph.D., of Harvard and Innovative Training Systems, for his monumental contributions to our knowledge of brief therapy.

2001   Morris F. Collen, M.D., retired cofounder of the Kaiser Permanente health system, for making possible the first co-located integrated behavioral/primary-care setting in the early 1960s.

Recipients of the Cummings *Psyche* Award have been chosen through 2003 and will be announced annually. Nominations are solicited from the greater behavioral healthcare community by Janet L. Cummings, Psy.D., president of The Nicholas & Dorothy Cummings Foundation.

The Cummings Collaborative Healthcare Medal

The Cummings Foundation established the Cummings Collaborative Healthcare Medal to celebrate the establishment of the first large-scale, fully integrated behavioral/primary-care system. The nominations for the Cummings *Psyche* Award will be interrupted so that the first practitioner(s) to achieve a fully integrated program may be recognized in a timely fashion. To be eligible for the medal, the program establishment must have all of the following characteristics:

1. The integrated system must be a substantial one, covering at least a quarter to half a million lives for at least two years.
2. Behavioral care must be on co-location with primary care, with every clinic and program having such co-location.
3. The behavioral-health practitioners must provide a round-the-clock coverage and make extensive use of disease- and population-based group psychotherapy/treatment programs.
4. There must be an obliteration of the departments of medicine and psychiatry, or pediatrics and psychiatry, in favor of interdisciplinary teams of practitioners responsible for a predetermined cohort of covered lives.

A $100,000 tax-free prize will accompany the Cummings Collaborative Healthcare Medal, which will be awarded only once, with the prize to be distributed among the primary leaders, not to exceed three, who were responsible for establishing the successful system.

The Nicholas Cummings Chair in Organized Behavioral Care Delivery

To create an educational venue for the training of the behavioral-health practitioner of the future, who will work in primary care, and to develop optimal curricula and settings for the integrated health system of the future, the Cummings Foundation allocated $1 million to establish an endowed chair. It would have been easy to establish such a chair in name only, suffering a great deal of dilution and compromise, as universities are eager to accept such a gift. The task of doing it correctly proved much more formidable than had been anticipated.

Since I had founded the California School of Professional Psychology (CSPP), it would seem logical that the Cummings Foundation would seek to establish such a chair on one of the CSPP campuses. President John O'Neil expressed an interest, and in 1996, contact was made with the Los Angeles and Alameda/Berkeley campuses. Enthusiasm was expressed by the chancellors of the two campuses, and especially by the CSPP-Los Angeles chancellor, Lisa Porche-Burke, and the process was begun on both campuses. Two faculty members undertook the task of spearheading the endeavor, Michael Pallak, Ph.D., at Alameda/Berkeley, and Warwick Troy, Ph.D., at Los Angeles. The latter had just completed his tenure as chair of the APA Curriculum Committee, whose well-thought-out reforms were crafted in committee over three years, but were never allowed by the APA governance structure to see the light of day. Drs. Pallak and Troy agreed between them that the first task was to rewrite a curriculum in clinical psychology that would merit the support of both the faculty and the administration. There followed a flurry of activity in which I was invited to present colloquia on the campuses, deliver commencement addresses at graduation exercises, receive awards and acknowledgments, and participate in a number of meetings and social events. In the last analysis, however, after 18 months, the proposed initiatives did not receive the necessary support from either the faculty or the administration. Both men were disappointed. They had expended a great deal of effort, much of it on their own time, and were understandably upset when the Cummings Foundation withdrew from the negotiations. In the meantime, Sam Mayhew, Ph.D., who was CEO of a small MBHO, had contributed a stream of money sufficient to keep the initiative alive during the interim. In spite of his generosity and interest, it was apparent to Dorothy and me that the environment was ill-prepared to accept our $1 million gift, and even less inclined to implement our initiative.

It was suggested to us that perhaps a more established university would be better prepared to entertain our initiative, and several universities were approached. The most promising seemed to be the University of Missouri at Columbia, where Charles Kiesler, Ph.D., was the chancellor. I had worked with Chuck when I was APA president and he was the executive officer. Furthermore, he had transformed the medical school into a successful HMO serving 300,000 covered lives, which was so well accepted and successful that it kept the commercial HMOs out of central Missouri. At Chuck's invitation, I traveled to Columbia to observe and evaluate the system, and came away highly impressed. Unfortunately, Chuck left the university shortly thereafter. Not only did this abort any early thought of establishing a chair there, but it became apparent within eight months or so that the usual university was incapable of understanding, much less of accepting and implementing, our initiative. We decided it had to be done right or not at all, and came to the disappointing conclusion that it was not at all.

Early in 1991, Dorothy and I moved to Reno, Nevada, where we kept a low profile. In time, I joined the Nevada State Psychological Association (NSPA) by invitation, and I declined, with regrets, because I would be traveling, an invitation from Steven Hayes, Ph.D., to participate in a working conference on campus. Steve is chair of the Department of Psychology at the University of Nevada at Reno (UNR), and a nationally respected behaviorist. He contacted me again once or twice, but nothing came of it. It was at about this time that two faculty members, William T. O'Donohue, Ph.D., and Jane Fisher, Ph.D., a husband-and-wife team, approached us. They wanted to involve us on campus, but I held back. In time, we attended a faculty party at their home where I was prepared to observe the usual academic contentiousness. Instead, we saw a very friendly, cohesive group. Dorothy commented that the children were the congeniality barometer, as they were jumping on various faculty members' laps and hugging them. She added, "You can't fool the children." We decided to explore possibilities, and with unanimous faculty concurrence, I was named Distinguished Professor soon after.

I continue to enjoy my affiliation in this remarkable setting, warmly and respectfully chaired by Steve Hayes. This is especially so because I am exempt, at my request, from attending faculty meetings. We did not approach the campus with our idea of an endowed chair until we had enjoyed the congenial atmosphere for almost two years. In that time, we became convinced that our initiative might thrive here, and we approached Steve Hayes and Bill O'Donohue, who put us in touch with Ken Hunter, Ph.D., vice president for academic affairs. Within a remarkably short period, we had been encouraged by everyone, up to and including the president, Joe Crowley. By July 1999, we had arrived at an agreement with the university. It would match in cash and in kind our $1 million, and our gift would remain in a special financially managed fund for three years. If all the conditions had been met by July 2002, the gift would be transferred to the UNR Foundation. In the interim, subject to certain considerations, the proceeds from the annual $1 million fund could be tapped for approved projects. We were enabled to conduct a national search for the endowed professor.

The final name, the Nicholas Cummings Chair in Organized Behavioral Care, was chosen with Janet's and Andy's urging that it bear my name. It came to be known at UNR as the Cummings Initiative, as it encompassed three thrusts. The first was to develop an educational arm. Within the doctoral clinical program, a curriculum and training sequence reflecting the needs of the future integrated behavioral-care practitioner would be established. Second, the chair would be occupied by a clinician with practice experience who not only could promote clinical excellence, but could create a clinical/research/program planning arm. Third, an entrepreneurial endeavor would be founded as a showcase encouraging integration of behavioral care into primary care, and providing clinical placement settings for the students in the program. All three define the endowed chair, and with the understanding that all three attributes had to be present in the same individual, the UNR conducted a national search for an unlikely individual.

For the selection of the first Cummings Professor only, Dorothy and I were on the search committee. To guarantee that the first selection would be in keeping with our vision, we were also given veto authority. The person chosen must have the academic and intellectual achievements that would meet the eligibility criteria for a full professorship, and would have to be an accomplished clinician and researcher with a successful grant record, as well as an entrepreneur. This was a difficult tripartite requirement, and Paul Page, vice president for development at UNR, mused that Nick Cummings might be the only possible candidate. The national search attracted a number of prominent applicants, several of whom were well known in managed care. Others were more identified with the academic side, but not surprisingly, none were topnotch in all three: academic, clinical, and entrepreneurial. Nonetheless, the field was whittled down to three finalists, who were invited to the campus for interviews and to give a colloquium.

It was the unanimous conclusion of the search committee that none of the three finalists was satisfactory. Since I knew most of the players in managed care who had applied, there was an unusually large amount of fallout at not making the final cut. But this paled in comparison with the disappointment expressed by the finalists at not being selected. Each was a close friend of one or more persons on the selection committee, and each expected to be the one who would be chosen. The basis for rejection of each of the finalists was that they all manifested the same feature: each seemed to know more about what was to be done and how it should be done than did the architects and founders of the chair. Successful as they were, they reflected a better way of doing what was now extant, rather than totally out-of-the-box future. All of us at UNR were disappointed, for it seemed we were back to square one.

It was Dorothy who came up with the solution. She reminded me that we all knew from the beginning that it would be unlikely that someone would possess all three of the attributes to the degree required. Then she further reminded me that American Biodyne was built at a time when no one had the required experience in organized behavioral care. She pointed out that I hired trained psychologists who may have lacked entrepreneurial experience, but were eager to learn and to be on the cutting edge. All of them had to be retrained, and most of them proved to be successful hires. She suggested that we had in our midst such a young psychologist who lacked entrepreneurial experience, but was eager to learn. His name was Bill O'Donohue. A light went off in my head: once again, Dorothy was right. I approached Bill, who expressed two appropriate emotions, enthusiasm and terror. After giving it some thought, and discussing it with Jane, he agreed to be an applicant. Several hurdles created by Bill's having been chair of the search committee had to be surmounted, but not too long after that, William T. O'Donohue became the first occupant of the Nicholas Cummings Chair in Organized Healthcare Delivery. Shortly thereafter, he was named by the Psychology Department to be a full professor, thus holding the academic rank envisaged by the donors.

Successes of the Cummings Professor

Within a short time, the new training track had a dozen doctoral students who eagerly gravitated to it, even though the additional courses added a full year to the curriculum. A number of persons outside the Psychology Department were engaged to teach the new courses: a highly regarded consultant to the Reno business community to teach finance, a member of the economics faculty to teach health economics, Janet Cummings to teach medical psychology and psychopharmacology, and I to teach the Biodyne boot camp. Others are in the offing, but individuals such as Stuart Feigan, one of the six original founders, with Larry Ellison, of Oracle, would be coming on campus for one-time presentations.

With the invaluable help of Steve Hayes, the chair of the Department of Psychology, and with his own adroit and collegial demeanor, Bill established the Cummings Initiative as a welcomed, valuable, and accepted part of the department. This could not have been accomplished without his having been a highly respected colleague, to which he added his characteristic conciliatory firmness. With Bill, this attribute is not an oxymoron.

The new program has attracted considerable attention, and the first students to finish their course work in the year 2001 were rewarded with enthusiastic acceptance as they applied for internships. During an era of a shortage of internships, these students were sought after, and each was hired by her first choice. One student, Michelle Byrd, was hired to join the faculty of Eastern Michigan University (Ypsilanti) when she completes her internship next year. This is unprecedented, and points to the impact that the new program already has had.

The national impact, however, is limited by the few doctorates that are granted each year in university programs. Consequently, the Cummings Initiative is applying to UNR for permission to grant a new degree: master of behavioral healthcare administration (M.B.H.A.). This would be a postprofessional degree somewhat like the master of medical management (M.M.M.) program offered to physicians at Tulane, Georgetown, and other universities. It is planned that the M.B.H.A. will be a learning-at-a-distance program, to be augmented by periods of time on campus. Thus, it will be possible to complete the degree while continuing employment.

Bill O'Donohue has been instrumental in promoting national working conferences in Reno on managed care and medical cost offset, with a follow-up in 2002 on how to do it for the latter topic. He has been active in grant writing and a number of possibilities are in the offing. A demonstration program entitled Hawaii Project II, taking the findings of Hawaii Project I into behavioral/primary-care integration, began in 2001. It has attracted pending cosponsorship from SAMHSA, an assistant surgeon general, and the HMSA Foundation, with additional funds coming from UNR's match of the original Cummings Foundation gift.

The University Alliance for Behavioral Care, Inc. (U/ABC)

After the first two arms of the Cummings Chair were well underway, and even before most of the events just described had occurred, it was time to begin the third, or entrepreneurial, arm. A start-up was incorporated in Nevada in November 1999 as the University Alliance for Behavioral Care (U/ABC), and soon after, began the process of capitalization and activation, both of which were completed in November of the following year. The Cummings Foundation and UNR each owns a 10% nondiluted share (Class A stock), with both (or 20%) vested in the Cummings Foundation until July 2002, when the $1 million gift and the university's 10% are transferred to UNR. Additionally, four investors capitalized the company equally with a total of over half a million dollars (Class B stock): Ronald Fish, Ira Godwin, William O'Donohue, and myself. This commitment by management is, in the words of my late friends Dave Packard and Bill Hewlett, a formula for success. Finally, Class C stock is reserved for senior management on a five-year vesting schedule.

U/ABC is patterned after the alliance model, in which affiliations are made with existing health-delivery systems to assist them in integrating behavioral health with primary care. This assistance may range from helping the company to do it in-house, to providing the integrated practitioners. In both instances, U/ABC provides the necessary training, monitoring, and tracking of the medical savings. It is structured to participate in the venture by doing the work of integration at cost, and then sharing the medical savings with the affiliated health system. The new company is not a carve-out and has no intention of getting into the carve-out business, a model that is a mature industry that has probably outlived most of its usefulness. The U/ABC's alliances are attractive because our company shares the risk: if there are no medical savings, it has cost the allied company little and U/ABC does not make a profit.

I chair the board of directors, with Ira Godwin, M.D., serving as vice-chair, Bill O'Donohue as president, Ron Fish as vice-president, and Janet Cummings as secretary and treasurer. Bill is the CEO, Ron is Vice President of marketing, and Janet is assistant clinical officer, with a full-time chief clinical officer to be hired in the future. Critical is the position of the chief operations officer, and after interviewing a number of MBHO experienced executives, we were fortunate in hiring Ian A. Shaffer, M.D. He is the former chief medical officer and executive vice-president at Value and its successor, Value/Options, and one of the most respected executives in the behavioral healthcare industry. He is also a past chair of AMBHA. With his arrival at U/ABC just a few days before the beginning of 2001, the company began intensive marketing. A demonstration grant such as Hawaii Project II, a commercially contracted pilot program, or both, are part of the plan to provide marketing showcases.

Reflections

FROM OVER FOUR DECADES of my creating my new psychological organizations, the editors of Volume II of my papers have chosen the foregoing from a list that could have included others, such as the Golden Gate Mental Health Center founded in San Francisco in 1957. This was a privately funded organization that anticipated by several years the Kennedy Community Mental Health Centers Act, and resulted in my being invited to join President John Kennedy's Mental Health Task Force in 1961. Their selection of these enduring organizations demonstrates the importance of psychological organizations in enhancing the evolution of a profession, often in directions it had been strongly resisting for years.

To me, it reflects the importance of the lessons I learned from my early mentors, such as Henry J. Kaiser, Sidney Garfield, and Morris F. Collen. All three were outstanding founders of enduring organizations, all of which changed history. Kaiser was a leading industrialist whose Liberty ships, built in five days, may have saved Great Britain during the days after Dunkirk when the isolated islands desperately needed food, munitions, and hope to prevent falling to Hitler's blitzkrieg. Those of us who served in World War II will never forget his simple, but hardy, Jeep, and how it helped us win the war. He teamed up with Dr. Garfield, and later with Dr. Collen, as the three of them revolutionized healthcare. They created the first HMO before there was even a name for it and, to this day, health economists regard it as the gold standard for organized health industry. I was fortunate as a young psychologist to work with these giants. The lessons they taught me they had learned the hard way, as I, too, had to make my own mistakes.

One of my worst errors was the founding in 1975 of Blue PSI (Psycho-Social Insurance), 10 years before the founding of the inordinately successful American Biodyne, and six years before commencing the Hawaii Project. I had anticipated the need for organized cost-effective treatment, but I was much too far ahead of my time. Kaiser had taught me to find a need and fill it, but the need was in my forward vision, not in reality. Mental health was costing only 1% of the healthcare dollar, and third-party payers regarded it as an inconsequential. I had ignored Kaiser's and Garfield's exhortations that the timing must be exquisite. Additionally, I overlooked Collen's oft-repeated admonition that you cannot create something with helpers who have no understanding of what you are attempting to do. I had surrounded myself with experts who understood the old psychological structures, not the new. My good friend Rogers Wright, with whom I fought the wars of the Dirty Dozen for over three decades, was one such. Together, we had made psychology an autonomous, reimbursable profession. To him, that was the Nirvana, to be protected at all cost, while I was ready to move from the private solo practice of long-term psychotherapy to organized systems of care. Ernie Lawrence, another member of the Dirty Dozen, was also on the team. He went on to found a professional school that give a doctorate in psychoanalysis. Obviously, he was not on board. John Armer, another member of the Blue PSI team, was a successful insurance broker who never understood the definition of capitation, even though I meticulously explained it to him at every one of our company meetings. Finally, there was Ernie Leff, the CSPP lawyer who betrayed me during the very time we were founding Blue PSI. It soon became painfully apparent that there was no need for what we were doing, and even if there were, this was the wrong team at the wrong time with the wrong name. Contrast the name Blue PSI, trying to capitalize on the household name of the "Blues" (Blue Cross and Blue Shield), with that of Biodyne, which is a combination of two classical Greek words meaning life change. I closed down Blue PSI around the time we formed the Foundation for Behavioral Health (the Biodyne Institute) to begin the necessary research that would lead to the creation of the organized behavioral healthcare of the future.

My mentors had a decided impact on me in their insistence that it is much easier to form a new organization than it is to change an entrenched one. Whenever I was confronted by stonewalling, I formed an organization that would bypass the impediment. But even they at some point commented that they never dreamed that anyone would tackle so many obstacles and form so many organizations to circumvent them. I took these comments as compliments, for if there was a message to the effect that I should slow down, I did not want to hear it.

The Hawaii Medicaid Project would never have been completed successfully if I had not formed the Foundation for Behavioral Health (FBH, or the Biodyne Institute) to house it. It was being eviscerated in its two previous homes. If I had not conducted the medical cost offset research at Kaiser that demonstrated the effectiveness of behavioral interventions, who knows how long it would have been before psychotherapy would be recognized by the insurance industry as a financially viable covered benefit? Healthcare moves slowly and conservatively. I am persuaded that had I not founded the National Academies of Practice (NAP), there still would not be a national, interdisciplinary healthcare organization of the 10 Academies representing the professions that are recognized by the federal government as practicing independently and as eligible for direct reimbursement. Doing demonstration projects in traditional settings is most often an exercise in futility, while creating a new mental-health delivery system at Kaiser Permanente, and later in Hawaii, was a piece of cake by comparison, because I was able to exert the control needed for change. Until the change takes place, with its attendant results, you can't say, "There's the beef."

The APA is an organization that resisted change in practice issues until someone did it first. Thus, the APA would not have become a practitioner advocacy organization without there first having been a CAPPS. It would not have empowered practitioners to become faculty in APA-approved doctoral programs without CSPP having done it so successfully that it inspired many copycats. Even then, it would have found a way to snuff out the professional schools, as it adroitly sidestepped the formulation of the Vail Model, were it not for the only moderately effective, but necessary, NCSPP. It would not have made reimbursement of psychologists APA policy without COHI's having forged ahead to pass freedom-of-choice legislation in several states without APA help.

American Biodyne demonstrated that psychologists could create an effective, clinically driven system that had a sound economic base in spite of conventional wisdom to the contrary. Even Wall Street was startled that psychologists could form a company that grew in seven years to 14.5

million covered lives without a single malpractice suit, and with unprecedented consumer satisfaction. But most of all, Wall Street blinked with amazement that psychologists could form a company that paid investors well over $100 for every dollar invested by actually increasing covered services. Our secret weapon was effective psychotherapy that saved money by doing the job, but this was contrary to the practices of most psychologists, who were ignoring the burgeoning array of behavioral-health technologies. To attend to these technologies constituted a quantum leap that the APA, held back by its own constituents, could not make. Rank-and-file practitioners did not want to change. The consequences for psychological practice are now a matter of history.

It is apparent that I enjoy starting new companies, especially those whose concepts have never before existed. The more difficult the challenge, the more I enjoy it. I am the first to admit that once a company is mature, the day-to-day management is tedious and boring to me. On the other hand, ongoing managers seldom manifest the qualities required of an entrepreneur. These are characteristics I share with most entrepreneurs, and I saw these propensities first in Henry J. Kaiser many years ago. When he had mastered shipbuilding, he started an automotive company. When that was going well, he founded a steel company, and still later an aluminum company. Throughout all of these endeavors, his greatest joy was construction, and he added to the building of the Hoover Dam aqueduct the Grand Coulee Dam and a surprising number of other such projects throughout the world. This particular company was called the Kaiser Engineers, and it was world famous for undertaking tasks regarded as nearly impossible and performing them cost effectively. When he died, all began to unravel, the sole survivor being the health plan named for him, and which he had long before turned over to a select group of physician founders.

A number of organizations I founded later took different directions than had been intended. The most frequent question I am asked by colleagues, and one that Levinson (2000) posed in his commentary on the founding of American Biodyne, is whether I could have prevented these subsequent disparities by keeping closer ties with the entities I created. For several reasons, this was not possible. Had I kept one foot in each previous company as I went on to the next one, in time I would have been spread so thin that I never would have been able to create over two dozen enterprises. Additionally, I am not like many successful psychologists who enjoy assuring a following, either through a so-called "school" of psychology, or even a "cult," as some others have done. I do not relish power, and see it only as a necessity in accomplishing a goal. Once the mission is accomplished, I quickly relinquish the power, preferring that my colleagues remember me for my ideas, not for any axe I might wield. This does not mean I am not tough-minded, and I have successfully fought every lawsuit or onslaught, even when an insurance company wanted to settle for reasons of parsimony. I have faced a number of legal challenges (never for malpractice), and have won all of them, just as I have fought off political and financial incursions. Success invites hostility from the envious, and I have learned to take the heat and ward off those who would be destructive.

I must agree with Levinson, however, that it would have been nice if American Biodyne could have maintained fidelity to its outstanding beginnings. This might have prevented the industry I founded from becoming managed-cost, rather than managed-care, companies. This would have required a number of sacrifices for my family and me. I would have had to continue as CEO, with 90-hour weeks, well into my 70s. The American corporation is structured so that extensive changes are inevitable once a CEO turns over the reins. Further, once there has been an initial public offering (IPO), the now public company assumes a mind of its own.

Three of the board members and I arrived at a plan that would have kept American Biodyne privately held into perpetuity. This would mean that it would stay much smaller than the giant MBHOs of today, but as a boutique company limited to 15 to 20 million covered lives, it could remain the one quality, clinically driven company in the industry. Robert Bulla, president of Blue Cross/Blue Shield of Arizona, a board member and a fan of the Biodyne Model, was the principal proponent of this plan, along with board member Albert Yuen, former president of the Hawaii Medical Services Association (HMSA). By the time this course was considered, I had already stepped down as CEO, and the new CEO went ahead with the IPO while Dorothy and I were in London. We contemplated opposing going public, but it would be a fight that we might well lose as the investors were ready to cash in. Financially, the time could not have been more right, and the pressure exerted to go forward with the IPO was intense. So I spent three days in the business center of the London Marriott reading and signing the necessary papers as chair of the board, all of which were faxed back and forth between London and the lawyers in New York.

In retrospect, it is apparent that the Biodyne Model was incompatible with the giant companies of today, created by a series of mergers that took the industry through successive distancing from being clinically driven. In addition, the megamergers were a series of cultural clashes, with little hope of assimilation. Rather, one culture would become dominant, and often the one that was more business than clinical-delivery driven would prevail. Thus, when Value and Options merged, the latter became the dominant culture that was far from the original concepts of Value Behavioral Health, which resulted from the merger of Preferred Health (Alex Rodriguez) and American Psych Management (Ken Kessler). Similarly, Greenspring remained the dominant culture when Magellan acquired Merit, again very far from the original Biodyne Model from which Merit had emerged. Again, had business interests not taken the dominant role, it is unlikely that the MBHO industry would now be covering 175 million lives.

It would seem in retrospect that as an organization matures, it becomes mainstream, and there is regression to a conceptual mean. This many not necessarily be a bad thing, as the problem for whose solution I founded the company has been resolved and the organization now has to serve a broader constituency. Thus, an organization needs to become mainstream in order to grow and prosper. Dr. Albino is taking CSPP, during a time of diminishing student interest in clinical psychology, to a larger university structure that will serve other needs, along with those of CSPP.

On reflection, I am pleased with the current status of some of the organizations I founded, and I am disappointed with others, but there are no regrets. I am reminded of how Satchel Page, the star player of the old Negro Baseball League, responded to a question. Jackie Robinson had just become the first African-American to play in the "big leagues." Asked if he had any regrets that he had retired before this event, Satchel replied, "I never look back." I feel the same way as I participate with a new group of colleagues in our initiatives for the 21st century.

References

Baker, G. P., & Smith, G. D. (1998). *The new financial capitalists: Kohlberg Kravis Roberts and the creation of corporate value*. New York: Cambridge University Press.

Bethune, G., & Huler, S. (1998). *From worst to first: Behind the scenes of Continental's remarkable comeback*. New York: Wiley.

Butcher, L. (1988). *Accidental millionaire: The rise and fall of Steven Jobs at Apple Computer*. New York: Paragon.

Cummings, N. A. (1986). The dismantling of our health system: Strategies for the survival of psychological practice. *American Psychologist, 41*, 426–431.

Cummings, N. A. (1988). The emergence of the mental health complex: Adaptive and maladaptive responses. *Professional Psychology: Research and Practice, 19* (III), 308–315.

Cummings, N. A. (1991). Arguments for the financial efficacy of psychological services health care settings. In J. J. Sweet, R. G. Rozensky, & S. M. Tovian (Eds.), *Handbook of clinical psychology in medical settings* (pp. 113–126). New York: Plenum Press.

Cummings, N. A. (1994). The successful application of medical cost offset in program planning and clinical delivery. *Managed Care Quarterly, 2*, 1–6.

Cummings, N. A. (1996). The search for capital: Positioning for growth, joint venturing, acquisition and public offering. In N. A. Cummings, M. S. Pallak, & J. L. Cummings (Eds.), *Surviving the demise of solo practice: Mental health practitioners prospering in the era of managed care* (pp. 205–216). Madison, CT: Psychosocial Press.

Cummings, N. A. (1999). Managing a managed care organization. In W. T. O'Donohue, & J. Fisher, *Management and administrative skills for the mental health professional* (pp. 133–151). New York: Academic Press.

Cummings, N. A. (2000). A psychologist's proactive guide to managed care: New roles and opportunities. In A. J. Kent, & M. Hersen (Eds.),

A psychologist's proactive guide to managed mental health care (pp. 141–152). Mahwah, NJ: Lawrence Erlbaum.

Cummings, N. A. (1997). Behavioral health in primary care: Dollars and sense. In N. A. Cummings, J. L. Cummings & J. Johnson (Eds.), *Behavioral health in primary care: A guide for clinical integration.* Madison, CT: Psychosocial Press.

Cummings, N. A., Cummings, J. L., & Johnson, J. (Eds.). (1997). *Behavioral health in primary care: A guide for clinical integration.* Madison, CT: Psychosocial Press.

Cummings, N. A., Dorken, H., Pallak, M. S., & Henke, C. J. (1993). The impact of psychological intervention on health care costs and utilization: The Hawaii Medicaid project. In *Medicaid, managed behavioral health and implications for public policy: Vol. 2. Healthcare and utilization cost series* (pp. 3–23). San Francisco: Foundation for Behavioral Health.

Cummings, N. A., & Follette, W. T. (1968). Psychiatric services and medical utilization in a prepaid health plan setting: Part 2. *Medical Care, 6,* 31–41.

Cummings, N. A, Kahn, B. I., & Sparkman, B. (1965). *The effect of psychological intervention on medical utilization: A pilot project.* Oakland, CA: Kaiser Foundation Reports.

Cummings, N. A., Pallak, M. S., & Cummings, J. L. (Eds.). (1996). *Surviving the demise of solo practice: Mental health practitioners prospering in the era of managed care.* Madison, CT: Psychosocial Press.

Cummings, N., & Sayama, M. (1995). *Focused psychotherapy: A casebook of brief, intermittent psychotherapy throughout the life cycle.* New York: Brunner/Mazel.

Cummings, N. A. & VandenBos, G. R. (1981). The twenty-year Kaiser Permanente experience with psychotherapy and medical utilization: Implications for national health policy and national health insurance. *Health Policy Quarterly, 1*(2), 159–175.

Delbecq, A. L. (1999). Organizing to stimulate "entrepreneurship" and innovation. Keynote address to *Behavioral Healthcare Tomorrow,* San Francisco (September 24).

DeLeon, P. H., VandenBos, G. R. & Bulatao, E. Q. (1991). Managed mental health care: A history of the federal policy initiative. *Professional Psychology: Research and Practice, 22,* 15–25.

Dell, M. (1999). *Direct from Dell: Strategies that revolutionized an industry.* New York: Harperbusiness.

Drucker, P. F. (1985). *Innovation and entrepreneurship: Practice and principles*. New York: Harper Row.

Farrell, L. C. (2001). *The entrepreneurial age*. New York: Allworth Press.

Follette, W. T., & Cummings, N. A. (1967). Psychiatric services and medical utilization in a prepaid health plan setting. *Medical Care, 5*, 25–35.

Gates, B. (2000). *Business @ the speed of thought: Succeeding in the digital economy*. New York: Warner Books

Iacocca, L. A., & Novack, W. (1984). *Iacocca: An autobiography*. New York: Bantam Books.

Jones, K. R., & Vischi, T. R. (1979). Impact of alcohol, drug abuse and mental health treatment on medical utilization: A review of the literature. *Medical Care, 17*(suppl.), 1–82.

Jones, K. R., & Vischi, T. R. (1980). *The Bethesda Conference on Medical Cost Offset*. Washington, DC: ADAMHA Report.

Levinson, H. (2000). On becoming an entrepreneur. *The Psychologist-Manager Journal, 4*(1), 91–96.

McGrath, R. G., & MacMillan, I. (2000). *The entrepreneurial mindset*. Boston: Harvard Business School Press.

Morthland, J. (1996). Richard Rainwater. The invisible man behind one of the year's biggest deals. Retrieved from the World Wide Web: www.texasmonthly.com/archive/tex20/rainwater.html.

Nickels, W. G., McHugh, J. M., & McHugh, S. M. (1999). *Understanding business*. Boston: Irwin McGraw-Hill.

Packard, D., Kirby, D., & Lewis, K. (1996). *The HP Way: How Bill Hewlett and I built our company*. New York: Harperbusiness.

Pallak, M. S., & Cummings, N. A. (1992). Inpatient and outpatient psychiatric treatment: The effect of matching patients to appropriate level of treatment on psychiatric and medical-surgical hospital days. *Applied & Preventative Psychology, 1*, 83–87.

Raphael, M. J. (2000). *Bill W. and Mr. Wilson: The legend and life of AA's cofounder*. Amherst: University of Massachusetts Press.

Sculley, J., & Byrne, J. A. (1987). *Odyssey: Pepsi to Apple — A journey of adventure, ideas, and the future*. New York: Harper & Row.

Senior, N. (1989). Regulation and review of psychiatric services in the United States. *Psychiatric Annals, 19*, 415–420.

Stevens, M. (1993). *King Icahn: The biography of a renegade capitalist*. New York: Dutton.

Thomas, J. L., & Cummings, J. L. (Eds.). (2000). *The value of psychological treatment. The collected papers of Nicholas A. Cummings, Volume I*.

Phoenix: Zeig, Tucker & Theisen.

Wright, R. H. (1991, Spring). Toward a national health plan. *Advance Plan, 1,* 14–16.

Wright, R. H. (1992). Toward a political solution to psychology's dilemmas: Managing managed care. *Independent Practitioner, 12*(3), 111–113.

Wright, R. H., & Cummings, N. A. (2001). *The practice of psychology: The struggle for professionalism.* Phoenix, AZ: Zeig, Tucker & Theisen.